Prentice Hall
WRITING and GRAMMAR

Communication in Action

Gold Level

Grammar Exercise Workbook

Teacher's Edition

Prentice Hall

Upper Saddle River, New Jersey
Glenview, Illinois
Needham, Massachusetts

Teacher's Edition

ISBN 0-13-0434825

2 3 4 5 6 7 8 9 10   04 03 02 01

Contents

Note: This workbook supports Chapters 16–29, (Part 2: Grammar, Usage, and Mechanics) of Prentice Hall *Writing and Grammar*.

16.1 Nouns (Names, Compound Nouns) • Practice 1

Nouns as Names   A noun is the name of a person, place, or thing. Some of the things nouns name can be seen or touched; some cannot.

People	Places	Things
Mrs. Jones	field	deer
friend	Ohio	holiday
cousin	post office	crime

Compound Nouns   A compound noun is a noun that is made up of more than one word. The chart shows the three ways compound nouns can be written.

Separated	Hyphenated	Combined
sweet potato	send-off	tablecloth
inner tube	son-in-law	handbook

▶ **Exercise 1**   **Recognizing Nouns.**   Underline the two nouns in each sentence. Some nouns may be compound.

EXAMPLE: <u>Charlotte</u> helped us win the <u>championship</u>.

1. Each February, there is a major snowstorm.
2. The daisies in the garden are dying.
3. The children on the merry-go-round were laughing.
4. There are no longer any animals in that zoo.
5. Uncle Pete has been studying to become a pilot.
6. After the party there were dirty plates everywhere.
7. Poverty has always been a problem.
8. Her dream is to visit the Far East.
9. All of the silverware fell out of the drawer.
10. "This is not a good sign," said Dennis.

▶ **Exercise 2**   **Adding Nouns to Sentences.**   Fill in each blank with a noun. Use at least one compound noun.

EXAMPLE: _____Christopher_____ will visit us this ___year___ .

1. The _____ we saw was a _____ .
2. We went to the _____ to see a _____ .
3. Afraid of the _____ , the _____ cried out.
4. _____ is not my favorite _____ .
5. She must leave at _____ for _____ .
6. In three _____ the _____ will be over.
7. Many of the _____ were not ready for the _____ .
8. Put your _____ on the _____ .
9. We must remember that _____ is not a _____ .
10. Walking through the _____ , they found a _____ .

16.1 Nouns (Names, Compound Nouns) • Practice 2

▶ **Exercise 1**   **Identifying Nouns as People, Places, or Things.**   Underline the two nouns in each group. Then label each pair as *people, places,* or *things.*

EXAMPLE: <u>tree</u>   funny   <u>dandelion</u>   _things_

1. able   baby   musician   _____
2. rabbit   really   chair   _____
3. prison   mountainside   write   _____
4. misery   rusty   success   _____
5. only   forest   swamp   _____
6. sailor   tiny   explorer   _____
7. tame   table   dog   _____
8. destroy   dentist   mayor   _____
9. rock   clever   pie   _____
10. beach   pasture   foolish   _____
11. carry   courage   freedom   _____
12. lion   kindly   kite   _____
13. conductor   do   woman   _____
14. grim   king   president   _____
15. bedroom   school   rough   _____
16. jolly   desk   thought   _____
17. construction   pain   pretty   _____
18. hunter   nurse   into   _____
19. pelican   shouted   honor   _____
20. plaza   library   ill   _____

▶ **Exercise 2**   **Recognizing Compound Nouns.**   Underline the compound noun or nouns in each sentence.

EXAMPLE: Last <u>weekend</u> Jane received an invitation to visit her <u>grandparents</u>.

(1) As soon as she arrived at the airport, Jane became excited about her first flight alone. (2) Once the ticket agent had given her a boarding pass, she kissed her parents, went on board, and fastened her seatbelt. (3) Shortly after takeoff, the flight attendant brought her a soft drink. (4) Later, the passengers lunched on meatloaf, string beans, and fruit salad. (5) Soon she heard the landing gear come down and returned her tray table to its correct position. (6) In a few minutes, she felt the gentle bump of the touchdown.

(7) Inside the terminal, next to the runway, her grandmother and grandfather were waiting for her. (8) A slight mix-up over her suitcases was soon solved. (9) With the help of a porter, they carried the luggage to the station wagon. (10) Jane couldn't believe her luck as she watched the beautiful scenery along the freeway on the way into town.

16.1 Nouns (Common and Proper Nouns) • Practice 1

Common and Proper Nouns   A common noun names any one of a class of people, places, or things. A proper noun names a specific person, place, or thing. Proper nouns take capitals.

Common Nouns		Proper Nouns	
river	book	Hudson River	*The Pearl*
friend	group	Chris	Senate
battle	language	World War I	English

▷ **Exercise 1**   **Recognizing Proper Nouns.**   Write the proper noun in each sentence in the blank at the right, adding the missing capitalization.

EXAMPLE: We greatly admired aunt clare.   _Aunt Clare_

1. She decided that she would write to mark twain. _____
2. When we were in texas, we saw a huge ranch. _____
3. Do you think our ships will ever reach mars? _____
4. The moving van took a detour at maple avenue. _____
5. His favorite language is german. _____
6. They saw the guards at buckingham palace. _____
7. There must be a way to arouse school spirit here at emerson high school. _____
8. In seville, the people have a festival every year. _____
9. Finally, we had to ask donna what to do. _____
10. The leaves are now turning scarlet in vermont. _____

▷ **Exercise 2**   **Adding Proper Nouns to Sentences.**   Fill in each blank with a proper noun.

EXAMPLE: In ____Chicago____ there are many famous buildings.

1. After much thought, he gave the bracelet to _____ .
2. The author she likes the least is _____ .
3. The sight of the _____ filled us with awe.
4. On _____ there were two new houses being built.
5. We finally decided to buy a _____ .
6. During _____ there was very little to do around here.
7. Some day I would like to see _____ .
8. After a heated contest, we beat _____ by two points.
9. Television just isn't the same without _____ .
10. The explorers crossed the _____ during their first expedition.

16.1 Nouns (Common and Proper Nouns) • Practice 2

▶ **Exercise 1** **Distinguishing Between Common and Proper Nouns.** Write the one proper noun in each group, adding the necessary capitalization.

EXAMPLE: planet   neptune   star   _____Neptune_____

1. town   village   smithville   _____
2. black beauty   horse   pony   _____
3. state   region   texas   _____
4. river   nile   stream   _____
5. landmark   memorial   washington monument   _____
6. whitman   poet   writer   _____
7. french   people   language   _____
8. dog   puppy   lassie   _____
9. paris   capital   city   _____
10. country   nation   italy   _____
11. holiday   season   thanksgiving   _____
12. sea   mediterranean   ocean   _____
13. september   month   autumn   _____
14. street   avenue   maple lane   _____
15. pet   sophie   cat   _____

▶ **Writing Application** **Writing Sentences with Nouns.** Use the following instructions to write ten sentences of your own.

EXAMPLE: Write a sentence about flowers that includes two common nouns.

_____They planted pansies and marigolds._____

1. Write a sentence about sports that includes one proper noun and one compound common noun.

_____

2. Write a sentence about animals that includes two common nouns.

_____

3. Write a sentence about an interesting place that includes one compound proper noun and two common nouns.

_____

4. Write a sentence about your school that contains one compound proper noun and one proper noun.

_____

5. Write a sentence about music that includes one compound proper noun and two common nouns.

_____

16.2 Pronouns (Antecedents, Personal Pronouns)
• Practice 1

Antecedents of Pronouns   A pronoun is a word used to take the place of a noun. The noun a pronoun substitutes for is called an antecedent.

PRONOUNS AND ANTECEDENTS
ANTECEDENT   PRONOUN   PRONOUN
Elizabeth Macintosh asked *her* parents if *she* could go.
PRONOUN   ANTECEDENT
Because of *his* sore knee, the star *quarterback* couldn't play.

Personal Pronouns   Personal pronouns refer to (1) the person speaking, (2) the person spoken to, or (3) the person, place, or thing spoken about.

First Person	Second Person	Third Person
I, me, my, mine we, us, our, ours	you, your, yours	he, him, his, she, her, hers, it, its, they, them, their, theirs

▶ **Exercise 1**   **Recognizing Pronouns and Antecedents.**   Underline the personal pronoun in each sentence. Then, circle its antecedent.

EXAMPLE: The (team) lost its nerve in the third quarter.

1. Lisa, are you going to the party tonight?

2. When Paul drove up, everyone piled into his car.

3. Phyllis said that she would be absent today.

4. During the storm, the house lost its antenna.

5. "I must not forget, " the child said over and over again.

6. With their suitcases packed, the Joneses left forever.

7. Joel, please take all of these gadgets with you.

8. The woman across the street left her trash in the driveway.

9. When he was very young, Mozart wrote beautiful music.

10. Why are you going to sleep, Tom?

▶ **Exercise 2**   **Using Personal Pronouns.**   Fill in each blank with a personal pronoun.

EXAMPLE: Parker never remembers ___his___ lines.

1. Emily Dickinson spent much of _____ life in Amherst.

2. Randy, would _____ please give us a hand?

3. All of her friends sent her _____ best wishes.

4. With _____ motor running, the car sounded like a washing machine.

5. Tom Sawyer didn't always do _____ own work.

6. With _____ money ready, Trudy stood in the long line.

7. Many countries have _____ capitals in a central location.

8. These books are so good that I wish _____ were longer.

9. Charles Lindbergh flew _____ small plane across the Atlantic.

10. Anne Morrow Lindbergh features nature in many of _____ books.

16.2 Pronouns (Antecedents, Personal Pronouns)
• Practice 2

▶ **Exercise 1** **Recognizing Antecedents.** Circle the antecedent for each underlined pronoun.

EXAMPLE: Did Amy write both of the (letters)?

1. Some of the children are afraid of mice.
2. Andrea usually brings her lunch to school.
3. This is not the CD I ordered.
4. The horse has broken out of its stall.
5. Frank asked his father to help build the fire.
6. The explorers loaded supplies into their boat.
7. The Joneses enjoyed themselves at the picnic.
8. Did Joe bring his camera?
9. The boat with the red sail is the one that won.
10. The twins ordered strawberry milkshakes to drink with their lunches.
11. The fans jumped to their feet and cheered loudly.
12. That was the first time Sara had ever seen Jules.
13. Marcia bought herself a new jacket at the sale.
14. The umpire changed his call after seeing the tape.
15. The mayor wore a red suit to her inauguration.

▶ **Exercise 2** **Identifying Personal Pronouns.** Underline the two personal pronouns in each sentence. Then draw an arrow from each personal pronoun to its antecedent.

EXAMPLE: Liz handed her brother his coat.

1. Alice asked Henry if he had brought his bike.
2. Paul baked his parents a cake for their party.
3. The twins took their skis with them.
4. Jody put down her pencil when she was finished.
5. Dad helped the Grants select their new piano and move it into the house.
6. The fans rose to their feet when they realized that the ball had gone over the fence.
7. The movie doesn't live up to its ads, but it does have an exciting ending.
8. Tracy enjoyed her trip and was sorry when it was over.
9. Ned decided he would order cake since it looked so good.
10. Ellen helped her brother find his baseball.
11. After paying for his purchases, Todd picked up the bag and carried it to the car.
12. Diane arranged her roses in a vase, filling the room with their delightful fragrance.
13. O. Henry got many of his story ideas when he was in prison.
14. Jamie likes the poems of Robert Frost because he can understand them.
15. In the attic, Annie found her mother's wedding dress and tried it on.

16.2 Pronouns (Reflexive and Intensive Pronouns)
• Practice 1

Reflexive and Intensive Pronouns   A reflexive pronoun ends in *-self* or *-selves* and adds information to a sentence by pointing back to a noun or pronoun that appears earlier in the sentence. An intensive pronoun has the same ending as a reflexive pronoun but simply adds emphasis to a noun or pronoun in the same sentence.

REFLEXIVE AND INTENSIVE PRONOUNS		
	Singular	**Plural**
First Person	myself	ourselves
Second Person	yourself	yourselves
Third Person	himself, herself, itself	themselves

▶ **Exercise 1**   **Distinguishing Between Reflexive and Intensive Pronouns.**   On the blank, write whether each sentence has a *reflexive* or *intensive* pronoun.

EXAMPLE: The article itself contains no new information.   ___*intensive*___

1. Ted promised himself to work harder next semester. _____
2. The jurors could not agree among themselves. _____
3. The students made the scenery themselves. _____
4. Ethel promised herself a reward for her hard work. _____
5. The mayor presented the new program herself. _____
6. We cooked the whole meal ourselves. _____
7. Some animals protect themselves through camouflage. _____
8. The pitcher scored the winning run himself. _____
9. Have you asked yourselves why you arc herc? _____
10. The playcrs prepared themselves by staying in shape. _____

▶ **Exercise 2**   **Adding Reflexive and Intensive Pronouns to Sentences.**   Fill in each blank with an appropriate reflexive or intensive pronoun.

EXAMPLE: Do ___*yourself*___ a favor.

1. Many young children cannot amuse _____ easily.
2. Ms. Willard said little about _____.
3. Now my little brother can tie his shoes _____.
4. Mr. Holmes supervised the experiment _____.
5. Ivy easily attaches _____ to brick or stone walls.
6. You must trust _____ to make the right decision.
7. Only the teachers _____ know where we are having the picnic.
8. We made up the rules _____.
9. I gave _____ a break after an hour of studying.
10. You can help _____ to another piece of cake.

16.2 Pronouns (Reflexive and Intensive Pronouns)
• Practice 2

Exercise 1 **Distinguishing Between Reflexive and Intensive Pronouns.** Underline the reflexive or intensive pronoun in each sentence. Then label each as *reflexive* or *intensive*.

EXAMPLE: The wind itself blew the door shut. _____*intensive*_____

1. I myself have never questioned Janet's loyalty. _____
2. We all enjoyed ourselves at the picnic. _____
3. The author described the plot to us herself. _____
4. Helen wallpapered her bedroom herself. _____
5. The governor himself answered our questions. _____
6. Paul kept telling himself he wasn't afraid. _____
7. The children went to the park by themselves. _____
8. The guests helped themselves from the heaping platters. _____
9. Pete had a hard time defending himself. _____
10. Rita found herself the only one left. _____
11. If you run with scissors, you might hurt yourself. _____
12. You yourselves are responsible for the decorations. _____
13. Speaking for myself, I don't agree with the senator. _____
14. Harry painted the room himself. _____
15. Gloria has always taken good care of herself. _____

Exercise 2 **Writing Sentences with Pronouns.** Write a sentence for each pronoun, using the pronoun in the manner indicated in parentheses.

EXAMPLE: himself (reflexive) _____*He bought the gifts himself.*_____

1. herself (intensive) _____
2. herself (reflexive) _____
3. myself (intensive) _____
4. myself (reflexive) _____
5. ourselves (intensive) _____
6. ourselves (reflexive) _____
7. yourself (intensive) _____
8. yourself (reflexive) _____
9. himself (intensive) _____
10. itself (intensive) _____
11. itself (reflexive) _____
12. yourselves (intensive) _____
13. yourselves (reflexive) _____
14. themselves (intensive) _____
15. themselves (reflexive) _____

16.2 Pronouns (Demonstrative, Relative, and Interrogative Pronouns) • Practice 1

Demonstrative, Relative, and Interrogative Pronouns   A demonstrative pronoun directs attention to a specific person, place, or thing.

DEMONSTRATIVE PRONOUNS			
this	that	these	those

A relative pronoun begins a subordinate clause and connects it to another idea in the sentence.

RELATIVE PRONOUNS				
that	which	who	whom	whose

An interrogative pronoun is used to begin a question.

INTERROGATIVE PRONOUNS				
what	which	who	whom	whose

▷ **Exercise 1**   **Identifying Demonstrative, Relative, and Interrogative Pronouns.**   Write whether each underlined word is a *demonstrative*, a *relative*, or an *interrogative* pronoun.

EXAMPLE: Which of the cars is yours? _____*interrogative*_____

1. Are these your keys? _____
2. Is she the girl whom you met at the party? _____
3. Whom have you asked for information? _____
4. Tom is a person that everyone likes. _____
5. Which of the twins was born first? _____
6. This is the first edition of our school paper. _____
7. What have you done with your umbrella? _____
8. Have you found the book that you need? _____
9. Is that your final decision? _____
10. She is an artist whose work I admire. _____

▷ **Exercise 2**   **Adding Demonstrative, Relative, and Interrogative Pronouns to Sentences.**   Fill in each blank with an appropriate *demonstrative*, *relative*, or *interrogative* pronoun.

EXAMPLE: These shirts look brighter than ____*those*____ .

1. _____ is your favorite kind of ice cream?
2. Are _____ the books you ordered?
3. I got the directions from someone _____ lives nearby.
4. Never make a promise _____ you cannot keep.
5. _____ will pitch for the Bombers tonight?
6. _____ is another book by the same author.
7. _____ invited you to enter the essay contest?
8. Is there anyone _____ can help you with your problem?
9. Is there any way in _____ I can help you?
10. With _____ did you leave a message?

16.2 Pronouns (Demonstrative, Relative, and Interrogative Pronouns) • Practice 2

▷ **Exercise 1** **Recognizing Demonstrative, Relative, and Interrogative Pronouns.** Underline the pronoun in each sentence. Then label each as *demonstrative*, *relative*, or *interrogative*.

EXAMPLE: Alice chose the book that Paul wanted. _____*relative*_____

1. Which of the candidates is more likely to win? _____
2. Ralph was the person who told Lisa. _____
3. What will happen next? _____
4. This is a book by the same author. _____
5. Who was elected to represent the class? _____
6. Jake has a pen pal who lives in New Guinea. _____
7. Is that the jacket with the broken zipper? _____
8. What is Paul having for dinner? _____
9. Darryl's aunt is the lawyer who won the case. _____
10. These are the tomatoes from Mom's garden. _____
11. For whom are you baking the cookies? _____
12. Are those the apple trees Fiona mentioned earlier? _____
13. Whose baby is crying so loudly? _____
14. The person to whom Sally is writing is named Franklin. _____
15. Which of these three shades of pink do you prefer? _____

▷ **Exercise 2** **Using Pronouns in Sentences.** Fill in each blank with the kind of pronoun indicated in parentheses.

EXAMPLE: (1) _____*That*_____ (demonstrative) was the most exciting trip I have ever taken. We visited a castle (2) _____*that*_____ (relative) was four hundred years old.

Carlito declared, (1) "_____ (demonstrative) is the best movie I have seen all year. The star, (2) _____ (relative) I have always liked, did a terrific job."

Roseanne answered, (3) "_____ (interrogative) was the name of the movie?"

"The strange thing," Carlito said, "is (4) _____ (relative) I can't remember the title."

(5) "_____ (interrogative) of the three theaters in town is showing it?" asked Roseanne.

"It's at the Roxie, (6) _____ (relative) is over on Tenth Avenue. It's also at the Star 12 on Eureka Road."

(7) "_____ (demonstrative) are both comfortable theaters," said Roseanne. "With (8) _____ (interrogative) did you attend the movie?"

"Well, (9) _____ (demonstrative) is something I do remember. It was the person (10) _____ (relative) drove me there: my mom!"

16.2 Indefinite Pronouns • Practice 1

Indefinite Pronouns   Indefinite pronouns refer to people, places, or things, often without specifying which ones. Some indefinite pronouns may have an antecedent, but many do not have a specific antecedent.

INDEFINITE PRONOUNS			
Singular		**Plural**	**Singular or Plural**
another	much	both	all
anybody	neither	few	any
anyone	nobody	many	more
anything	no one	others	Most
each	nothing	several	None
either	one		Some
everybody	other		
everyone	somebody		
everything	someone		
little	something		

> **Exercise 1**   **Recognizing Indefinite Pronouns.**   Underline each indefinite pronoun in the sentences below.

EXAMPLE: Only one of the speakers answered any of the questions.

1. Each of the players maintained a strict training schedule.
2. Everyone had some of the cake.
3. Many of the families offered their homes to some of the visitors.
4. Few of the speakers had anything new to add.
5. No one was able to answer all of the questions.
6. Some of the books have been moved from that shelf to another.
7. Most of the neighbors knew something about the legend.
8. Janet suggested that little could be done to help.
9. Neither of the plans was very attractive.
10. We knew most of the guests at the party.

> **Exercise 2**   **Adding Indefinite Pronouns to Sentences.**   Fill in each blank with an indefinite pronoun that makes sense. Circle any antecedents for the pronouns you write.

EXAMPLE: _____None_____ of the (cake) was left.

1. _____ of the players were familiar with the rules.
2. The emcee asked _____ of the contestants the same question.
3. The children asked for _____ to eat.
4. The speaker knows _____ about her subject.
5. _____ of the test questions were easy.
6. Jon is always considerate of _____.
7. Three days before the opening, _____ of the tickets had been sold.
8. _____ of the candidates promised to lower taxes.
9. My grandfather worries about _____.
10. _____ of the fans shouted enthusiastically.

16.2 Indefinite Pronouns • Practice 2

▶ **Exercise 1** **Identifying Indefinite Pronouns.** Underline the indefinite pronoun or indefinite pronouns in each sentence.

EXAMPLE: Most of us know something about insects.

(1) Although animals throughout the animal kingdom are adaptable, none have shown greater ability to adapt than insects. (2) Everyone knows that insects thrive in hot and humid jungle regions, but did you know that some also live in frozen polar regions? (3) Deserts, caves, lakes, and mountains provide homes for still others. (4) Few, however, are found in the Earth's oceans. (5) Scientists have already identified more of these small creatures than the average person would guess—over 800,000 different kinds. (6) No one is sure, but it seems likely that many remain to be discovered. (7) Some of the scientists who study insects estimate that there may be up to ten million kinds still to be identified. (8) All have six legs, three main body parts, and external skeletons that have helped them to survive. (9) One has a wingspan of about ten inches; another is only about one hundredth of an inch long. (10) Their great numbers and variety seem to have equipped insects with the ability to survive almost anything.

▶ **Writing Application** **Writing Sentences with Pronouns.** Use the following instructions to write ten sentences of your own.

EXAMPLE: Write a sentence that includes a personal pronoun and a reflexive pronoun.

_____ *I invited myself to dinner.* _____

1. Write a sentence that includes two personal pronouns.

   _____

2. Write a sentence that includes a personal pronoun and an intensive pronoun.

   _____

3. Write a sentence that includes a demonstrative pronoun followed by the word *is*.

   _____

4. Write a sentence that includes a personal pronoun and a relative pronoun.

   _____

5. Write a sentence that includes an interrogative pronoun or an indefinite pronoun, followed by the word *of*.

   _____

6. Write a sentence that includes two personal pronouns and an indefinite pronoun.

   _____

7. Write a sentence that includes an intensive pronoun and a demonstrative pronoun.

   _____

8. Write a sentence that includes a reflexive pronoun, a personal pronoun, and a relative pronoun.

   _____

9. Write a sentence that includes an interrogative pronoun and two demonstrative pronouns.

   _____

10. Write a sentence that includes a relative pronoun, an intensive pronoun, and an indefinite pronoun.

   _____

17.1 Action Verbs • Practice 1

Visible and Mental Action   A verb is a word that expresses time while showing an action, a condition, or the fact that something exists. An action verb is a verb that tells what action someone or something is performing. An action verb may show mental action as well as visible action.

Visible Action		Mental Action	
dig	yell	wonder	hope
measure	play	believe	think

Transitive and Intransitive Verbs   An action verb is transitive if it directs action toward someone or something. An action verb is intransitive if it does not direct action toward someone or something.

Transitive	Intransitive
Angie *played* baseball.	Danny *played* well.
(played what?) baseball	(played what?) no answer

> **Exercise 1**   **Recognizing Visible and Mental Actions.**   Underline each verb that shows visible action. Circle each verb that shows mental action.

EXAMPLE: No one (understood) the question.

1. Hansel and Gretel wandered through the forest.

2. The teacher carefully considered the question.

3. Grandma always gives me a treat.

4. David wrote an excellent essay.

5. The plane glided to a stop.

6. We wanted to surprise Jessica with a birthday party.

7. Our team built the best sand castle.

8. Last night our family talked about our summer vacation.

9. Darin wished for a career in music.

10. We planted marigolds all around the vegetable garden.

> **Exercise 2**   **Distinguishing Between Transitive and Intransitive Verbs.**   On each blank at the right, write *transitive* or *intransitive* to describe the action verb in each sentence.

EXAMPLE: Janet studied hard for the test. ___*intransitive*___

1. My mother studied Latin in high school. _____

2. All the scout troops marched in the holiday parade. _____

3. Dana entered her poem in the contest. _____

4. The chef prepared spectacular desserts. _____

5. The cowhand swung his lariat high above his head. _____

6. The monkeys swung from tree to tree. _____

7. Prairie dogs tunnel underground. _____

8. We divided the rest of the cake among us. _____

9. The train departed an hour late. _____

10. After their long trek, the hikers ate greedily. _____

17.1 Action Verbs • Practice 2

Exercise 1 **Recognizing Action Verbs.** Underline the action verb in each sentence. Then label each as *visible* or *mental*.

EXAMPLE: Sarah attended the concert. _____*visible*_____

1. The posse drove the bank robbers out of town. _____
2. I learned that song in kindergarten. _____
3. Some people worry about everything. _____
4. A nurse held the baby up to the nursery window. _____
5. Mom jogs two miles every morning. _____
6. The secretary filed the letter in the wrong drawer. _____
7. Paul often sleeps for twelve hours straight. _____
8. Our dog chased the squirrel up the tree. _____
9. We appreciated Elena's kindness. _____
10. The mayor wondered about the voters' reaction. _____

Exercise 2 **Distinguishing Between Transitive and Intransitive Verbs.** Underline the action verb in each sentence. Then label each as *transitive* or *intransitive*.

EXAMPLE: The puppy growled at me. _____*intransitive*_____

1. Who called? _____
2. Someone ate my sandwich. _____
3. Mark reads the dictionary for pleasure. _____
4. Icicles hung from the roof. _____
5. Kelly often reads until bedtime. _____
6. We saw Grandma last night. _____
7. Sheila searched frantically for her umbrella. _____
8. The campers feared the bears. _____
9. A guide directed us back to our hotel. _____
10. The fans shouted their approval. _____
11. Eric shouted to his friend. _____
12. We crawled carefully under the fence. _____
13. The raindrops danced on the pavement. _____
14. A stray dog followed us home from the park. _____
15. The campers pitched their tent near the brook. _____
16. Helen pitched for nine straight innings. _____
17. Portia walks her dog before school every morning. _____
18. The speaker walked to the front of the platform. _____
19. We waited for three hours at the station. _____
20. The king offered a reward for the missing jewels. _____

Name _____ Date _____

 17.2 # Linking Verbs (*Be*, Other Linking Verbs) • Practice 1

Forms of *Be*   A linking verb is a verb that connects a word at or near the beginning of a sentence with a word at or near the end. In English the most common linking verb is some form of *be*.

THE FORMS OF *BE*					
am	am being	can be	shall be	have been	might have been
are	are being	could be	should be	has been	must have been
is	is being	may be	will be	had been	shall have been
was	was being	might be	would be	could have been	should have been
were	were being	must be		may have been	will have been
					would have been

Other Linking Verbs   Other verbs may be used in the same ways as *be* to link two parts of a sentence.

OTHER LINKING VERBS					
appear	feel	look	seem	sound	taste
become	grow	remain	smell	stay	turn

▶ **Exercise 1**   **Recognizing Forms of *Be* Used as Linking Verbs.**   Circle the form of *be* in each sentence below. Then underline the words in the sentence that the verb links.

EXAMPLE: Geoff (may be) our new class president.

1. The fans were eager for a win.

2. The purpose of the experiment was not clear to us.

3. Some of the council members were angry about the tax proposal.

4. Like my mother, I am an ardent music lover.

5. Both candidates were optimistic throughout the day.

6. One of the boxes was completely empty.

7. Reviews in both major papers were unfavorable.

8. Some people are anxious about dental appointments.

9. This colorful poster is suitable for framing.

10. T-shirts are popular dress among young people.

▶ **Exercise 2**   **Recognizing Other Linking Verbs.**   Circle the linking verb in each sentence. Then underline the words that the verb links.

EXAMPLE: Aunt Ethel (seemed) happy with our visit.

1. The patient looks better today.

2. The lemonade tastes sour.

3. The crowd became angry.

4. The old barn smelled musty.

5. That music sounds too loud.

17.2 Linking Verbs (*Be*, Other Linking Verbs) • Practice 2

▶ **Exercise 1**   **Recognizing Forms of *Be* Used as Linking Verbs.**   Underline each linking verb. Then draw a double-headed arrow to show which words are linked by the verb.

EXAMPLE: Ms. Hughes was happy about the promotion.

1. Helena is our new president.

2. Both candidates were certain of victory.

3. The patient was a man with great courage.

4. I am nervous about the interview.

5. The play was a huge success.

6. The Homans are our new neighbors.

7. The governor is always considerate of her staff.

8. The press was critical of the mayor's plan.

9. I am always the last person in line.

10. The score was lopsided almost from the kick-off.

11. The campers should have been afraid of the bears.

12. Darlene could be Donna's twin sister.

13. You must have been thrilled at the news.

14. The children were being extremely rude to the newcomer.

15. The error must have been serious.

▶ **Exercise 2**   **Identifying Other Linking Verbs.**   Underline each linking verb. Then draw a double-headed arrow to show which words are linked by the verb.

EXAMPLE: Sean felt better after his nap.

1. The book became a classic.

2. Erica sounded happy about the results.

3. Peter Pan stayed a child all of his life.

4. Everyone feels a little lonely at times.

5. The bill became law despite the President's veto.

6. The boys remained good friends all their lives.

7. That style looks good on you.

8. The weather turned suddenly colder during the night.

9. The smaller car seemed more attractive.

10. The child grew sleepy after a long day at the beach.

17.2 Linking Verbs (Linking Verb or Action Verb?)
• Practice 1

Linking Verb or Action Verb? Some verbs may be used as an action verb in one sentence and as a linking verb in another. If a verb is a linking verb, *am, are,* or *is* will make sense when substituted for it in a sentence.

Linking Verbs	Action Verbs
Robbie *grew* quite tall. (Robbie *is* tall?) linking	Robbie *grew* tomatoes. (Robbie *is* tomatoes?) not linking
The pizza *smells* good. (The pizza *is* good?) linking	Tanya *smelled* the rose. (Tanya *is* the rose?) not linking

▶ **Exercise 1** **Distinguishing Between Linking Verbs and Action Verbs.** On each blank at the right, write whether each sentence contains a linking verb or an action verb.

EXAMPLE: This soup tastes too salty. ___*linking*___

1. The chef tasted the sauce. _____
2. The lemon juice turned the milk sour. _____
3. The driver turned the corner carefully. _____
4. I looked carefully through the book. _____
5. I felt refreshed after my catnap. _____
6. We stayed for three hours. _____
7. Erin remains friends with Dawn even now. _____
8. Mom felt the fabric before buying it. _____
9. The nurse sounded the alarm. _____
10. The baby looks a little pale. _____

▶ **Exercise 2** **Adding Verbs to Sentences.** Fill in each blank within the sentence with an appropriate verb. On each blank line at the right, write whether the verb is an action verb or a linking verb.

EXAMPLE: Everyone ___*stayed*___ calm during the emergency. ___*linking*___

1. Cold lemonade _____ refreshing on a warm day. _____
2. Last night I _____ squid for the first time. _____
3. Since his illness, Grandpa _____ tired easily. _____
4. Litmus paper _____ red in an acid solution. _____
5. The bus _____ left into the service area. _____
6. Our neighbor _____ prize-winning roses. _____
7. I _____ interested in coins a year ago. _____
8. Each bird's call _____ different. _____
9. We _____ at four different models. _____
10. The jeweler _____ closely at the ring. _____

17.2 Linking Verbs (Linking Verb or Action Verb?)
• Practice 2

▶ **Exercise 1**   **Distinguishing Between Linking Verbs and Action Verbs.**   Underline the verb in each sentence. Then label each as *linking* or *action*.

EXAMPLE: The baby gently felt the kitten's fur. _____action_____

1. The kiss turned the handsome prince into an ugly frog. _____
2. The vegetables tasted salty. _____
3. Archie tasted the snails after a little hesitation. _____
4. Fred smelled the flowers. _____
5. The star always grows nervous before a performance. _____
6. The bridge looked sturdy enough. _____
7. The crowd became restless. _____
8. The grass turned brown during the drought. _____
9. This milk smells sour. _____
10. Dad stayed at home with the children. _____
11. The guard sounded the alarm. _____
12. The groundhog appeared on schedule. _____
13. The detective looked closely at the fingerprints. _____
14. The two remained friends through the years. _____
15. The candidate appeared confident during the campaign. _____
16. Two tourists remained in the museum. _____
17. We all felt cooler after a dip in the ocean. _____
18. Our neighbor grows magnificent roses. _____
19. The troops stayed loyal to the general during the battle. _____
20. Sharon sounds happy about her job. _____

▶ **Writing Application**   **Writing Sentences with Linking and Action Verbs.**   Use each verb in two sentences of your own, first as a linking verb, then as an action verb.

EXAMPLE: remain _____*Even after eating, the boys remained hungry.*_____
_____*Three students remained in the gym.*_____

1. turn _____
_____

2. look _____
_____

3. sound _____
_____

4. taste _____
_____

5. feel _____
_____

17.3 # Helping Verbs • Practice 1

Recognizing Helping Verbs Helping verbs are verbs that can be added to another verb to make a single verb phrase. Any of the many forms of *be* as well as some other common verbs can be used as helping verbs.

HELPING VERBS OTHER THAN THE FORMS OF *BE*			
do	have	shall	can
does	has	should	could
did	had	will	may
		would	might
			must

VERB PHRASES	
Helping Verbs	**Key Verbs**
am	talking
can	write
will be	studying
should have been	considered

Finding Helping Verbs in Sentences Other words may sometimes separate helping verbs from key verbs.

VERB PHRASES SEPARATED
Mom *will* certainly not *allow* anyone in the kitchen at that time. *Has* anyone *seen* my keys to the apartment?

▷ **Exercise 1** **Adding Helping Verbs to Sentences.** Fill in each blank with an appropriate helping verb.

EXAMPLE: You _____*should*_____ _____*have*_____ come with us.

1. I _____ _____ studying for two hours.

2. Who _____ running for student council?

3. We _____ never _____ done it without your help.

4. Dinner _____ not be ready for a while.

5. _____ the show _____ starting soon?

6. I _____ going to camp this summer.

7. We _____ _____ prepared more food.

8. The first guests _____ _____ arriving at any moment.

9. The runner _____ not even seem winded.

10. The diver _____ _____ positioned herself more carefully.

▷ **Exercise 2** **Identifying Helping Verbs.** Underline each helping verb in the sentences below. Circle the key verb in each verb phrase.

EXAMPLE: <u>Will</u> Tasha <u>be</u> (arriving) today?

1. Phil should never have repeated that remark.

2. Ms. Wilkins does not always announce tests.

3. Will your sister be starting college this fall?

4. How could I have been so mistaken?

5. Did you make your train on time?

6. What else do you need?

7. They must have left late.

8. Bill may not call tonight.

9. Why is Tracy crying?

10. Where have you put it?

17.3 Helping Verbs • Practice 2

> **Exercise 1** **Supplying Helping Verbs.** In each sentence, write one helping verb for each blank.

EXAMPLE: Al ___will___ ___be___ waiting for me.

1. Judd _____ written a poem about growing up.
2. _____ you finished your homework?
3. I still _____ not found my record album.
4. The governor _____ _____ speaking.
5. The party _____ _____ ended by now.
6. _____ Ellie ever visited San Francisco?
7. Gary _____ not _____ delayed.
8. The game _____ not _____ delayed.
9. When _____ the furniture _____ delivered?
10. Janet _____ not _____ _____ chosen.

> **Exercise 2** **Locating Helping Verbs.** Underline the verb phrase in each sentence. Include all helping verbs but do not include any words that interrupt the verb phrase.

EXAMPLE: Most of the earth has been explored thoroughly.

(1) Explorers have been faced with many obstacles. (2) They may spend days looking for a shallow place in a river to cross safely. (3) Canyons and ravines can often not be crossed at all. (4) Instead, people must travel long distances around them. (5) Mountain ranges have always presented a challenge. (6) Explorers must search for a pass through them. (7) Some explorers searching for mountain passes have been killed by storms, severe cold, or landslides. (8) Desert heat can also be dangerous. (9) Even insects can be a hazard. (10) Would you explore the few areas that remain?

> **Writing Application** **Writing Sentences with Helping Verbs.** Use the following instructions to write five sentences of your own.

EXAMPLE: Use the verb phrase *has seen* in a question.

_____Has Liz seen that movie yet?_____

1. Interrupt the verb phrase *can be fixed* with the word *not.*

_____

2. Use the verb phrase *does work* in a question.

_____

3. Interrupt the verb phrase *should have started* with the words *never really.*

_____

4. Interrupt the verb phrase *must have been running* with the word *definitely.*

_____

5. Use the verb phrase *will succeed* in a question.

_____

Name _____ Date _____

 18.1 # Adjectives (Modification, Articles) • Practice 1

The Process of Modification   An adjective is a word used to describe a noun or pronoun, or to give a noun or pronoun a more specific meaning. Adjectives answer the questions *What kind? Which one? How many?* or *How much?* about the nouns or pronouns they modify.

ADJECTIVE QUESTIONS		
What Kind?	*rare* coin	*lucky* one
Which One?	*first* try	*that* dog
How Many?	*seven* days	*few* people
How Much?	*adequate* time	*no* money

Articles   The definite article, *the*, indicates that the noun it modifies refers to a specific person, place, or thing. The indefinite articles, *a* and *an*, indicate that the nouns they modify may refer to any one of a class of people, place, or things. The following chart summarizes the rules for choosing between *a* and *an*.

Consonant Sounds	Vowel Sounds
a *book*	an *incident*
a *horn* (h sound)	an *honorable* decision (no h sound)
a *one-day* sale (w sound)	an *open* door (o sound)
a *unicycle* (y sound)	an *umbrella* (u sound)

▶ **Exercise 1**   **Identifying Adjectives.**   Underline the two adjectives in each sentence. Do not count *a, an,* and *the.*

EXAMPLE: The <u>final</u> play in the game was <u>spectacular</u>.

1. Dad divided the apple pie among the eager guests.

2. The runner was proud of setting a new record.

3. The passengers remained calm in spite of the turbulent weather.

4. The giant spacecraft orbited Earth for ten days.

5. Everything always looks fresher and greener after a rainfall.

6. No one in the class had the correct answer to the last question.

7. Cellars of old houses near the river flood during heavy rains.

8. The first speaker raised an interesting point.

9. At the last debate, Collins seemed the stronger candidate.

10. The new students were eager to volunteer.

▶ **Exercise 2**   **Using Articles in Sentences.**   Fill in each blank with the correct article called for in parentheses.

EXAMPLE: _____*a*_____ Halloween costume (indefinite)

1. _____ exotic flower (indefinite)

2. _____ plaid coat (definite)

3. _____ one-horse town (indefinite)

4. _____ unanimous vote (indefinite)

5. _____ honorary degree (indefinite)

6. _____ final episode (definite)

7. _____ unique opportunity (indefinite)

8. _____ new book (definite)

9. _____ travel agent (definite)

10. _____ unusual bird (indefinite)

18.1 Adjectives (Modification, Articles) • Practice 2

▷ Exercise 1   **Recognizing Words Modified by Adjectives.**   Circle the word or words modified by each underlined adjective.

EXAMPLE: In the green (meadow) stood an ugly, old (ram).

1. A strange creature crept out of the murky water.
2. A steady diet of any food will not provide sufficient nutrients.
3. The winner, weary but happy, gave us a broad grin.
4. The big game was played on a raw, cold day.
5. A long drive lined with stately, old oaks led to an old mansion.
6. Many people watched as a new record was set.
7. You were generous to give me the larger piece.
8. Alice wasted the first wish because she had not given the matter enough thought.
9. Dana tried a third time, and then she was successful.
10. The pale and wintry sun gave little warmth.
11. Over short distances, cheetahs are the fastest land animals.
12. The yellowish fur of a leopard has black spots.
13. Eagles and hawks are carnivorous birds with long, sharp claws.
14. A few eagles are so big that they can catch small deer.
15. Young ducks and geese have short, thick feathers called *down*.

▷ Exercise 2   **Using Definite and Indefinite Articles.**   Write the article needed to complete each sentence.

EXAMPLE: I had ____an____ apple for dessert. (indefinite)

1. Joey studied hard for _____ exam. (definite)
2. Alison is _____ one-woman band. (indefinite)
3. That book has _____ unusual title. (indefinite)
4. Did you find _____ car keys? (definite)
5. Grandma always keeps _____ cookie jar full. (definite)
6. June will give us _____ honest answer. (indefinite)
7. Dad fixed us _____ omelet for lunch. (indefinite)
8. _____ agent showed us several houses. (definite)
9. We stayed in _____ hotel just outside town. (indefinite)
10. Liz had brought _____ umbrella. (indefinite)
11. Deer's antlers fall off in _____ winter. (definite)
12. The bird looked for _____ good place for her nest. (indefinite)
13. Jake picked up _____ apple that had fallen to the ground. (indefinite)
14. _____ largest bird is the ostrich. (definite)
15. We saw _____ hummingbird at our new feeder. (indefinite)

Name _____ Date _____

18.1 Adjectives (Nouns Used as Adjectives, Proper and Compound Adjectives) • Practice 1

Nouns Used as Adjectives A noun used as an adjective answers the question *What kind?* or *Which one?* about a noun that follows it.

Nouns	Nouns Used as Adjectives
Snack	snack food (*What kind* of food?)
ring	ring finger (*Which* finger?)

Proper and Compound Adjectives A proper adjective is a proper noun used as an adjective or an adjective formed from a proper noun.

Proper Nouns as Adjectives	Proper Adjectives from Proper Nouns
Boston newspaper	Bostonian dialect
India ink	Indian curry

A compound adjective is an adjective made up of more than one word.

Hyphenated Compound Adjectives	Combined Compound Adjectives
long-distance operator	bedtime story
saber-toothed tiger	household goods

> **Exercise 1** Recognizing Nouns Used as Adjectives, Proper Adjectives, and Compound Adjectives. On each blank at the right, write *noun, proper adjective,* or *compound adjective* to describe the underlined adjective in that sentence.

EXAMPLE: We had dinner in a Greek restaurant. _____*proper adjective*_____

1. The decision had far-reaching effects. _____
2. Ms. Wallace is running for a town office. _____
3. David Copperfield is a favorite Dickensian character. _____
4. My mother raises African violets. _____
5. Those children like peppermint-flavored ice cream. _____
6. Dairy products are good sources of calcium and protein. _____
7. Each camper had a bottle of insect repellent. _____
8. The Parkers are very closemouthed about their new business. _____
9. We have a birdbath in our rose garden. _____
10. This juice comes from Florida oranges. _____

> **Exercise 2** Using Proper and Compound Adjectives to Modify Nouns. Rewrite each word group below to contain a proper adjective or a compound adjective before the main noun.

EXAMPLE: Lens with a wide angle _____*wide-angle lens*_____

1. cafe on a sidewalk _____
2. hat of a cowboy _____
3. serape from Mexico _____
4. streets of the inner city _____
5. island in Hawaii _____

© Prentice-Hall, Inc.

Adjectives (Nouns Used as Adjectives, Proper and Compound Adjectives) • 23

18.1 Adjectives (Nouns Used as Adjectives, Proper and Compound Adjectives) • Practice 2

Exercise 1   **Identifying Nouns Used as Adjectives.**   Underline the noun or nouns that are used as adjectives in each sentence. Make sure each one modifies another noun.

EXAMPLE: Good family members should be careful shoppers.

(1) When you go to the grocery store, do you look for a breakfast cereal, fruit drink, or soap powder with a famous name? (2) If so, you probably pay more than you would if you bought another household product.

(3) Name brands—products with well-known names—are sold across the country. (4) As a result, name brands are usually more costly than regional products, which are sold in a limited area. (5) Producers of national brands know the value of package design and spend money to give products shelf appeal.

Exercise 2   **Recognizing Proper and Compound Adjectives.**   Underline the proper and compound adjectives in each sentence.

EXAMPLE: German shepherds make high-spirited pets.

(1) From the days of the Egyptian and Mesopotamian empires, people have valued dogs because many of their senses are much stronger than ours. (2) A dog's sense of smell is keen, as can be seen in the fugitive-hunting activities of the bloodhound. (3) A dog's sense of hearing is acute, especially for high-pitched sounds. (4) Though dogs are nearsighted and colorblind, their eyes can detect the slightest movement.

(5) In far-off days, dogs first served people as hunters. (6) Mesopotamian records from 3000 B.C. describe greyhound-like dogs. (7) Labrador retrievers, Irish setters, and Russian wolfhounds are a few descendants of early hunters. (8) Work dogs also have a long-lived history. (9) German shepherds, English collies, and Siberian huskies belong to the hard-working group. (10) Today, most breeds, such as the Yorkshire terrier, the Mexican chihuahua, and the French poodle, are kept mainly for companionship.

Writing Application   **Writing Sentences with Adjectives.**   Write each sentence, adding one or more adjectives. Include at least one noun used as an adjective, one proper adjective, and one compound adjective.

EXAMPLE: The team won a game.
_____*The basketball team won a tournament game.*_____

1. We moved the table out under the tree.

   _____

2. The house on our street has a fence around it.

   _____

3. We had food for dinner.

   _____

4. The child played with the ball.

   _____

5. The driver couldn't read the sign.

   _____

Pronouns Used as Adjectives • Practice 1

Possessive Pronouns or Adjectives A pronoun is used as an adjective if it modifies a noun. A personal pronoun used as a possessive adjective answers the question *Which one?* about a noun that follows it.

POSSESSIVE ADJECTIVES
my   your   his   her   its   our   their

Demonstrative, Interrogative, and Indefinite Adjectives A demonstrative, interrogative, or indefinite pronoun used as an adjective answers the question *Which one? How many?* or *How much?* about the noun that follows it.

Demonstrative Adjectives	Interrogative Adjectives
this, that, these, those	what, which, whose

INDEFINITE ADJECTIVES			
Singular	**Plural**	**Singular or Plural**	
another	both	all	other
each	few	any	some
either	many	more	
neither	several	most	

 Exercise 1 **Recognizing Possessive Adjectives.** Underline the possessive adjective in each sentence and circle the noun it modifies.

EXAMPLE: We were late because our (car) broke down.

1. Is your typewriter broken?
2. The cat cleaned its paws.
3. The jurors have taken their seats.
4. The mayor is in her office.
5. Who broke my tennis racquet?
6. We take our vacation in August.
7. Several guests brought their records.
8. I left my notes in school.
9. The boat came off its moorings.
10. Did Dad tell you his surprise?

Exercise 2 **Adding Other Pronouns Used as Adjectives.** Fill in each blank with the kind of pronoun given in parentheses.

EXAMPLE: _____Whose_____ notebook is this? (interrogative)

1. _____ tomatoes are bigger than last year's. (demonstrative)
2. _____ prominent citizens oppose the bill. (indefinite)
3. _____ student completed a questionnaire. (indefinite)
4. _____ career are you thinking of? (interrogative)
5. _____ class are you in for math? (interrogative)

18.1 # Pronouns Used as Adjectives • Practice 2

▶ **Exercise 1** **Recognizing Personal Pronouns That Act as Adjectives.** Underline the possessive pronoun used as an adjective in each of the following sentences. Circle the word it modifies.

EXAMPLE: The lion paced restlessly up and down in its (cage).

1. Have you asked your parents for permission to go to the movies?

2. Stan offered his help to the motorist stranded by the side of the road.

3. All of the players carried their helmets.

4. After the game Tess and her friends waited for the bus.

5. Our grandparents are coming to visit us next week.

6. She helped me with my homework.

7. The dog wagged its tail at us.

8. Jed and Michael rode their bicycles to school.

9. The baby robin fell from its nest during the storm.

10. Please put the books back on their shelves.

▶ **Exercise 2** **Recognizing Other Pronouns Used as Adjectives.** Underline the pronouns used as adjectives. Label each as *demonstrative, interrogative,* or *indefinite.*

EXAMPLE: Did you catch all of these trout? _____*demonstrative*_____

1. Some students still have tickets for the game. _____

2. Which sport is Judy trying out for? _____

3. All citizens have a duty to vote. _____

4. What subject do you like best? _____

5. Are these sunglasses yours or mine? _____

6. We visited several museums last summer. _____

7. Each teacher must hand in a written report. _____

8. That car seldom starts easily on cold mornings. _____

9. Whose trumpet did you borrow? _____

10. Please mail those letters. _____

▶ **Writing Application** **Writing Sentences with Pronouns Used as Adjectives.** Use each pronoun as an adjective in a sentence of your own. Then draw an arrow from each pronoun to the word it modifies.

EXAMPLE: both _____*Julie wore both sweaters.*_____

1. each _____

2. its _____

3. this _____

4. that _____

5. which _____

Name _____ Date _____

 18.2 **Adverbs** (Modifying Verbs) • **Practice 1**

Adverbs Modifying Verbs An adverb is a word that modifies a verb, an adjective, or another adverb.
An adverb modifying a verb answers the question *Where? When? In what manner?* or *To what extent?*

ADVERBS MODIFYING VERBS		
Where?	looked *around*	turned *right*
When?	awoke *early*	arrived *yesterday*
In What Manner?	*easily* won	ran *fast*
To What Extent?	had *barely* touched	*thoroughly* understood

▷ **Exercise 1** **Recognizing Adverbs That Modify Verbs.** Underline the adverb that modifies a
verb in each sentence. On each line at the right, write the question the adverb answers.

EXAMPLE: I have <u>seldom</u> seen a better performance. _____*when*_____

1. The ice storm completely destroyed several buildings. _____

2. The emergency crew arrived promptly. _____

3. New condominiums will be built nearby. _____

4. Leave the packages here. _____

5. The aerialist cautiously tiptoed across the rope. _____

6. The sailor pulled the anchor up. _____

7. Our neighbors will be moving away. _____

8. The children laughed hard at the clown's pranks. _____

9. Ellen spelled one word incorrectly. _____

10. Did you return the call immediately? _____

▷ **Exercise 2** **Adding Adverbs to Modify Verbs.** Fill in the blank in each sentence below with an
adverb that modifies the verb.

EXAMPLE: We ____*usually*____ go away during the month of August.

1. The plane gradually moved _____.

2. The guests _____ ate anything that was offered.

3. The writer worked _____ on the revisions.

4. Several musicians will perform _____.

5. Our connecting flight from Chicago arrived _____.

6. Phyllis solved every problem _____.

7. My grandfather _____ does the Sunday crossword puzzle.

8. The siren wailed _____ in the distance.

9. That meat should be cooked _____.

10. Please meet me _____.

18.2 Adverbs (Modifying Verbs) • Practice 2

▶ **Exercise 1** **Recognizing Adverbs That Modify Verbs.** Write the adverb in each sentence in the correct column.

EXAMPLE: We have almost finished our work.

Where?	When?	In What Manner?	To What Extent?
			almost

1. The pork chops are being served now.
2. The child behaved badly at the circus.
3. Several guests arrived late.
4. Julia beat the eggs briskly.
5. Have any of the tomatoes ripened completely?
6. You'll find the package inside.
7. Our neighbors are moving away.
8. Ted bravely answered the question.
9. The patient has fully recovered from surgery.
10. Jason finished the test early.
11. The pianist performed brilliantly.
12. I will meet you there.
13. The new mayor spoke confidently about the future of the city.
14. Yesterday I forgot my lab notebook.
15. The leaves rustled softly.

Where?	When?	In What Manner?	To What Extent?
1.			
2.			
3.			
4.			
5.			
6.			
7.			
8.			
9.			
10.			
11.			
12.			
13.			
14.			
15.			

18.2 Adverbs (Modifying Adjectives and Other Adverbs)
• Practice 1

Adverbs Modifying Adjectives   An adverb modifying an adjective answers only one question: *To what extent?*

MODIFYING ADJECTIVES	
too eager	*very* far
slightly nervous	*nearly* ready

Adverbs Modifying Other Adverbs   An adverb modifying another adverb also answers just one question: *To what extent?*

MODIFYING ADVERBS	
worked *very* carefully	followed *too* closely
visits *almost* daily	*only* slightly hungry

▷ **Exercise 1**   **Recognizing the Words Adverbs Modify.**   On each blank at the right, write whether each underlined adverb modifies an adjective or another adverb.

EXAMPLE: The President was <u>extremely</u> upset by the news leak. _____*adjective*_____

1. The end of the movie was <u>rather</u> unsatisfying. _____
2. Alison will <u>almost</u> certainly finish the course. _____
3. That is an <u>exceptionally</u> good novel. _____
4. The alarm clock <u>hardly</u> ever wakes me up. _____
5. Dad seemed <u>genuinely</u> surprised by the party. _____
6. The mayor was <u>quite</u> strongly opposed to the new law. _____
7. The patient seemed <u>somewhat</u> stronger today. _____
8. <u>Hardly</u> any cookies were left over. _____
9. The student worked <u>very</u> diligently. _____
10. That building is <u>extraordinarily</u> beautiful. _____

▷ **Exercise 2**   **Adding Adverbs to Sentences.**   Fill in the blank in each sentence with an adverb that answers the question *To what extent?* Underline the word it modifies.

EXAMPLE: _____*Not*_____ many people attended the concert.

1. The bride looked _____ beautiful.
2. The earthquake _____ completely destroyed the city.
3. Several people were _____ unhappy about the decision.
4. The situation seemed _____ hopeless.
5. The hedge _____ partially hid the town dump.
6. _____ early this morning, the repair crew arrived.
7. Mr. Hillyer looks _____ tired today.
8. Jerry is _____ always on time for appointments.
9. We were _____ thoroughly confused by the diagrams.
10. Her compliment sounded _____ sincere.

18.2 Adverbs (Modifying Adjectives and Other Adverbs)
• Practice 2

▶ **Exercise 1** **Recognizing Adverbs That Modify Adjectives.** Underline the adverb in each sentence. Then circle the adjective it modifies.

EXAMPLE: This soup is <u>extremely</u> (hot).

1. That child seems unusually bright.
2. Are you nearly ready for the party?
3. The road was barely visible through the dense fog.
4. Your answer is partially correct.
5. The candidate was thoroughly upset by the question.
6. Lisa looked extremely pale.
7. The auditorium was almost full on opening night.
8. The doctors remained somewhat hopeful.
9. A very sharp noise woke us at three a.m.
10. I was especially happy to see Gladys.
11. As a basketball coach, Pat is quite talented.
12. The rock concert was surprisingly brief.
13. Cynthia was an exceptionally beautiful baby.
14. The skier was particularly careful near the trees.
15. The conductor was visibly moved by the music.

▶ **Exercise 2** **Recognizing Adverbs That Modify Other Adverbs.** Underline the adverb that modifies another adverb in each sentence. Then circle the adverb it modifies.

EXAMPLE: The movie ended <u>too</u> (quickly).

1. The flood waters spread very rapidly.
2. The train arrived unusually late.
3. The horse ran surprisingly fast.
4. The dog moved somewhat closer to the squirrel.
5. The turtle moved more quickly than we had expected.
6. Arnold just barely finished in time.
7. Clare speaks more clearly than her brother.
8. The cookies are almost completely gone.
9. The jury reached its verdict unexpectedly soon.
10. Please move the couch farther forward.
11. Stan takes himself too seriously.
12. The speaker pronounced every word very carefully.
13. Joseph speaks annoyingly slowly.
14. The car was moving frighteningly fast.
15. The driver applied the brakes quite suddenly.

18.2 Adverbs (Adverb or Adjective?) • Practice 1

Adverb or Adjective?   Some words can be either adjectives or adverbs. Remember that an adverb modifies a verb, an adjective, or another adverb. An adjective modifies a noun or a pronoun.

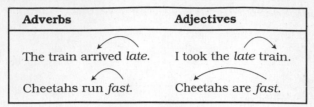

Adverbs	Adjectives
The train arrived *late*.	I took the *late* train.
Cheetahs run *fast*.	Cheetahs are *fast*.

▶ **Exercise 1**   **Distinguishing Between Adjectives and Adverbs.**   Write whether the underlined word in each sentence is an adjective or an adverb.

EXAMPLE: The children seemed <u>excited</u>.   *adjective*

1. The lions ate <u>greedily</u>. _____
2. Glynnis regretted her <u>past</u> mistakes. _____
3. My cousin is an <u>only</u> child. _____
4. Pamela always studies very <u>hard</u>. _____
5. <u>Early</u> dinner guests can be quite unnerving. _____
6. We have <u>only</u> enough money to get home. _____
7. The judge's decision seemed <u>just</u>. _____
8. The Olympic torch went <u>past</u> too quickly. _____
9. I never get up <u>early</u> on weekends. _____
10. My grandmother has <u>just</u> arrived for a visit. _____

▶ **Exercise 2**   **Adding Adverbs and Adjectives to Sentences.**   If an adjective is needed in a sentence below, write the word given in parentheses in the blank. If an adverb is needed, add *-ly* to the given word.

EXAMPLE: Dad told the story _____*amusingly*_____. (amusing)

1. The children seemed _____ to please the teacher. (eager)
2. Ms. Bascomb always walks with a _____ step. (quick)
3. The parents looked _____ at their sleeping infant. (fond)
4. The speaker _____ approached the microphone. (nervous)
5. My aunt is quite _____ of artichokes. (fond)
6. Paul felt _____ about his unkind remark. (bad)
7. After our hot walk, we _____ drank the lemonade. (eager)
8. Many actors feel _____ just before curtain time. (nervous)
9. The waiter brought our food _____. (prompt)
10. The child behaved _____ during the play. (bad)

18.2 Adverbs (Adverb or Adjective?) • Practice 2

▶ **Exercise 1** **Distinguishing Between Adverbs and Adjectives.** Write whether the underlined word in each sentence is an *adjective* or an *adverb*.

EXAMPLE: Agnes looks exceptionally happy today.   *adverb*

1. I spoke too hastily. _____
2. Faith always avoids early classes. _____
3. Jesse seems like a very friendly person. _____
4. The lawyer argued her case convincingly. _____
5. Alice took the late bus back to Minneapolis. _____
6. Many of the guests stayed very late. _____
7. Sid offered me a little brotherly advice. _____
8. Yesterday's game was a close one. _____
9. Christine is extremely athletic. _____
10. Mr. Hawkes gave us a neighborly wave. _____
11. This past year has been a busy one. _____
12. My French teacher lives close to the school. _____
13. We waited eagerly for the election results. _____
14. A butterfly just flew past. _____
15. Lancelot's courtly gesture pleased King Arthur. _____
16. The cyclists began at a leisurely speed. _____
17. The audience applauded enthusiastically. _____
18. Sedwick's punishment was only fair. _____
19. Her stately appearance on stage surprised us all. _____
20. The President openly admitted his mistake. _____

▶ **Exercise 2** **Using Adverbs in Sentences.** Complete each sentence by writing one adverb in each blank.

EXAMPLE: The story of Helen Keller's life is ____*truly*____ inspiring.

(1) Illness _____ destroyed Helen Keller's sight and hearing when she was eighteen months old. (2) For _____ five years, she lived in a dark, silent world, shrieking _____ when she was unhappy or wanted something. (3) Her father _____ hired Anne Sullivan to teach Helen. (4) _____, Anne managed to establish contact with Helen. (5) She spelled words _____ on Helen's hand with her fingers.

(6) Helen _____ made the connection between the words spelled on her hand and the things the words stood for. (7) Her progress _____ became _____ rapid. (8) She _____ learned how to speak _____ _____. (9) With Anne Sullivan to interpret the lectures, Helen _____ completed her degree at Radcliffe College in 1904. (10) For the rest of her life, Helen worked _____ _____ to improve conditions for other blind and deaf-blind people.

Name _____   Date _____

19.1 **Prepositions** • **Practice 1**

Words Used as Prepositions   A preposition is a word that relates a noun or pronoun that appears with it to another word in the sentence. The choice of preposition affects the way the other words in a sentence relate to each other.

PREPOSITIONS
The actors performed { for / without / with } the children.

Prepositional Phrases   A prepositional phrase is a group of words that includes a preposition and a noun or pronoun called the object of the preposition.

PREPOSITIONAL PHRASES	
Prepositions	**Objects of the Prepositions**
about	*whom*
near	the *river*
next to	the *baby*

▶ **Exercise 1**   **Identifying Prepositions.**   Underline each preposition in the sentences below.

EXAMPLE: Elsa brought her camera <u>with</u> her <u>to</u> the museum.

1. Snacks before dinner may spoil your appetite.
2. We agreed to the plan without any hesitation.
3. The wagon in the barn once belonged to my grandfather.
4. Paul Revere rode through the countryside on his horse.
5. According to the newspaper, the play will open in three weeks.
6. We walked along the riverbank until sundown.
7. Mom found my keys in the clothes hamper.
8. The wood stove in the kitchen heats the whole house.
9. Jerry hasn't changed much since last year.
10. Everyone but me had a good view of the runner.

▶ **Exercise 2**   **Identifying Prepositional Phrases.**   Underline each preposition and circle its object. The number in parentheses tells you how many phrases to look for.

EXAMPLE: The girl <u>in front of</u> the (line) came <u>from</u> (Germany). (2)

1. Among the five of us, we had just enough money for a pizza. (3)
2. The sirens could be heard throughout the town. (1)
3. The woman with the tan briefcase is the mayor. (1)
4. A statue of a figure on horseback is an equestrian statue. (2)
5. Despite the sudden shower, we enjoyed our day in the park. (2)
6. Please put this vase of flowers in front of the fireplace. (2)
7. Several guests were late because of the traffic. (1)
8. During the summer everyone met often at the playground. (2)
9. We could see the crab among the rocks beneath the surface. (2)
10. I laughed in spite of myself. (1)

19.1 Prepositions • Practice 2

▶ **Exercise 1** **Recognizing Prepositions.** Write each prepositional phrase, replacing the given preposition with a new one that makes sense.

EXAMPLE: The reporter stood in front of the candidate.

The reporter stood behind the candidate.

1. Please put this under the counter. _____
2. The child played outside the pool. _____
3. I'd like my pizza with anchovies. _____
4. The secret service rode ahead of the President. _____
5. I finished my homework after dinner. _____
6. We carried the packages into the house. _____
7. The runners raced up the hill. _____
8. The senator spoke prior to the press conference. _____
9. The branch fell onto the woodpile. _____
10. The child ran from its mother. _____
11. The party started without Benjamin. _____
12. This gift from you means a great deal. _____
13. Jasmine sat between Roland and Stephen. _____
14. Katherine walked out the door. _____
15. In addition to apples, I bought some peaches. _____

▶ **Exercise 2** **Identifying Prepositional Phrases.** Underline the prepositional phrase or prepositional phrases in each sentence. The number at the end of each sentence tells how many prepositional phrases the sentence has.

EXAMPLE: Please hand me the book with the red cover. (1)

1. Very little could be seen through the fog. (1)
2. In spite of his low test scores, he was admitted to the program. (2)
3. The children dropped their mittens into the muddy creek. (1)
4. The squirrels chased each other around the park. (1)
5. The huge dog dragged his master along the path. (1)
6. Cars and trucks streamed across the bridge during the rush hour. (2)
7. You will find the beach house next to the pier and in back of the parking lot. (2)
8. For three years she traveled the same road. (1)
9. They hiked in the Rocky Mountains for two weeks. (2)
10. Every morning, he passes by on roller skates. (1)
11. The path winds through the hills and into a valley. (2)
12. The person standing near the kitchen seems angry. (1)
13. Life on a raft on the Mississippi gave Huck a chance for adventure. (3)
14. After an hour I finally arrived at the home of my new friend. (3)
15. The book opens with a mystery concerning a lost bracelet. (2)

19.1 Preposition or Adverb? • Practice 1

Preposition or Adverb?   Many words can be either prepositions or adverbs, depending on how they are used. Remember that prepositions always have objects. Adverbs do not.

Prepositions	Adverbs
We walked *along* the *path*.	Will Adam come *along*?
Perry sits *behind me*.	The dog followed *behind*.

▶ **Exercise 1**   **Distinguishing Between Prepositions and Adverbs.**   On each line at the right, write whether the underlined word in each sentence is a *preposition* or an *adverb*.

EXAMPLE: We planted marigolds <u>around</u> the vegetable garden. ___*preposition*___

1. The children enjoyed playing <u>outside</u>. _____

2. A beautiful cherry tree grows <u>outside</u> my bedroom window. _____

3. An eager autograph-seeker slipped <u>past</u> the doorman. _____

4. A fire engine just sped <u>past</u>. _____

5. These belong on the shelf <u>above</u> the encyclopedia. _____

6. A seagull circled high <u>above</u>. _____

7. It was too warm to leave our jackets <u>on</u>. _____

8. Burt was wobbly <u>on</u> his new ice skates. _____

9. I must have left my notebook <u>behind</u>. _____

10. We sat <u>behind</u> a woman with a big hat on. _____

▶ **Exercise 2**   **Adding Prepositions and Adverbs to Sentences.**   In each blank fill in a word that is appropriate for the meaning of both sentences in each pair. In the sentence in which the word is used as a preposition, underline its object.

EXAMPLE: The cake has plenty of raisins ___*throughout*___ .

    The baby was restless ___*throughout*___ the <u>night</u>.

1. a. It is cooler _____ the house than outside.

   b. Please take these packages _____ .

2. a. The diver had enough air to stay _____ the water for hours.

   b. The sailors stayed _____ during the storm.

3. a. We heard strange noises _____ .

   b. That information is to be kept strictly _____ the family.

4. a. Jeanne had never seen a movie star _____ .

   b. The cast arrived at the theater an hour _____ the play.

5. a. Timmy often comes _____ for a visit with my grandmother.

   b. Have you read any other books _____ that author?

19.1 Preposition or Adverb? • Practice 2

▶ **Exercise 1** **Distinguishing Between Prepositions and Adverbs.** Label each underlined word as a *preposition* or an *adverb*.

EXAMPLE: The car was rusted <u>underneath</u> in three places. _____*adverb*_____

1. Please take your coat <u>off</u> the table. _____

2. After I sent the letter <u>off</u>, I remembered the stamp. _____

3. The crowd would not allow him <u>through</u>. _____

4. Alicia skied easily <u>through</u> the dense pine trees. _____

5. Three beautiful boats sank slowly <u>in</u> the waves. _____

6. Although the space was tight, Dave fit his car <u>in</u>. _____

7. The crew went <u>below</u> after they heard the order. _____

8. <u>Below</u> the surface, I saw green and blue fish. _____

9. Entering the apartment, she turned the radio <u>on</u> to catch the news. _____

10. Bill enjoys water skiing <u>on</u> one ski. _____

▶ **Writing Application** **Writing Sentences with Prepositions.** Use each prepositional phrase in a sentence of your own.

EXAMPLE: before school

_____*I usually do my homework in the morning before school.*_____

1. into the water

_____

2. above the clouds

_____

3. except for one student

_____

4. toward my house

_____

5. until next Saturday

_____

6. in addition to soccer

_____

7. outside the window

_____

8. without any fear

_____

9. in front of the post office

_____

10. in spite of the rain

_____

Name _____ Date _____

19.2 Conjunctions and Interjections (Different Kinds of Conjunctions) • Practice 1

Different Kinds of Conjunctions A conjunction is a word used to connect other words or groups of words. Coordinating conjunctions and correlative conjunctions join similar kinds of words or word groups. Subordinating conjunctions connect two ideas by making one of them less important than the other.

COORDINATING CONJUNCTIONS			
and	for	or	yet
but	nor	so	

CORRELATIVE CONJUNCTIONS	
both ... and	not only ... but also
either ... or	whether ... or
neither ... nor	

FREQUENTLY USED SUBORDINATING CONJUNCTIONS					
after	as long as	before	since	till	whenever
although	as soon as	even though	so that	unless	where
as	as though	if	than	until	wherever
as if	because	in order that	though	when	while

▶ **Exercise 1** **Identifying Conjunctions.** Underline the conjunction in each sentence. Write whether it is *coordinating, correlative*, or *subordinating* in each blank at the right.

EXAMPLE: After the race, we were not only tired but also thirsty. _____correlative_____

1. Mr. Kellogg phoned while you were out. _____
2. Alison knew the answer, yet she did not volunteer. _____
3. The swimmer was exhausted but proud. _____
4. We need both cucumbers and tomatoes for the salad. _____
5. I waited in the car while Ted got his bathing suit. _____
6. Katie is a better swimmer than I am. _____
7. Neither Pete nor Carol solved the last problem correctly. _____
8. We will leave as soon as the car is loaded. _____
9. Dad leaves an hour early so that he can avoid traffic. _____
10. Put the packages down wherever there is room for them. _____

▶ **Exercise 2** **Adding Conjunctions in Sentences.** Fill in each blank with a conjunction of the kind given in parentheses.

EXAMPLE: Aunt Joan came with us, ____but____ Uncle Jack stayed home. (coordinating)

1. _____ you need any help, please call me. (subordinating)
2. The food was _____ delicious _____ appealing to the eye. (correlative)
3. The fans were clapping _____ cheering wildly. (coordinating)
4. Al's last book has made him _____ rich _____ famous. (correlative)
5. _____ the cake looked delicious, it was not on my diet. (subordinating)
6. The bus broke down, _____ many students were late. (coordinating)
7. _____ she has the time, Mom volunteers at the hospital. (subordinate)
8. Please type _____ print clearly. (coordinating)
9. The shortstop is good at _____ hitting _____ fielding. (correlative)
10. _____ you pass the high school, turn left. (subordinating)

19.2 Conjunctions and Interjections (Different Kinds of Conjunctions) • Practice 2

▶ **Exercise 1** **Identifying Conjunctions.** Underline the conjunction in each sentence. Then label each as *coordinating*, *correlative*, or *subordinating*.

EXAMPLE: As the rain ended, a rainbow appeared. _____*subordinating*_____

1. Either Elizabeth or Susanne would make a good class president. _____
2. Janet will never agree to that plan, nor will she support anyone who does. _____
3. When the bus was late, Carlos became impatient. _____
4. The pilot of the airplane waited until he received the signal for takeoff. _____
5. You must either leave for the movies immediately or forget about going. _____
6. Wherever the child went, she left cookie crumbs. _____
7. The runner was exhausted but happy. _____
8. Sandy ate not only her own dinner but also mine. _____
9. We waited for hours, yet no one came. _____
10. You will have to call after lunch because she is in a meeting now. _____
11. Both Kevin and Jennifer are working on the ticket committee. _____
12. As soon as he heard about the sale, he rushed to the department store. _____
13. Would you rather have a hot dog or a hamburger? _____
14. Neither the tomatoes nor the peppers are ripe yet. _____
15. If you hear of a part-time job, please let me know. _____
16. Would you please set the table for dinner while I finish the salad. _____
17. We had to take a detour because the bridge had been washed out. _____
18. The town has cleaned up Jones Park, so it is now a safe place to play. _____
19. We all went out for pizza after we finished painting the house. _____
20. The visiting team played hard and well. _____

▶ **Exercise 2** **Using Conjunctions in Sentences.** Fill in each blank with the kind of conjunction indicated in parentheses.

EXAMPLE: The day started out normally, (1) *but* (coordinating) soon things began to change.

Jason had always wanted to visit the Capitol, (1) _____ (coordinating) he signed up for the 1:00 tour. At the appointed time, the tourists (2) _____ (coordinating) their guide set out on the tour of the famous building. The guide pointed out interesting items (3) _____ (subordinating) the group got close to them.

It was (4) _____ hot _____ (correlative) extremely humid, (5) _____ (coordinating) Jason could barely concentrate.

(6) _____ (subordinating) he had looked forward to the tour, he was now eager for it to end.

Jason looked at his watch, (7) _____ (coordinating) he was wondering how much longer the tour would continue. It was 3:00, (8) _____ (coordinating) the tour was supposed to be over. It seemed (9) _____ (subordinating) the tour guide would never stop talking. (10) "_____ this guide ends the tour immediately _____ (correlative) I will have to be rude and leave," thought Jason.

19.2 Conjunctions and Interjections • Practice 1

Conjunctive Adverbs   A conjunctive adverb is an adverb that acts as a conjunction to connect complete ideas.

FREQUENTLY USED CONJUNCTIVE ADVERBS		
accordingly	finally	nevertheless
again	furthermore	otherwise
also	however	then
besides	indeed	therefore
consequently	moreover	thus

Interjections   An interjection is a word that expresses feeling or emotion and functions independently of a sentence.

SOME COMMON INTERJECTIONS		
aha	goodness	tsk
alas	hurray	well
darn	oh	whew
golly	ouch	wow

▶ **Exercise 1**   **Recognizing Conjunctive Adverbs.**   Underline each conjunctive adverb in the sentences below. If a sentence does not have a conjunctive adverb, write *none* in the blank at the right.

EXAMPLE: We waited for the bus; not a single one came by.   ___*none*___

1. Ellen's new bike was a bargain; besides, she needed one. _____
2. I overslept this morning; therefore, I was late for school. _____
3. The phone rang ten times; no one answered. _____
4. It is not unusual for Phil to be late; indeed, he is seldom on time. _____
5. Louise had never eaten snails; nevertheless, she was willing to try. _____
6. Please eat your potatoes; they are getting cold. _____
7. The third batter struck out; again, the Pirates had not scored. _____
8. Len finished his homework; then, he was ready to relax. _____
9. One twin is extremely cautious; the other is impulsive. _____
10. We were caught in traffic; consequently, we missed the overture. _____

▶ **Exercise 2**   **Adding Interjections to Sentences.**   Fill in each blank with an interjection that shows the feeling or emotion given in parentheses.

EXAMPLE: _____ This tastes terrible! (disgust)

1. _____ I just bit my tongue. (pain)
2. _____ The stain will not come out. (regret)
3. _____ What a terrific car that is! (delight)
4. _____ It's just what I always wanted. (surprise)
5. _____ What a close game this is! (excitement)
6. _____ I'm trapped in here! (fear)
7. _____ I knew I got that one wrong. (annoyance)
8. _____ The game has been rained out. (disappointment)
9. _____ Our team is winning. (enthusiasm)
10. _____ What a workout that was! (exhaustion)

19.2 Conjunctions and Interjections • Practice 2

▶ **Exercise 1** **Recognizing Conjunctive Adverbs.** Read each sentence to see whether or not it has a conjunctive adverb. If it does, underline the conjunctive adverb. If it does not, write a conjunctive adverb in the blank and mark where it belongs in the sentence.

EXAMPLE: Eat your breakfast; ∧ go to school. _____*then,*_____

1. Several accidents have occurred on that ride; nevertheless, people wait in line for their turn on it.

_____

2. I saw that movie; however, I did not enjoy it. _____

3. The train arrived late; we missed the concert. _____

4. The book was exciting; I read it all evening. _____

5. Her car broke down; consequently, she had to walk home. _____

6. Finish your dinner; you will have no dessert. _____

7. Al is reliable; moreover, he is never late. _____

8. The fans waited for hours; finally, the star arrived. _____

9. Your appointment was at 6:00; you arrived at 7:00. _____

10. We ran out of gas; we had a flat tire. _____

▶ **Exercise 2** **Supplying Interjections.** Complete each sentence by writing an interjection that shows the indicated emotion.

EXAMPLE: _____*Whew!*_____ This has been a long day. (weariness)

1. _____ I lost my keys. (annoyance)

2. _____ I was hoping for that. (surprise)

3. _____ I stubbed my toe. (pain)

4. _____ What a beautiful cake you made. (delight)

5. _____ It's starting to rain. (disappointment)

▶ **Writing Application** **Using Conjunctions and Conjunctive Adverbs to Combine Sentences.** Turn each pair of sentences into a single sentence by using the kind of conjunction or conjunctive adverb indicated.

EXAMPLE: I keep fit. I swim every day. (subordinating conjunction)

_____*I keep fit because I swim every day.*_____

1. The team practiced hard all week. They did not win the match. (coordinating conjunction)

_____

2. We yanked the door open. Jody stumbled out. (coordinating conjunction)

_____

3. I will go. I will stay. (correlative conjunction)

_____

4. He insisted on driving. He had never driven a truck before. (subordinating conjunction)

_____

5. It rained. The game was canceled. (conjunctive adverb)

_____

20.1 The Sentence (Complete Subjects and Predicates)
• Practice 1

Complete Subjects and Predicates   A sentence is a group of words with two main parts: a complete subject and a complete predicate. Together these parts express a complete thought.

Complete Subjects	Complete Predicates
Everyone in our family	likes Mexican food.
The house down the street	has been for sale for months.
Fish	swim.

Exercise 1   **Recognizing Complete Subjects and Predicates.**   On the blank after each sentence, write *S* or *P* to tell whether the underlined word or group of words is the complete subject or the complete predicate.

EXAMPLE: The bike with the missing reflector is mine.   ___P___

1. Azaleas do well in acid soil. _____
2. The last essay question was really challenging. _____
3. Most of the students in my class study hard. _____
4. The player with the most points at the end of the game loses. _____
5. Weather forecasters predict another storm front from the west. _____
6. The first volunteer fire company in the United States was in Philadelphia. _____
7. Benjamin Franklin organized it. _____
8. Franklin was once ambassador to France. _____
9. Many American towns and cities are named for places in England. _____
10. You may have a little trouble with the lock. _____

Exercise 2   **Identifying Complete Subjects and Predicates.**   In each sentence underline the complete subject once and the complete predicate twice.

EXAMPLE: The tall ships sailed up the Atlantic Coast.

1. Several members of that family have served in the armed forces.
2. Louise borrowed my sweater last week.
3. A pane in one of the bedroom windows cracked.
4. Lemmings follow their leader to their death.
5. A portrait of my grandmother hangs above the mantel.
6. The first pianist on the program seemed nervous.
7. All the children in the neighborhood enjoyed the new playground.
8. Searchlights from the rescue ships flashed across the water.
9. The fans of the losing team groaned.
10. Philip or his brother will surely help you.

20.1 The Sentence (Complete Subjects and Predicates)
• Practice 2

▶ **Exercise 1**   **Recognizing Complete Subjects and Predicates.**   In each sentence, underline each complete subject once and each complete predicate twice.

EXAMPLE: The tall pine trees swayed in the wind.

1. The car swerved away from the child.
2. My favorite radio station plays all of the hit songs.
3. Grandfather Kim owns an art gallery in Chicago.
4. Mexico City was built on a lake.
5. The evening news summarizes the day's events.
6. Shakespeare's father was a glove maker.
7. Computers process information very quickly.
8. My older brother has a telephone shaped like Mickey Mouse.
9. The bags of coins were placed in an armored truck.
10. Damascus, the capital of Syria, has been continuously inhabited for over four thousand years.
11. Mr. Axelrod worked for years as a traveling salesman.
12. The magma in a volcano is called lava when it reaches the air.
13. The ancient Greeks were the first people to have free public museums.
14. People in ancient times used the abacus to compute numbers.
15. Some museums are devoted entirely to computers.
16. Some species of bats are very beneficial to the environment.
17. More than five hundred volcanoes have erupted over the centuries.
18. Our sun is a typical, medium-sized star.
19. The gravity of the sun is almost twenty-eight times the gravity of Earth.
20. Some planets have one or more moons.

▶ **Exercise 2**   **Recognizing Complete Subjects and Predicates.**   In each sentence underline the complete subject once and the complete predicate twice.

EXAMPLE: The blue-eyed Siamese cat curled up on the oak desk.

(1) The giant panda lives in the remote mountains of southern China. (2) This animal is a frustrating mystery to zoologists. (3) The Chinese name for the panda is *xiong-mao*, or "bear-cat". (4) However, the animal is not a cat. (5) Zoologists do not agree about its identity. (6) Some call it a bear. (7) Others place it in the same family as the raccoon. (8) Sadly, the panda is becoming rare. (9) The reason for this is the scarcity of bamboo, its main food. (10) The panda populations can be saved only through worldwide efforts.

The Sentence (Sentence or Fragment?) • Practice 1

Sentence or Fragment?   A fragment is a group of words that does not express a complete thought.

Fragments	Complete Sentences
Early Sunday afternoon	Our weekend guests left early Sunday afternoon.
The beautiful phoenix	The beautiful phoenix was a mythical bird.
Rose from its own ashes	The phoenix rose from its own ashes.

Fragments as Sentence Parts   To turn fragments into sentences, add whatever sentence parts are needed to express a complete thought. The chart below explains what sentence parts were added to the fragments in the chart above.

SENTENCE PARTS ADDED
Complete subject and predicate areas were added.
A predicate area was added.
A subject area was added.

▶ **Exercise 1**   **Distinguishing Between Sentences and Fragments.**   In the blanks below, write *S* for each sentence and *F* for each fragment.

EXAMPLE: throughout the day and into the night. ____*F*____

1. Without any trouble at all. _____

2. Played quietly after dinner. _____

3. Pete plays the piccolo. _____

4. Beyond our wildest expectations. _____

5. Yellowstone Park attracts many tourists. _____

6. People from all parts of the world. _____

7. The contestant with the most unusual costume. _____

8. Has traveled widely throughout the United States. _____

9. The prospector struck oil. _____

10. Robins fly south for the winter. _____

▶ **Exercise 2**   **Adding Words to Make Sentences from Fragments.**   Rewrite five of the fragments above as complete sentences.

EXAMPLE: _____*Snow fell throughout the day and into the night.*_____

1. _____

2. _____

3. _____

4. _____

5. _____

20.1 The Sentence (Sentence or Fragment?) • Practice 2

Exercise 1 **Distinguishing Between Sentences and Fragments.** Identify each item as a *sentence* or a *fragment*.

EXAMPLE: Worked for many hours _____*fragment*_____

1. In the woods almost until dawn. _____

2. A few inches of snow. _____

3. The grizzly bear needs large territories undisturbed by people. _____

4. Have been unusually high because of the very heavy rains this season. _____

5. Herds of thousands of caribou. _____

6. Haste makes waste. _____

7. Dived in search of food. _____

8. Cousteau believes artificial islands could be built off the coast. _____

9. About a great white shark, one of the largest ones ever caught. _____

10. Cougars have become increasingly rare. _____

11. Is the last frontier. _____

12. There he sat, totally content. _____

13. In the day in order to hunt at night. _____

14. Ice-covered Mount McKinley in Alaska attracts many tourists. _____

15. Wolves, jaguars, and grizzly bears once numerous in North America. _____

Writing Application **Using Fragments to Make Sentences.** Combine each of the ten complete subjects on the left with one of the ten complete predicates on the right to make ten logical sentences.

EXAMPLE: The umpire at yesterday's game   told me to watch my temper.

_____*The umpire at yesterday's game told me to watch my temper.*_____

1. His Roman costume   took the wrong bus.
2. The children   stuck to the stage.
3. The girl with butterflies in her stomach   wandered into the tack room.
4. The curious horse   can fool people.
5. The boy with the confused expression   was tangled in the stage scenery.
6. Lemon jello inside empty eggshells   put sugar at the bottom of her sleeping bag.
7. Their cousins coming for dinner   was wearing his shirt inside out.
8. The man standing on the corner   scored a goal for the opposing team.
9. Her long, pointed putty nose   thought the raccoon was a ghost.
10. Her friends at the slumber party   spoke to the flag instead of to the class.

1. _____

2. _____

3. _____

4. _____

5. _____

6. _____

7. _____

8. _____

9. _____

10. _____

20.1 Subjects and Verbs (Simple Subjects and Predicates) • Practice 1

Simple Subjects and Predicates   The simple subject is the essential noun, pronoun, or group of words acting as a noun that cannot be left out of the complete subject. The simple predicate is the essential verb or verb phrase that cannot be left out of the complete predicate. In the chart below, each simple subject and simple predicate is in darker type.

Complete Subjects	Complete Predicates
Tired of arguing, **Maria**	finally **agreed** to the plan.
Like many others in my class, **I**	**do** not especially **like** homework.
Many **citizens** in town	**oppose** higher taxes.
Others	**agree**.

Focusing on Subjects and Verbs   Being able to locate subjects and verbs quickly in sentences will help you to determine that a sentence is clear and grammatically correct.

FINDING SUBJECTS AND VERBS
To find the subject, ask "What word is the sentence telling about?"   To find the verb, look for a word or word group that expresses action, existence, or a linking relationship.

▷ **Exercise 1**   **Recognizing Complete and Simple Subjects and Predicates.**   Draw a line between the complete subject and the complete predicate in each sentence. Then circle each simple subject and predicate.

EXAMPLE: That tall (girl) in the red dress | usually (gets) the best grades.

1. The album with the original cast is now available in most stores.

2. Senator Billings will propose the new law.

3. The fourth Thursday in November is celebrated as Thanksgiving Day.

4. The skydiver landed safely.

5. Youngsters sometimes jump from those high rocks.

6. Dignitaries from all over the world attended the reception.

7. The children's elaborate skyscraper collapsed.

8. Ghosts are popular Halloween characters.

9. Several students from Europe are staying with local families.

10. The mysterious figure in black vanished.

▷ **Exercise 2**   **Adding Sentence Parts.**   Each word group below is missing either a complete subject or a complete predicate. On the line write a missing part to create a complete sentence. Circle the simple subject and simple predicate in the final sentence.

EXAMPLE: ____(Most) of the people passing by____ (did) not (offer) to help.

1. From among the many entries, only one _____.

2. Every visitor to our school _____.

3. _____ gradually overcame the fear of heights.

4. My younger brother _____.

5. _____ has misplaced a library book.

20.1 Subjects and Verbs (Simple Subjects and Predicates) • Practice 2

▶ **Exercise 1** **Recognizing Simple Subjects and Predicates.** Draw a line between the complete subject and complete predicate. Then underline each simple subject once and each simple predicate twice.

EXAMPLE: A <u>friend</u> of mine | <u>plays</u> chess with me.

1. A sixteen-year-old girl from California gave the best dramatic interpretation.
2. A muddy dog of unknown breed ran away with Bernard's lunch.
3. Her friends at school helped her get a job.
4. The weary commuters were angry about the delay.
5. The freshman with the most unusual hat won the contest.
6. The boxes under the sink are empty.
7. The frightened witnesses wrote reports for the police.
8. The speaker caught his fishing pole on the light fixture.
9. Students going on the trip left early this morning.
10. The forward with the knee brace made ten baskets.

▶ **Exercise 2** **Finding Subjects and Verbs.** Underline the subject once and the verb twice.

EXAMPLE: Many <u>people</u> <u>visit</u> the Grand Canyon.

(1) A tourist gets a spectacular view at the Grand Canyon. (2) Curious visitors can take nature walks along the trails on the edge of the canyon. (3) Hikers may want to venture down the steep trails into the canyon. (4) However, the crumbling walls of the canyon's sides make mountain climbing dangerous. (5) A guided mule trip is a safer way to see the canyon. (6) Trips down the Colorado River also enable tourists to see the canyon from the inside.

(7) Tourists can also take a helicopter or an airplane ride over the canyon. (8) From the helicopter or plane, passengers can see the different branches of the canyon. (9) The aircraft can fly into the canyon for a closer view of the river and rock formations. (10) With all of these approaches, tourists can see the canyon from above, from the inside, or from the edge.

▶ **Writing Application** **Using Subjects and Verbs to Write Sentences.** Use each subject and verb in a sentence of your own.

EXAMPLE: robins   chirped

_____*In the nest baby robins chirped for food.*_____

1. truck   is stopping _____
2. girl   jumped _____
3. steak   shriveled _____
4. wind   was shrieking _____
5. radio   blared _____
6. lawnmower   sputtered _____
7. automobile   is wobbling _____
8. water   feels _____
9. waiter   dropped _____
10. newscaster   hiccupped _____

20.1 # Compound Subjects and Verbs • **Practice 1**

Compound Subjects   A compound subject is two or more subjects that have the same verb and are joined by a conjunction such as *and* or *or*.

COMPOUND SUBJECTS
Mother or Dad will pick us up after the movie.
Lobsters, shrimp, and crabs are popular shellfish.

Compound Verbs   A compound verb is two or more verbs that have the same subject and are joined by a conjunction such as *and* or *or*.

COMPOUND VERBS
The waves crested and broke against the rocks.
The passers-by did not move on but stopped to watch the mime.
Paul and Andrew write, direct, and star in their own plays.

▷ **Exercise 1**   **Recognizing Compound Subjects.**   Underline the nouns or pronouns that make up each compound subject below.

EXAMPLE: High winds and freezing rain caused the power failure.

1. Carrots or small tomatoes would make an attractive garnish.
2. Cheese and whole-wheat crackers are a healthful snack.
3. Nancy, Darryl, and I worked on the decorations.
4. Time and the tide wait for no one.
5. In the forest, ferns and wildflowers abound.
6. Neither my brother nor I felt comfortable with those people.
7. Without your help, the table and the food would not have been ready.
8. Jason and Ulysses are characters from Greek mythology.
9. Pueblos, hogans, and tepees were common Indian dwellings.
10. In colonial times, stocks and pillories were used for punishment.

▷ **Exercise 2**   **Recognizing Compound Verbs.**   Underline the verbs that make up each compound verb below.

EXAMPLE: The masked stranger mounted his horse and galloped away.

1. The baby eats and sleeps on a regular schedule.
2. The photographer checked the lighting, posed the subject, and snapped the picture.
3. The paramedic did not hesitate but acted at once.
4. The captain hoisted the sail and pulled up the anchor.
5. The sick puppy neither ate nor drank.
6. The whole family baked and cooked for days before the holiday.
7. Brenda organized her note cards and began her rough draft.
8. Mike pruned and fertilized the grapefruit plant.
9. The departing dignitary neither waved nor looked back.
10. Some students seldom study but still do well.

20.1 Compound Subjects and Verbs • Practice 2

▶ **Exercise 1**   **Recognizing Compound Subjects.**   Underline the nouns that make up each compound subject.

EXAMPLE: The <u>windows</u> and <u>doors</u> are locked.

1. Both flowers and perfume cause her to sneeze.

2. David and Marie both failed to win the prize.

3. Neither pets nor pianos are allowed in the apartment.

4. Lettuce, tomatoes, peppers, and cucumbers grew in the garden.

5. Hurricanes and tornadoes cause much damage to property every year.

▶ **Exercise 2**   **Recognizing Compound Verbs.**   Underline the verbs that make up each compound verb.

EXAMPLE: I <u>studied</u> hard and <u>passed</u> the test.

1. The car suddenly skidded on the ice and hit the curb.

2. Winds howled through the night but died down at dawn.

3. Hercules lifted Antaeus from the ground and crushed him.

4. Sports medicine is a relatively new field and offers many opportunities for careers.

5. The duck waddled down the bank, splashed into the water, and paddled to safety.

6. My brother and I built a rowboat in 1979 and used it on the lake the next year.

7. We washed the dishes and put them away.

8. He survived the war but died soon after.

9. The Romans erected buildings in brick and then faced them with marble.

10. We rehearsed the play for three weeks, had a dress rehearsal, and then gave a performance.

▶ **Writing Application**   **Writing Sentences with Compound Subjects and Verbs.**   Use the following items to write ten sentences of your own. Use the first three items as compound subjects, the next three as compound verbs, and the last four as compound subjects and verbs.

EXAMPLE: dog   squirrel
   _____*Our dog and a squirrel raced around the yard.*_____

1. jumper   sprinter _____

2. beaches   docks _____

3. guitarist   drummer   composer _____

4. stamped   screamed _____

5. dribbled   tossed _____

6. nods   smiles _____

7. orchestra   conductor   bowed   disappeared _____

   _____

8. horses   riders   galloped   trotted _____

   _____

9. clown   acrobat   stumbled   fell   rose _____

   _____

10. vans   trucks   cost   carry _____

   _____

20.2 Hard-to-Find Subjects (in Orders and Directions, in Questions) • Practice 1

Subjects in Orders and Directions   In sentences that give orders or directions, the subject is understood to be *you*.

Orders or Directions	With Understood Words Added
Return your library books immediately.	[You] return your library books immediately.
David, answer the door.	David, [you] answer the door.

Subjects in Questions   In questions the subject often follows the verb. To find the subject in a question, mentally rephrase the question as a statement.

Questions	Reworded as Statements
Is this your address?	This is your address.
Can we eat now?	We can eat now.
Where are you going ?	You are going where.

▶ **Exercise 1**   **Finding the Subject in Orders or Directions.**   Write the subject of each sentence in the blank at the right. Put a caret (^) where the subject belongs in the sentence.

EXAMPLE: André,^ please clear the table. _____*you*_____

1. A block past the First Bank, turn left. _____
2. Whatever the difficulties, do your best. _____
3. Please take out the trash. _____
4. Alison, don't forget your lunch. _____
5. Blacken in the grid with a soft pencil. _____
6. Derek, please give your mother a message. _____
7. Meet me at the library after school. _____
8. Mandy, please let me copy that recipe. _____
9. Before starting out, buckle your safety belt. _____
10. Help yourself, everyone. _____

▶ **Exercise 2**   **Finding the Subject in Questions.**   Underline the simple subject in each question below.

EXAMPLE: How much do these shoes cost?

1. Do you know the combination to this lock?
2. Have your parents given their permission for the class trip?
3. How is that casserole prepared?
4. What color did you paint the kitchen walls?
5. Did anyone bring directions to the farm?
6. Where are the Claytons going for the weekend?
7. Didn't Shakespeare write sonnets as well as plays?
8. Who brought the sandwiches?
9. Whom did Sue invite on the picnic?
10. Whose story should we believe?

20.2 Hard-to-Find Subjects (in Orders and Directions, in Questions) • Practice 2

▶ **Exercise 1** **Finding Subjects in Orders or Directions.** Rewrite each sentence, inserting the understood subject in brackets.

EXAMPLE: During your break, take the dog out.

During your break, [you] take the dog out.

1. After school, come straight home.

   _____

2. Joanne, give me a quarter.

   _____

3. Now tell me what happened.

   _____

4. When using that machine, always wear safety goggles.

   _____

5. Sue, order me a milkshake, please.

   _____

6. After class, meet me at the library.

   _____

7. Pete, during takeoff, keep your seatbelt fastened.

   _____

8. Before leaving, pack a good lunch.

   _____

9. Dad, turn left at the end of the exit ramp.

   _____

10. When filling out that form, use ink.

   _____

▶ **Exercise 2** **Finding Subjects in Questions.** Underline the subject of each sentence.

EXAMPLE: Where did they spend their last winter vacation?

1. Have you seen the new horror movie?
2. When will Sally be home?
3. Who baked this cake?
4. About what will Andy write?
5. Are the final reports complete?
6. Is the story ready for publication?
7. Why hasn't Judy answered my note?
8. What did Jack wear to the game?
9. Has Joyce finished her term paper yet?
10. Which team won the championship?

20.2 Hard-to-Find Subjects (in Sentences Beginning with *There* or *Here*, in Sentences Inverted for Emphasis)
• Practice 1

Subjects in Sentences Beginning with *There* or *Here* The subject of a sentence is never *there* or *here*. Like inverted questions, such sentences can usually be rephrased as statements to find the subject.

Sentences Beginning with *There* or *Here*	Reworded with Subjects First
There goes my best friend.	My best friend goes there.
Here is your tennis racquet.	Your tennis racquet is here.

Subjects in Sentences Inverted for Emphasis In some sentences the subject is placed after the verb in order to receive greater emphasis. Such sentences can be mentally rephrased in normal subject-verb order to find the subject.

Inverted Word Order	Rephrased in Subject-Verb Order
After the elephants came the *clowns*.	The *clowns* came after the elephants.
Beyond the river lay the *cliffs*.	The *cliffs* lay beyond the river.

Exercise 1 **Finding the Subject in Sentences Beginning with *There* or *Here*.** Underline the subject in each sentence below.

EXAMPLE: Here comes the circus parade.

1. There is the new mayor.
2. Here are the proofs from the photographer.
3. There has seldom been a more beautiful sunset.
4. There is little undeveloped land in this part of town.
5. Here comes the custodian with the keys.
6. There must be a better restaurant in town than this one.
7. Here is the newest book by my favorite author.
8. There is no doubt about the outcome.
9. There went our last chance at the championship.
10. Here comes the President's helicopter.

Exercise 2 **Finding the Subject in Inverted Sentences.** Underline the subject in each sentence below.

EXAMPLE: Over the mantel hangs a beautiful landscape.

1. Right before our eyes appeared a white rabbit.
2. Between the creek and the dirt road stretches a lush meadow.
3. Throughout the town flew rumors about the bank manager.
4. Outside my bedroom window blooms a beautiful lilac bush.
5. On the front page appeared a story about the student of the year.
6. Into the stadium filed the throng of eager fans.
7. Through these halls have passed generations of dedicated lawmakers.
8. In the center of the harbor stands the Statue of Liberty.
9. From every window streamed tons of ticker tape and confetti.
10. Along the cobblestone streets stood restored colonial houses.

20.2 Hard-to-Find Subjects (in Sentences Beginning with *There* or *Here*, in Sentences Inverted for Emphasis)
• Practice 2

▶ **Exercise 1**   Finding Subjects in Sentences Beginning with *There* or *Here*.   Underline the subject of each sentence.

EXAMPLE: Here <u>she</u> is.

1. There are your keys on the table.
2. Here comes the bus.
3. There was no excuse for his behavior.
4. There goes the kite into the tree.
5. Here is your pizza with mushrooms and extra cheese.
6. There is the rest of the strawberry pie.
7. There are last week's papers.
8. Here are the poppy-seed rolls from the bakery.
9. There went my sister in her new car.
10. There were only three seeds left in the birdfeeder.

▶ **Exercise 2**   Finding Subjects in Inverted Sentences.   Underline the subject of each sentence.

EXAMPLE: In her hand was the missing <u>letter</u>.

1. After the rain came a beautiful rainbow.
2. All about us rang the bells of the village's three churches.
3. To the south rose the snow-covered peaks of the lofty mountains.
4. Ahead of the couple ran four noisy children.
5. All around them lay the scattered leaves.
6. With their safe arrival came a feeling of great happiness and relief.
7. Among the people in the crowd were our neighbors.
8. Beside the fire sat an old man.
9. On a raft floating down the river were their treasured possessions.
10. From the distance came the sound of thunder.

▶ **Writing Application**   Writing Sentences with Hard-to-Find Subjects.   Write four sentences of your own. The first sentence should give an order; the second should ask a question; the third should be an inverted sentence that begins with *there* or *here*; and the fourth sentence should be inverted for emphasis.

EXAMPLE: _____ *Lisa, leave right away.* _____

1. _____
   _____
2. _____
   _____
3. _____
   _____
4. _____
   _____

20.3 Direct Objects (The Direct Object, Compound Direct Objects) • Practice 1

The Direct Object   A direct object is a noun, pronoun, or group of words acting as a noun that receives the action of a transitive verb.

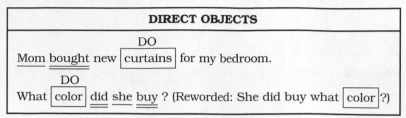

Compound Direct Objects   A compound direct object is more than one noun, pronoun, or group of words acting as a noun that receives the action of the same transitive verb.

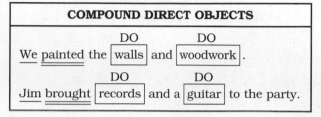

Exercise 1   **Recognizing Direct Objects.**   Draw a box around the direct object in each sentence.

EXAMPLE: Please set this |vase| in the center of the table.

1. What tapes did you bring?
2. Everyone enjoyed the performance.
3. Who will teach classes during Mr. Roper's leave of absence?
4. The owner of the missing dog has offered a reward.
5. Too much sugar may promote tooth decay.
6. Did you make this long-distance call to Denver?
7. Tanya likes basketball better than I do.
8. The campers took a wrong turn.
9. On the day of the test, bring two sharpened pencils.
10. Phyllis's parents surprised her with a new bike.

Exercise 2   **Recognizing Compound Direct Objects.**   Draw a box around the nouns or pronouns that make up each compound direct object.

EXAMPLE: Would you rather have |sausage| or |pepperoni| on your pizza?

1. Mandy plays both basketball and soccer.
2. The new album brought fame and fortune to the young singer.
3. Should we serve the soup or the salad first?
4. The contestant won not only the car but also a cash jackpot.
5. Would you rather play chess or checkers?
6. Did the painter use a roller or a brush?
7. The chef will prepare pancakes or omelets.
8. The shopper bought both the knee-high boots and the matching purse.
9. For a bedtime snack, Fran has a sandwich and milk every night.
10. Are you taking biology or chemistry next term?

20.3 Direct Objects (The Direct Object, Compound Direct Objects) • Practice 2

▶ **Exercise 1** **Recognizing Direct Objects.** Underline the direct object in each sentence.

EXAMPLE: Most people own umbrellas.

(1) Umbrellas have a long history. (2) Even the ancient Egyptians used them. (3) The umbrella symbolized royal and religious power to the Egyptians. (4) Assyrian tablets from 1350 B.C. show an umbrella-shaded king. (5) The early Greeks also used the umbrella symbol. (6) Religious festivals and parades featured it prominently. (7) The later Greeks used the umbrella shape more practically. (8) They invented the sunshade. (9) They even developed a sunshade hat. (10) Later still, the Romans used parasols.

▶ **Exercise 2** **Recognizing Compound Direct Objects.** Underline the nouns or pronouns that make up each compound direct object.

EXAMPLE: Maggie knitted a hat and mittens.

1. Don't forget the hammer and nails.
2. Mike bought a new jacket, shirt, and trousers.
3. The fire destroyed both the main house and the barn.
4. Who invited Joan and Jack?
5. That factory produces cars and trucks.
6. The baby doesn't eat fruit or cereal yet.
7. Which shrubs and bushes did the gardener trim?
8. The recipe requires cinnamon and sugar.
9. The waiter overlooked you and me.
10. Mom planted cabbage, tomatoes, lettuce, and peppers.
11. We read the bulletin board and the pamphlets carefully.
12. Susan had salad and soup for lunch.
13. The dog chased woodchucks and rabbits all over the field.
14. Caroline bought roses and carnations for the centerpiece.
15. My duties that summer included filing and word processing.
16. On our road trip, we visited Montana and Idaho.
17. William Shakespeare wrote sonnets and plays.
18. The mechanic replaced the points and plugs in the car.
19. Mabel added sprouts and radishes to the salad.
20. Winifred is studying history and literature.

20.3 Direct Objects (Direct Object or Object of a Preposition?) • Practice 1

Direct Object or Object of a Preposition   A direct object is never the noun or pronoun at the end of a prepositional phrase.

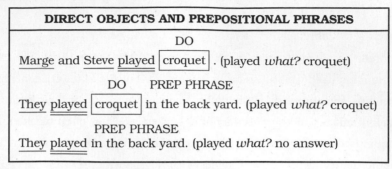

DIRECT OBJECTS AND PREPOSITIONAL PHRASES

DO
Marge and Steve played │croquet│ . (played *what?* croquet)

DO   PREP PHRASE
They played │croquet│ in the back yard. (played *what?* croquet)

PREP PHRASE
They played in the back yard. (played *what?* no answer)

▶ **Exercise 1**   **Distinguishing Between Direct Objects and Objects of Prepositions.**   Draw a box around only direct objects in the sentences. Do not box any objects of prepositions.

EXAMPLE: We joined │Kelly│ and │Tim│ for a picnic.

1. Please put the fruit into the refrigerator.
2. Several new families moved into our neighborhood.
3. A true story inspired the novel about Robinson Crusoe.
4. Alexander Selkirk survived on a desert island.
5. We changed planes in Chicago.
6. Betsy chose fruit instead of ice cream for dessert.
7. Linus carries his blanket everywhere.
8. We watched the sunset from the porch.
9. Eventually the cowboy overcame his fear of horses.
10. The guest of honor arrived in time for dinner.

▶ **Exercise 2**   **Writing Sentences with Direct Objects.**   Add words to each sentence beginning below to make a complete sentence. Be sure each sentence ending includes a direct object.

EXAMPLE: The singer performed _____*an old-time favorite*_____ .

1. My sister broke _____.
2. The teacher gave Ian _____.
3. We all enjoyed _____.
4. Some of the children followed _____.
5. Have you read _____.
6. My friend Jessica wrote _____.
7. The guests ate _____.
8. Robins built _____.
9. Our team won _____.
10. Please put _____.

20.3 Direct Objects (Direct Object or Object of a Preposition?) • Practice 2

▶ **Exercise 1** **Distinguishing Between Direct Objects and Objects of Prepositions.** Write the direct object in each sentence. If a sentence does not have one, write *none*.

EXAMPLE: People have used umbrellas for a long time. _____*umbrellas*_____

(1) The word umbrella has come to us from the Romans. (2) The Latin word *umbra* translates into our word "shade." (3) The Romans used umbrellas for protection against the sun. (4) People often carried them to chariot races. (5) Romans sometimes dyed the umbrellas with the colors of their favorite chariot team. (6) Eventually umbrellas at chariot races caused a public uproar. (7) They often blocked the view of other spectators. (8) The Roman emperor Domitian finally settled the dispute about umbrellas. (9) By his decree only sunshade hats could be used at the public games. (10) No one with an umbrella could attend the games.

1. _____   5. _____   8. _____
2. _____   6. _____   9. _____
3. _____   7. _____   10. _____
4. _____

▶ **Writing Application** **Writing Sentences with Direct Objects.** Use each subject and verb to write a sentence with a direct object. Then circle each direct object.

EXAMPLE: kittens   played

_____The kittens played ⟨tag⟩ with each other._____

1. police   will escort _____
2. truck   dented _____
3. Mr. Lopez   described _____
4. elephant   trampled _____
5. water   ruined _____
6. Eileen   organized _____
7. Craig   should have won _____
8. grasshoppers   destroy _____
9. detectives   found _____
10. noise   shook _____

20.3 Indirect Objects (Indirect Objects, Compound Indirect Objects) • Practice 1

Indirect Objects   An indirect object is a noun or pronoun that appears with a direct object and names the person or thing that something is given to or done for.

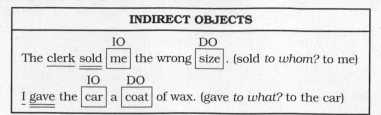

Compound Indirect Objects   A compound indirect object is two or more nouns or pronouns that appear with a direct object and name the people or things that something is given to or done for.

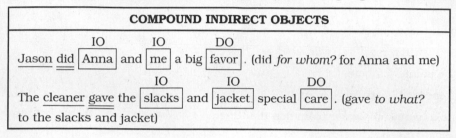

▶ **Exercise 1**   **Recognizing Indirect Objects.**   Draw a box around each indirect object.

EXAMPLE: My parents gave me an allowance for doing chores.

1. Grandma offered us another piece of pie.
2. The baby sitter read the children another story before bedtime.
3. Warren gave the teacher his first draft this morning.
4. The testing service will send the school our grades in a few weeks.
5. The prisoner passed the warden his empty cup.
6. The famous chef served the guests an elegant meal.
7. Who told you that secret?
8. Jimmy's parents allowed him one more chance.
9. Doris dealt each player thirteen cards.
10. Has anyone given the dog a bath this week?

▶ **Exercise 2**   **Recognizing Compound Indirect Objects.**   Draw a box around the nouns or pronouns that make up each compound indirect object.

EXAMPLE: Brenda showed her brother and me pictures from her vacation.

1. We fixed Mom and Dad a special anniversary dinner.
2. The PTA gave the teachers and aides an end-of-year luncheon.
3. Hannah brought the painter and his helper a cold drink.
4. The magician showed me and the others the secret compartment.
5. The principal handed Doug and Karen their diplomas first.
6. We gave Mom and Grandma corsages.
7. Aunt Paula always makes my cousins and me a special dessert.
8. The city gave the players and their families a ticker tape parade.
9. The mechanic gave the chain, sprocket, and axles a coat of oil.
10. The child left Santa and his reindeer a snack.

20.3 Indirect Objects (Indirect Objects, Compound Indirect Objects) • Practice 2

▶ **Exercise 1**   **Recognizing Indirect Objects.**   Underline the indirect object in each sentence.

EXAMPLE: He gave me his old tennis racquet.

1. He told his parents the news.
2. Greg ordered us seconds.
3. The receptionist gave the messenger an envelope.
4. The sitter read Paul two stories at bedtime.
5. I lent Amanda my pink sweater.
6. Ms. Hall showed us slides of Venice.
7. Who sent you these flowers?
8. Sandy hasn't written me a letter for weeks.
9. Mom left the painters a note.
10. Mr. Poirot teaches his students French.
11. You owe me a more complete explanation than that.
12. Please do Sylvia this favor.
13. Give James a call about your plans for the trip.
14. The federal government sent the flooded city aid.
15. Henry gave the school a memorial bench.
16. The coach handed the team members their new jerseys.
17. Mr. Costanza bought his daughter a new bicycle for her birthday.
18. Emma knitted her granddaughter a lavender blanket.
19. The store owner sold the young child a defective toy.
20. The politician told the people his plans for the future.

▶ **Exercise 2**   **Recognizing Compound Indirect Objects.**   Underline the nouns or pronouns acting as indirect objects in each sentence. Then circle the nouns or pronouns that make up each compound indirect object.

EXAMPLE: We wrote (Sue) and (Al) letters about our trip.

(1) Bart showed us the route for the trip. (2) Mr. Perkins rented Joyce and me bikes. (3) My mother packed us a snack. (4) I had already given the group the other food supplies. (5) I had also given Helen and Max the sleeping bags. (6) Our families wished us a pleasant trip. (7) At the campsite Bart showed Helen, Joyce, and Max the best way to make a fire. (8) We cooked ourselves a fine meal. (9) No one left the raccoons and other animals even a nibble. (10) Then Joyce told us ghost stories around the campfire.

20.3 Indirect Objects and Objective Complements • Practice 1

Indirect Object or Object of a Preposition   An indirect object never follows the word *to* or *for*.

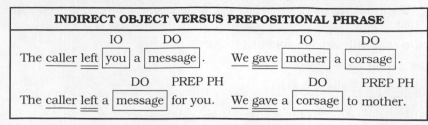

The Objective Complement   An objective complement is an adjective, noun, or group of words acting as a noun that follows a direct object and describes or renames it.

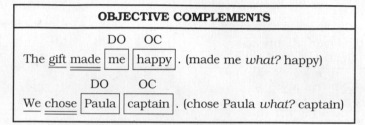

▶ **Exercise 1**   **Distinguishing Between Indirect Objects and Objects of Prepositions.**   In each blank at the right, write whether the underlined word is an *indirect object* or an *object of a preposition*.

EXAMPLE: Volunteers offered each <u>passer-by</u> a flyer.   _____*indirect object*_____

1. The realtor showed the <u>family</u> several houses. _____

2. The child brought an apple for the <u>teacher</u>. _____

3. Lana told <u>us</u> a funny joke. _____

4. A volunteer brought the <u>patient</u> a newspaper. _____

5. The messenger handed the envelope to the <u>secretary</u>. _____

6. Please give this note to <u>Phillip</u>. _____

7. Ms. Nelson gave <u>us</u> a surprise quiz. _____

8. The principal read the notice to the entire <u>school</u>. _____

9. The defendant told the <u>judge</u> his story. _____

10. Luis made his <u>father</u> a bookcase. _____

▶ **Exercise 2**   **Recognizing Objective Complements.**   Underline the objective complement in each sentence below. Then write whether it is a *noun* or an *adjective* in the blank to the right.

EXAMPLE: The race left us <u>exhausted</u>.   _____*adjective*_____

1. The team made the coach proud. _____

2. The class elected Harry treasurer. _____

3. The jury found the defendant not guilty. _____

4. The mechanical swing kept the baby quiet for hours. _____

5. Everyone in his family calls Jeremy "Jem." _____

20.3 Indirect Objects and Objective Complements • Practice 2

▶ **Exercise 1** **Distinguishing Between Indirect Objects and Objects of Prepositions.** In the following sentences, change each indirect object into a prepositional phrase. Change each prepositional phrase that you can into an indirect object.

EXAMPLE: Janet left a message for you.

Janet left you a message.

1. Last night at the restaurant, the chef prepared a special dessert for us.

_____

2. The sitter handed the baby the rattle.

_____

3. The realtor showed us four apartments.

_____

4. Alex sold his farm to the county.

_____

5. Did you bring some ice cream for the children?

_____

▶ **Exercise 2** **Recognizing Objective Complements.** Underline the objective complement in each sentence.

EXAMPLE: The movie made him very sad.

1. The third-period class nominated him treasurer.
2. The continuous rain made them depressed.
3. The cousins called their talented uncle a wizard.
4. The actor dyed his blond hair red.
5. My parents' rules sometimes make me angry.

▶ **Writing Application** **Using Indirect Objects to Combine Sentences.** Turn each pair of sentences into a single sentence with an indirect object.

EXAMPLE: I bought the album. I bought it for Mark.

I bought Mark the album.

1. The sitter prepared a snack. He prepared it for Paul.

_____

2. The waiter served my order. He served it to Ann.

_____

3. I made a macramé belt. I made it for my mother.

_____

4. The realtor rented the apartment. She rented it to us.

_____

5. The principal gave an award. He gave it to our class.

_____

Name _____ Date _____

20.3 Subject Complements (Predicate Nominative, Predicate Adjective) • Practice 1

Subject Complements A predicate nominative is a noun or pronoun that follows a linking verb and renames, identifies, or explains the subject of a sentence.

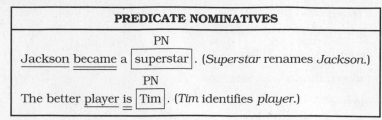

The Predicate Adjective A predicate adjective is an adjective that follows a linking verb and describes the subject of the sentence.

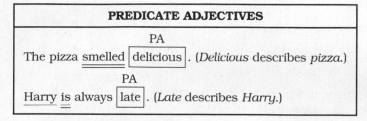

▷ **Exercise 1** **Recognizing Predicate Nominatives.** Underline each predicate nominative.

EXAMPLE: Helen has been my best <u>friend</u> since kindergarten.

1. The Tigers are the team to beat.
2. Math and science are my best subjects.
3. My sister became a lawyer after years of study.
4. The former President remained a prominent figure after leaving office.
5. The specialty of the house is cheese fondue.
6. Judy's plan seemed a workable one.
7. The understudy became an overnight success.
8. He is the best choice for the job.
9. The executive remained an officer even after her retirement.
10. Nero Wolfe is a famous fictional detective.

▷ **Exercise 2** **Recognizing Predicate Adjectives.** Underline each predicate adjective.

EXAMPLE: The movie sounds <u>ridiculous</u>.

1. The first plan seemed unworkable.
2. The color of that blouse is unbecoming.
3. Paul was disappointed with his strikeout.
4. Audrey sounded quite cheerful on the phone.
5. The crowd grew restless because of the long delay.
6. That centerpiece looks beautiful on the table.
7. The singer appeared nervous before the concert.
8. You will surely feel better after a nap.
9. The patient grows stronger every day.
10. The weather stayed sunny throughout the weekend.

© Prentice-Hall, Inc.

Subject Complements (Predicate Nominative, Predicate Adjective) • 61

20.3 Subject Complements (Predicate Nominative, Predicate Adjective) • Practice 2

Exercise 1 **Recognizing Predicate Nominatives.** Underline the predicate nominative in each sentence.

EXAMPLE: Carl is my brother.

1. Hawkins remained the best player on the team.
2. Some people stay children throughout their lives.
3. The first speaker was I.
4. Which of those records is a classic?
5. A hamburger seemed the safest thing to order.
6. The puppies in the corner are the ones for sale.
7. Our state senator may soon become governor.
8. The special today is broiled swordfish.
9. The girls have remained friends for years.
10. Ellen appears the strongest candidate.
11. Florence is Albert's youngest sister.
12. The result of the revolution was chaos.
13. The best item on the menu has always been the salmon.
14. The aroma in the air was clearly cinnamon.
15. Ramona is Rachel's best friend.

Exercise 2 **Recognizing Predicate Adjectives.** Underline the predicate adjective in each sentence.

EXAMPLE: Jean seems tired this afternoon.

1. The flowers smell heavenly.
2. I look awful in this shade of green.
3. Some of the cheese is moldy.
4. The pineapple tasted delicious.
5. The music sounds better from farther away.
6. The sky became cloudy toward evening.
7. I felt angry after our argument.
8. The weather remained hot all week.
9. The team's fans became more unhappy with each new setback.
10. The children grew tan from the summer sun.
11. The path is extremely treacherous.
12. The oatmeal seemed much too hot.
13. The moon was full last night.
14. The children looked very unhappy.
15. The price of the couch is much too high.

20.3 Subject Complements (Compound Subject Complements) • Practice 1

Compound Subject Complements   A compound predicate nominative is two or more nouns or pronouns that follow a linking verb and rename the subject of the sentence. A compound predicate adjective is two or more adjectives that follow a linking verb and describe the subject of the sentence.

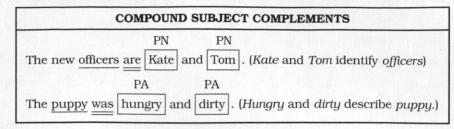

> **COMPOUND SUBJECT COMPLEMENTS**
>
> The new officers are | Kate | and | Tom | . (*Kate* and *Tom* identify *officers*)
>
> The puppy was | hungry | and | dirty | . (*Hungry* and *dirty* describe *puppy*.)

▶ **Exercise 1**   **Recognizing Compound Subject Complements.**   Underline the nouns or adjectives that make up each compound subject complement. On the line at the right, write *PN* for predicate nominative or *PA* for predicate adjective to describe each one.

EXAMPLE: The chair is neither <u>attractive</u> nor <u>sturdy</u>. ___*PA*___

1. The twins are Kim and Karen. _____
2. The main-course choices are steak, shrimp, or chicken. _____
3. That blazer is neither attractive nor affordable. _____
4. Cory will become either a lawyer or a politician. _____
5. When annoyed, the dog becomes mean and vicious. _____
6. After the long drought, the ground looks hard and dusty. _____
7. My favorite breakfast is pancakes and sausage. _____
8. The pizza will be ready and waiting in ten minutes. _____
9. Monsieur Henri is the owner and chef of that restaurant. _____
10. Without proper care, the plant may become bent or discolored. _____

▶ **Exercise 2**   **Writing Sentences with Compound Subject Complements.**   Each sentence below contains a subject complement. On each line to the right, add a conjunction and a noun or adjective to make the subject complement compound. Be sure the word you add is the same part of speech as the subject complement given.

EXAMPLE: The child became tired ____*and cranky*____ .

1. That remark sounded rude _____.
2. The stew tastes both rich _____.
3. Every visitor to their home feels comfortable _____.
4. The winner will surely be either Hank _____.
5. The best math students are Ellen _____.
6. All the fans felt proud _____.
7. A good snack would be fruit _____.
8. That star is both intelligent _____.
9. The losing team felt neither discouraged _____.
10. Her favorite months are January _____.

20.3 Subject Complements (Compound Subject Complements) • Practice 2

▶ Exercise 1 **Recognizing Compound Subject Complements.** Underline the nouns or adjectives that make up each compound subject complement. Then label each compound complement as a *predicate nominative* or *predicate adjective*.

EXAMPLE: The museum is <u>beautiful</u> and <u>interesting</u>. _____predicate adjective_____

(1) The most frequent visitors to the museum are foreign visitors or other out-of-towners. (2) The museum's treasures are mainly furniture and paintings. (3) Its collection grows larger and better every year. (4) The paintings are old and valuable. (5) Most of them are pastels, watercolors, or oils. (6) The majority of paintings are Dutch or Italian. (7) The museum's furnishings are graceful and elegant. (8) The most interesting pieces in the foyer are a colonial table, a Philadelphia clock, and a silver lamp. (9) Other museum highlights are its beautiful rugs and its formal gardens. (10) The museum is free to the public and open daily except holidays.

1. _____   6. _____
2. _____   7. _____
3. _____   8. _____
4. _____   9. _____
5. _____   10. _____

▶ Writing Application **Writing Sentences with Subject Complements.** Use each subject and verb to write a sentence with the kind of subject complement indicated.

EXAMPLE: Liz   seems   (predicate adjective)   _Liz seems excited about the trip._

1. friends   are   (compound predicate nominative)

_____

2. dogs   became   (predicate adjective)

_____

3. baby   grew   (compound predicate adjective)

_____

4. Eric   became   (predicate nominative)

_____

5. singer   was   (predicate nominative)

_____

6. leaves   turned   (compound predicate adjective)

_____

7. vegetables   are   (compound predicate nominative)

_____

8. guests   looked   (predicate adjective)

_____

9. voice   sounded   (predicate adjective)

_____

10. Agnes   remained   (predicate nominative)

_____

Name _____ Date _____

21.1 Prepositional Phrases • Practice 1

Adjective Phrases   A phrase is a group of words, without a subject and verb, that acts as one part of speech. An adjective phrase is a prepositional phrase that modifies a noun or pronoun by telling what kind or which one.

┌───┐
│   **ADJECTIVE PHRASES**   │
│   │
│ The woman *with the tan briefcase* is the mayor. (*Which* woman?) │
│   │
│ We have always liked the big house *on the hill.* (*Which* house?) │
└───┘

Adverb Phrases   An adverb phrase is a prepositional phrase that modifies a verb, adjective, or adverb by pointing out where, when, in what manner, or to what extent.

┌───┐
│   **ADVERB PHRASES**   │
│   │
│ *After the game*, we went *into town.* (*Went* when? *Went* where?) │
│   │
│ Tanya felt good *about her report card.* (*Good* to what extent?) │
└───┘

▶ **Exercise 1**   **Identifying Adjective Phrases.**   Underline the adjective phrase in each sentence below. Circle the noun or pronoun it modifies.

EXAMPLE: Someone should water the flower (bed) in the front yard.

1. Only one of us can play the guitar.
2. Several houses on our street have decks.
3. Each student will write a report about a different capital.
4. Louise gave a surprise party for Mary.
5. My grandmother collects teacups from different countries.
6. The bike in the shop window is expensive.
7. The only difference between Gerri and her twin sister is their names.
8. Someone just bought that empty lot down the street.
9. Eddy made a statue of a bird.
10. The top of the wall is barbed wire.

▶ **Exercise 2**   **Identifying Adverb Phrases.**   Underline the adverb phrase in each sentence below. Circle the word it modifies.

EXAMPLE: After our long workout, we (collapsed).

1. This coupon is good for another month.
2. Our next-door neighbors moved to New Mexico.
3. After all your hard work, you deserve a vacation.
4. With your help, I finished the job.
5. After high school, my sister became a computer programmer.
6. We arrived at the theater early.
7. With only slight hesitation, Diane approached the microphone.
8. Peter quickly slipped under the gate.
9. Outside the theater a large crowd watched the arriving celebrities.
10. We sometimes drive far into the country.

21.1 Prepositional Phrases • Practice 2

▶ **Exercise 1**   **Identifying Adjective Phrases.**   Underline the adjective phrase or adjective phrases in each sentence. Then draw an arrow from each phrase to the word it modifies.

EXAMPLE: Their house in the mountains is spectacular.

1. The price of the car was much too high.

2. Put that box of books down here.

3. My sister is the one in the yellow sweater.

4. The house on the corner of our street needs paint.

5. The cry of the wounded animal haunted us.

6. This is another book by the same author.

7. The shapes of the two objects are very similar.

8. Something in the corner of the room moved.

9. Did you close the window behind the couch?

10. I enjoyed your article about Mr. Hill.

▶ **Exercise 2**   **Identifying Adverb Phrases.**   Underline the adverb phrase or adverb phrases in each sentence. Then draw an arrow from each phrase to the word it modifies.

EXAMPLE: After school we went to the soccer game.

1. Simmer the stew over low heat.

2. The coach is always tougher on newcomers.

3. Louis delivered their anniversary present to the wrong house.

4. Lightning hit the barn during the storm.

5. The frightened squirrel ran across the roof and jumped into the tree.

6. Allie swam away from us.

7. The couple sailed their boat around the world.

8. They returned before dark.

9. The flood waters rose over the breakwater and onto the roadway.

10. Run into the backyard and take the lawnmower out of the rain.

21.1 Appositives and Appositive Phrases
• Practice 1

Appositives   An appositive is a noun or pronoun placed next to another noun or pronoun to identify, rename, or explain it.

APPOSITIVES
Robert Frost wrote the poem "*Birches*."
My new dog, *Max*, has a pedigree.

Appositive Phrases   An appositive phrase is an appositive with modifiers.

APPOSITIVE PHRASES
Robert Frost, *a New England poet*, wrote "Birches."
The dog, *a standard poodle with a brown coat*, has a pedigree.

▶ **Exercise 1**   **Identifying Appositives.**   Underline the appositive in each sentence. Circle the noun or pronoun it renames.

EXAMPLE: My (uncle), a dentist, favors fluoridating the water supply.

1. The play *Cats* is based on poems by T. S. Eliot.
2. Our first president, George Washington, was a native Virginian.
3. The story appeared in the popular magazine *Time*.
4. The film was nominated for Hollywood's top award, the Oscar.
5. The new park, Hammer Field, has three baseball diamonds.
6. I invited my best friend, Dora, to spend the weekend.
7. Please give this note to the principal, Mrs. Spiegel.
8. April 19, Patriots' Day, commemorates Paul Revere's famous ride.
9. Lou told only his brother Mike the secret.
10. The site of the fair will be Minnesota's capital, St. Paul.

▶ **Exercise 2**   **Identifying Appositive Phrases.**   Underline the appositive phrase in each sentence. Circle the noun or pronoun it renames.

EXAMPLE: The (centerpiece), an arrangement of roses, was beautiful.

1. Norma Ellis, a local TV reporter, was the first to report the fire.
2. My personal favorite is Talmadge, the candidate with the best record.
3. The unicorn, a creature with one horn, is a mythical animal.
4. That word comes from Natick, a Native American language.
5. Chinese cooking is often done in a wok, a large pan with a rounded bottom.
6. The movie, another in the popular science-fiction series, was awful.
7. Those flowers, members of the same family, grow in the woods.
8. The new road, a link between the two largest cities in the state, will be completed soon.
9. Please take this message to Judy, the girl in the last row.
10. My cousin, a senior at Eastern High, plans to become a nurse.

Name _____ Date _____

21.1 Appositives and Appositive Phrases
• Practice 2

Exercise 1 **Identifying Appositives.** Underline the appositive in each sentence. Then circle the word or words each appositive renames.

EXAMPLE: This (book), a <u>novel</u>, is extremely fast-paced.

1. Mr. Smith, a lawyer, is away on vacation.
2. My sister Alice is a medical student.
3. Our house, a saltbox, is typical of colonial New England architecture.
4. The reporter, Ms. Hughes, confirmed the story.
5. John Greenleaf Whittier wrote the poem "Snowbound."
6. My favorite teacher, Ms. Jenkins, will retire next year.
7. The artist Mary Cassatt painted mothers and their children.
8. Dad's special dessert, cheesecake, won a blue ribbon.
9. The poet Shelley drowned in a boating accident.
10. Ed ordered his favorite dinner, pizza.
11. My cousin Dorothy is coming to visit in December.
12. One candidate, Sharon, is the only one with a chance to win.
13. Rodin's work *The Thinker* is his most well-known sculpture.
14. A river, the Thames, runs through London.
15. The suspect, Bill Carlton, was arrested last night.

Exercise 2 **Identifying Appositive Phrases.** Underline the appositive phrase in each sentence. Then circle the word or words each appositive phrase renames.

EXAMPLE: Our new (pet), <u>a frisky puppy</u>, loves to play.

1. They hope to win the prize, a trip for two to Hawaii.
2. Mrs. Konevich fixed the car, an old station wagon.
3. Shelley's sister, a track star at UCLA, runs three miles daily.
4. He took her to a movie, a comedy about army life.
5. Two boys, friends of ours, gave us a ride.
6. The youngest player, a pitcher on the second team, received an award at the dinner.
7. We gave Mrs. Hunt, our noisy neighbor, a warning.
8. Amy's father, a federal court judge, will be the speaker.
9. Chess, her favorite game, can take hours to play.
10. He is an artist, a genius with a paint brush.
11. The story takes place in Thebes, an ancient city in Greece.
12. Stevie, a talented skateboarder, won a contest on Saturday.
13. The Morrises' house, a restored Victorian, needs a new paint job.
14. *Moby-Dick*, a novel by Herman Melville, is highly regarded by many critics.
15. The Amazon, the longest river in South America, is 4,000 miles in length.

21.1 Appositives and Appositive Phrases
(Compound Appositives) • Practice 1

Compound Appositives A compound appositive is two or more appositives or appositive phrases connected by a conjunction and used to identify the same noun or pronoun.

+--+
| **COMPOUND APPOSITIVES** |
| |
| Two cities, *Venice and Genoa*, were great rivals at one time. |
| |
| Any new car, whether *a small compact* or *a fancy sport model*, will be an improvement over |
| this one. |
+--+

▶ **Exercise 1** **Identifying Compound Appositives.** Underline each compound appositive in the sentences below. Then circle the word or words it renames.

EXAMPLE: The (puppies), a tiny hound and a winsome terrier, stared up at us.

1. I could not choose between the two desserts, cheesecake and brownies.

2. Which Shakespearean tragedy, *Hamlet* or *Macbeth*, is longer?

3. Our two newest states, Alaska and Hawaii, do not border other states.

4. The star added a Grammy to her other awards, a Tony, an Oscar, and an Emmy.

5. Sacajawea was a guide for the explorers Lewis and Clark.

6. The family could not decide between the houses, a small Cape Cod or a rambling ranch-style.

7. The battery, the pitcher and catcher, conferred on the mound.

8. We had a party for the new couple next door, a man and woman from Utah.

9. I like all movies by the Marx Brothers, Harpo, Groucho, Chico, Zeppo, and Gummo.

10. The ball was held for the visiting dignitaries, the King and Queen of Spain.

▶ **Exercise 2** **Writing Sentences with Appositives, Appositive Phrases, and Compound Appositives.** Turn each pair of sentences into a single sentence with an appositive, an appositive phrase, or a compound appositive.

EXAMPLE: The play was very amusing. The play was a farce.

The play, a farce, was very amusing.

1. Ed Jenkins went to college with my father. He is a local disc jockey.

_____

2. Scrooge is a symbol of miserliness. He is the main character in Dickens' A Christmas Carol.

_____

3. Mom had several choices for the main course. The choices were stuffed chicken, lasagna, or baked fish.

_____

4. Both home teams were high in the standings. The teams are the Bears and the Cubs.

_____

5. Their new apartment is quite spacious. It was once a loft with fourteen-foot ceilings.

_____

21.1 Appositives and Appositive Phrases
(Compound Appositives) • Practice 2

Exercise 1 **Identifying Compound Appositives.**   In each sentence, underline each part of each compound appositive. Then draw an arrow from each part to the word or words it renames.

EXAMPLE: Viewing ocean creatures, fish and other animals, is one reason that underwater diving is popular.

1. As early as 4500 B.C., people were diving in the ocean to bring up food, both fish and plants.

2. Early Greek and Roman divers also dived to retrieve the ocean's riches, pearls, sponges, and shells.

3. The most common diving method, skin diving or breath-hold diving, has been practiced the longest.

4. Skin diving, a very simple type of diving and a popular form of recreation today, requires little or no equipment.

5. The basic equipment, fins, masks, and snorkels, is easy to use.

6. Years ago, divers used natural equipment, hollow reeds for snorkels and tortoise shells for goggles.

7. Now, however, this equipment is made from more modern materials, glass and plastic.

8. In 1943, two Frenchmen, Cousteau and Gagnan, developed practical independent breathing equipment.

9. Improved equipment gives today's divers great advantages, more mobility and increased time under water.

10. Today, divers often use special gear, compressed-air tanks and wet suits, which allows them to swim underwater for long periods.

Writing Application **Using Appositives and Appositive Phrases to Combine Sentences.**   Turn each pair of sentences into one with an appositive or appositive phrase.

EXAMPLE: Sam typed his paper. It was a book report.

Sam typed his paper, a book report.

1. The book was published in many languages. It was an autobiography.

_____

2. A neighbor's tree became the graveyard for their colorful kite. The kite was a large dragon with a silver tail.

_____

3. Candice completed the race in spite of her injury. She had a twisted ankle.

_____

4. The memorial honors the people who died while in service during World War II. It is a simple, symbolic structure made of white stone.

_____

5. Mount Shasta towers thousands of feet above the surrounding valleys and plateaus. The mountain is a volcano.

_____

21.1 Participles and Participial Phrases
(Participles; Verb or Participle?) • Practice 1

Participles   A participle is a form of a verb that acts as an adjective and modifies a noun or pronoun.

Present Participles	Past Participles
A *bubbling* pot sat on the stove. *Purring*, the kitten settled into my lap.	A *typed* report looks neater. *Pleased*, Kimberly sat down.

Verb or Participle?   A verb phrase always begins with a helping verb, but a participle acting as an adjective stands by itself.

Verb Phrases	Participles
The crowd *was laughing* at the street corner clown. The taxpayers *were dismayed* at the latest increases.	*Laughing*, the children raced away. *Dismayed*, the librarian began to pick up the books.

▷ **Exercise 1**   **Identifying Participles.**   Underline the participle in each sentence and circle the word it modifies. On each line at the right, write *present* or *past* to tell which kind it is.

EXAMPLE: An <u>amused</u> ⟨smile⟩ played across her face. ___*past*___

1. Marilyn wished on the falling star. _____
2. Keith is the leading hitter on our team. _____
3. The detective had a puzzled expression on his face. _____
4. Can you repair this broken vase? _____
5. My favorite dessert is baked apples. _____
6. Marc auditioned for the casting director. _____
7. The dry cleaner had a pressing appointment. _____
8. The sitter soothed the frightened child. _____
9. In Davy's dream, he rode on a flying carpet. _____
10. Laura returned the borrowed book this morning. _____

▷ **Exercise 2**   **Distinguishing Between Verbs and Participles.**   On each line at the right, write whether each underlined word is a *verb* or a *participle*.

EXAMPLE: The <u>annoyed</u> customer spoke rudely to the clerk. ___*participle*___

1. The plane has been <u>delayed</u> by the weather. _____
2. The <u>delayed</u> game will be played next week. _____
3. A <u>growing</u> child needs nutritious food. _____
4. Queen Anne's lace was <u>growing</u> by the roadside. _____
5. You will find the information on the <u>following</u> pages. _____
6. Someone has been <u>following</u> me for the last block. _____
7. Some spots are <u>becoming</u> worn. _____
8. That dress is a very <u>becoming</u> color. _____
9. This restaurant has an interesting but <u>limited</u> menu. _____
10. My parents have <u>limited</u> my nights out to weekends. _____

21.1 Participles and Participial Phrases
(Participles; Verb or Participle?) • Practice 2

▶ **Exercise 1** **Identifying Participles.** Underline the participle in each sentence. Then label each as *present* or *past*.

EXAMPLE: The frightened cat ran up a tree. ___*past*___

1. The howling coyotes woke the neighborhood. _____
2. Raoul brought the injured hawk to a veterinarian. _____
3. The child gave his mother a crumbling cookie. _____
4. Stumbling, Nicole dropped her books in the hall. _____
5. A falling star streaked across the clear sky. _____
6. The frozen ice cream was too hard to eat. _____
7. The disappointed team vowed to practice harder. _____
8. Hurt, Vivian ate lunch by herself. _____
9. Howard turned off the blaring radio. _____
10. The torn tent was no protection against the wind. _____
11. The freezing rain made the roads quite treacherous. _____
12. The exhausted climbers were rescued after three days. _____
13. The dwindling water supply worried the city's residents. _____
14. Cornered, the thief finally gave up. _____
15. The carpenter fixed the child's broken toy. _____

▶ **Exercise 2** **Distinguishing Between Verbs and Participles.** Identify each underlined word as a *V* (verb) or *P* (participle). If the word is used as a participle, also write the word it modifies.

EXAMPLE: The cat frightened the bird. ___*V*___

1. The train is arriving on track 7. _____
2. Reporters interviewed the arriving delegation. _____
3. My little brother loves frozen yogurt. _____
4. Usually, by this time of year, the pond has frozen. _____
5. The theatrical company has been touring major cities. _____
6. The touring company will perform here next week. _____
7. The Baskins are moving to Toronto. _____
8. The moving truck arrived an hour late. _____
9. Have the police recovered the stolen jewels? _____
10. Someone has stolen a valuable painting from the museum. _____
11. Michael has grown at least three inches taller this year. _____
12. Axelrod, a fully grown poodle, is groomed regularly. _____
13. Kurt has written his thank-you notes already. _____
14. Jo memorized six of Shakespeare's beautifully written sonnets. _____
15. The speech was made to honor our fallen soldiers. _____

21.1 Participles and Participial Phrases
(Participial Phrases) • Practice 1

Participial Phrases   A participial phrase is a participle modified by an adverb or adverb phrase or accompanied by a complement. The entire phrase acts as an adjective.

PARTICIPIAL PHRASES
The man *holding the baby* is my uncle.
Feeling better, the patient ate some soup.
The boy *running down the street* is Eddy.
The woman *singing now* has a good voice.
Balancing himself carefully, the aerialist walked across the wire.

▶ **Exercise 1**   **Recognizing Participial Phrases.**   Underline the participial phrase in each sentence. Then circle the word it modifies.

EXAMPLE: (Games) played before opening day do not count toward the championship.

1. The train arriving on track 10 is an hour late.
2. A first-edition book signed by the author may become valuable.
3. Looking hot and tired, the tennis players rested in the shade.
4. All the seafood cooked in that restaurant is fried.
5. Found in an abandoned barn, the painting was in excellent condition.
6. Mandy is the girl passing out the programs.
7. Anyone wishing an application may get one in the office.
8. Frightened by the horror movie, the child had nightmares for weeks.
9. The bush growing beside the front steps is an azalea.
10. The dog, chained to a stake, barked loudly.

▶ **Exercise 2**   **Writing Sentences with Participial Phrases.**   Turn each pair of sentences into a single sentence with a participial phrase.

EXAMPLE: The money was stolen from First Bank. It was later recovered.

   The money stolen from First Bank was later recovered.

1. The small boy sits at the end of the pier. He has caught nothing all day.

   _____

2. The sun sets behind the mountains. It is a beautiful sight.

   _____

3. Many books have been written by that author. Many of them have been bestsellers.

   _____

4. The speaker appeared somewhat nervous. The speaker approached the microphone.

   _____

5. The players sat on the bench. They cheered for their teammates.

   _____

21.1 Participles and Participial Phrases
(Participial Phrases) • Practice 2

▶ **Exercise 1**   **Recognizing Participial Phrases.**   Underline the participial phrase in each sentence. Then draw an arrow from each participial phrase to the word it modifies.

EXAMPLE: Frightened by the cat, the bird flew away.

1. Our house, shaded by trees, stays cool in the summer.

2. Kicking stones, the children ran down the street.

3. They boarded the subway packed with people.

4. Frightened by the smoke, they called the fire department.

5. Ms. Foley served a pie steaming from the oven.

▶ **Writing Application**   **Using Participial Phrases to Combine Sentences.**   Turn each pair of sentences into one with a participial phrase. Then underline each participial phrase and draw an arrow from it to the word it modifies.

EXAMPLE: The palms sway in the wind. They are like dancers.

Swaying in the wind, the palms are like dancers.

1. The tollbooth would not accept the coins. It buzzed.

_____

2. The soft music flows out of the restaurant. It invites passersby to enter.

_____

3. The outrigger canoe sprayed water onto the faces of the crew. It raced along the tops of the waves.

_____

4. The telephone poles had been snapped by the hurricane. They hung dangerously over the road.

_____

5. Dolores placed her shot carefully. She hit the ball to her opponent's backhand.

_____

▶ **Writing Application**   **Writing Sentences with Participial Phrases.**   Use the following instructions to write five sentences with participial phrases.

EXAMPLE: Use *paint* as a past participle.

A picture painted on wet plaster is called a fresco.

1. Use *write* as a present participle.

_____

2. Use *laugh* as a present participle.

_____

3. Use *cook* as a past participle.

_____

4. Use *stamp* as a past participle.

_____

5. Use *amuse* as a present participle.

_____

21.1 Gerunds and Gerund Phrases (Gerunds; Verb, Participle, or Gerund?) • Practice 1

Gerunds   A gerund is a form of a verb that acts as a noun.

GERUNDS
Subject: Running has become very popular. *Direct Object:* Unfortunately, Susan adored *singing*. *Indirect Object:* Uncle Lew gave *skiing* a single try. *Predicate Nominative:* Her favorite activity was *riding*. *Object of a Preposition:* Steve was not very fond of *raking*. *Appositive:* Her hobby, *shopping*, tires me out.

Verb, Participle, or Gerund?   Words ending in *-ing* that act as nouns are gerunds. They do not have helping verbs, nor do they act as adjectives.

Verb	Participle	Gerund
Who *is cooking* tonight?	*Cooking* smells filled the house.	DO Paul enjoys *cooking*

▶ **Exercise 1**   **Recognizing Gerunds.**   Underline the gerund in each sentence. Then write whether each one is used as a *subject*, *direct object*, *indirect object*, *predicate nominative*, *object of a preposition*, or *appositive* on each line to the right.

EXAMPLE: Bill improved by <u>practicing</u>. ____*object of a preposition*____

1. Winning is less important than sportsmanship. _____
2. Since childhood, Tony has shown a love of learning. _____
3. The doctor recommended exercise instead of dieting. _____
4. Alice's knitting is quite remarkable. _____
5. Jody won several medals for swimming. _____
6. Jogging is a popular form of exercise. _____
7. During her free time, Michelle enjoys reading. _____
8. Chris turned his hobby, painting, into a profession. _____
9. The sound of drilling disturbed our sleep. _____
10. Dad's favorite sport is fishing. _____

▶ **Exercise 2**   **Distinguishing Between Verbs, Participles and Gerunds.**   Write *V*, *P*, or *G* on each line to the right to indicate whether the underlined word in each sentence is a verb, a participle, or a gerund.

EXAMPLE: A <u>rolling</u> stone gathers no moss. ___*P*___

1. Who is <u>pitching</u> today? _____
2. He has a strong <u>pitching</u> arm. _____
3. <u>Pitching</u> is our weakness. _____
4. Her great love is <u>acting</u>. _____
5. Who is <u>acting</u> in the play? _____
6. Portia was her first <u>acting</u> role. _____
7. The <u>moving</u> van was late. _____
8. <u>Moving</u> is always troublesome. _____
9. The Halls are <u>moving</u> away. _____
10. I am afraid of <u>flying</u>. _____

21.1 Gerunds and Gerund Phrases (Gerunds; Verb, Participle, or Gerund?) • Practice 2

▷ **Exercise 1** **Identifying Gerunds.** Underline the gerund or gerunds in each sentence. Label each one as a *subject, direct object, indirect object, predicate nominative, object of a preposition,* or *appositive.*

EXAMPLE: Swimming is her favorite activity. _____*subject*_____

1. She expanded her vocabulary by reading. _____
2. At the age of five, Winston began acting. _____
3. Dribbling requires coordination and dexterity. _____
4. On summer nights, the family enjoys picnicking. _____
5. One of Lenore's hobbies is sewing. _____
6. The parakeet's main pastime, chirping, prevents loneliness. _____
7. Loving is trusting. _____
8. Stephanie loved excitement and dancing. _____
9. Weeding has improved the appearance of the yard. _____
10. The team excelled in batting and running. _____
11. Swimming is an excellent way to stay in shape. _____
12. Unfortunately, studying is Raymond's least favorite activity. _____
13. Have you ever done any mountain climbing? _____
14. The judges gave Mel's skating a score of nine. _____
15. You'll never get anywhere by simply dreaming. _____

▷ **Exercise 2** **Distinguishing Between Verbs, Participles, and Gerunds.** Identify each underlined word as a *verb, participle,* or *gerund.*

EXAMPLE: The girls are swimming in the lake. _____*verb*_____

1. The losing team put up a good fight. _____
2. No one enjoys losing. _____
3. The home team was losing at the half. _____
4. The contractors are painting the exterior today. _____
5. Painting is more than a hobby to Chuck. _____
6. Have you seen my painting clothes? _____
7. Our meeting at the station was a surprise. _____
8. Hayes was a member of the delegation meeting the plane. _____
9. You will be meeting many new people at camp. _____
10. Why are you reading that book? _____
11. Reading is Ralph's favorite activity. _____
12. Once a month, the reading group meets for a book discussion. _____
13. The laughing children encouraged the clown to continue. _____
14. The children were laughing at the clown's antics. _____
15. The clown enjoys laughing. _____

21.1 Gerunds and Gerund Phrases (Gerund Phrases) • Practice 1

Gerund Phrases A gerund phrase is a gerund with modifiers or a complement, all acting together as a noun. In the chart, notice the words before the gerunds in the second and third examples. Remember that the possessive form of a noun or pronoun is used before a gerund.

GERUND PHRASES
Working hard usually pays off.
We were grateful for *Mary's careful planning*.
Our arriving so late caused a stir.
Paul surprised us by *hitting the ball so far*.

▶ **Exercise 1** **Recognizing Gerund Phrases.** Underline the gerund phrase in each sentence. Then write whether each one is used as a *subject*, *direct object*, *indirect object*, *predicate nominative*, *object of a preposition*, or *appositive* on each line to the right.

EXAMPLE: The comedian told the joke without cracking a smile. _____*object of a preposition*_____

1. Debby enjoys working in the garden. _____
2. Darryl's hobby is collecting old coins. _____
3. Practicing for several hours a day is not unusual for a musician. _____
4. Until the day before, we continued changing the menu. _____
5. Driving along the mountain road was a frightening experience. _____
6. This ice pack will reduce the swelling around the injury. _____
7. The candidate was gracious in thanking all her campaign workers. _____
8. Tonight's homework is writing a rough draft. _____
9. Her great love, cooking gourmet meals, delights her friends. _____
10. Damian dreams about becoming a rock star. _____
11. Tess entered the house without disturbing anyone _____
12. His honesty gave running for office a new respectability. _____
13. Recognizing shapes and colors is important for preschoolers. _____
14. Everyone rose for the singing of the national anthem. _____
15. My chores include setting the table before each meal. _____
16. All the guests raved about his exquisite cooking. _____
17. She was reprimanded for taking far too much time on the project. _____
18. Decorating the gym was one thing the committee looked forward to. _____
19. Beyond everything else, she liked working crossword puzzles. _____
20. He was intensely annoyed by her yawning so openly. _____

▶ **Exercise 2** **Writing Nouns and Pronouns Before Gerunds.** Fill in each blank with the correct word from the parentheses at the right.

EXAMPLE: _____*Her*_____ singing the lullaby put the baby to sleep. (She, Her)

1. Everyone appreciated _____ working so hard. (we, our, us)
2. _____ reading of the poem gave it new meaning. (He, His, Him)
3. We were surprised by _____ repeating that comment. (Tom, Tom's)
4. _____ snoring so loudly kept us all awake. (She, Her)
5. _____ being ready early amazed the family. (I, My, Me)

21.1 Gerunds and Gerund Phrases (Gerund Phrases) • Practice 2

▶ **Exercise 1** **Identifying Gerund Phrases.**   Underline the gerund phrase or gerund phrases in each sentence. Label each one as a *subject, direct object, predicate nominative,* or *object of a preposition.*

EXAMPLE: During our vacation last summer, we all enjoyed <u>swimming in the lake</u>.

_____ direct object _____

1. The pilot of a hang glider generally takes off by running down a hill. _____
2. Holly's favorite activity is climbing mountains in state parks. _____
3. Thousands of spectators showed their interest by following the pro golfers around the course. _____
4. After one night of mosquito attacks the Percivals regretted camping by the river. _____
5. In the 1800's some miners made as much as $5,000 in a few days of panning gold. _____
6. Flying an airplane in bad weather requires extensive training. _____
7. Running out of gas is a horrible experience. _____
8. Some body surfers use styrofoam boards for riding the waves. _____
9. Going to bed late and getting up early may lead to exhaustion. _____
10. Given the choice between hearing a story and playing a game, the children chose hearing a story. _____
11. Visiting the art museum was not Wesley's idea of fun. _____
12. Derek is an expert at flying kites. _____
13. Our music teacher enjoys conducting the choir. _____
14. One of the most dangerous sports is jumping from airplanes. _____
15. Watching television all day is not the best use of your time. _____

▶ **Writing Application**   **Writing Sentences with Gerund Phrases.**   Use the following instructions to write five sentences with gerund phrases. Then underline the gerund phrase in each.

EXAMPLE: Use *sneezing* as a subject.

_____ *Her violent sneezing startled me.* _____

1. Use *staring* as a subject.

   _____

2. Use *joking* as a predicate nominative.

   _____

3. Use *driving* as the object of a preposition.

   _____

4. Use *whispering* as a direct object.

   _____

5. Use *sliding* as a direct object.

   _____

21.1 # Infinitives and Infinitive Phrases (Infinitives;
Prepositional Phrase or Infinitive?) • Practice 1

Infinitives   An infinitive is a form of a verb that comes after the word *to* and acts as a noun, adjective, or adverb.

INFINITIVES
Subject: *To succeed* is not always easy. *Direct Object:* They promised *to remember*. *Predicate Nominative:* Her goal was *to act*. *Object of a Preposition:* He had no choice but *to relent*. *Appositive:* Andrea's decision, *to leave*, was a difficult one. *Adjective:* Her latest mystery is the book *to read*. *Adverb:* He struggled *to rise*. The loss was not easy *to accept*.

Prepositional Phrase or Infinitive?   A prepositional phrase always ends with a noun or pronoun. An infinitive always ends with a verb.

Prepositional Phrase	Infinitive
Will you drive me *to the store*?	I need *to shop*.

▶ **Exercise 1**   **Identifying Infinitives.**   Underline the infinitive in each sentence. Then write the part of speech it is used as on each line to the right.

EXAMPLE: The music began to play. ____*noun*____

1. The Bombers are the team to beat. _____
2. The offer was hard to refuse. _____
3. His greatest desire, to win, caused his ruthlessness. _____
4. Is this the right road to take? _____
5. This recipe is easy to make. _____
6. The whole class recognized Julie's ability to lead. _____
7. Dora always plays to win. _____
8. That will be a difficult promise to keep. _____
9. The new game is easy to learn. _____
10. Where is the best place to sit? _____

▶ **Exercise 2**   **Distinguishing Between Prepositional Phrases and Infinitives.**   Write *PP* for prepositional phrase or *Inf.* for infinitive on each line to the right to describe each underlined group of words.

EXAMPLE: I take the bus to school. ____*PP*____

1. Would you like to play? _____
2. Bud is kind to everyone. _____
3. Ben went to bed early. _____
4. This is no time to stop. _____
5. Please come to dinner. _____
6. It is too early to eat. _____
7. I need to rest. _____
8. Please give this to Jan. _____
9. Please try to relax. _____
10. This belongs to Pat. _____

21.1 Infinitives and Infinitive Phrases (Infinitives; Prepositional Phrase or Infinitive?) • Practice 2

Exercise 1   **Identifying Infinitives.**   Underline the infinitive in each sentence. Then label each as a *noun*, *adjective*, or *adverb*.

EXAMPLE: My friend started to laugh. _____*noun*_____

1. He wanted to protest. _____
2. Her only thought was to win. _____
3. She had no alternative except to drive. _____
4. Eager to succeed, he studied every night. _____
5. The ghost town to visit is on a deserted road. _____
6. Rob likes to swim. _____
7. Nadine told me what book to read. _____
8. To write takes more time than I have. _____
9. That is the most economical car to buy. _____
10. The bus to take stops only at major towns. _____
11. At eight o'clock exactly, the curtains began to open. _____
12. Paula must have forgotten to invite James to the party. _____
13. The push to reach the North Pole was dangerous and exciting. _____
14. Dean knows the best way to cook burgers. _____
15. Too scared to continue, Bill turned back toward the cave entrance. _____

Exercise 2   **Distinguishing Between Prepositional Phrases and Infinitives.**   Underline the prepositional phrase or infinitive beginning with *to* in each sentence. Then label each as a *prepositional phrase* or *infinitive*.

EXAMPLE: He had an essay to write. _____*infinitive*_____

1. Because the music was so loud, Pat found it hard to study. _____
2. To win was our only desire. _____
3. Have you ever been to Seattle? _____
4. My sister likes to ski. _____
5. When do we go back to school? _____
6. My grandparents are coming to visit. _____
7. Who phones in the message about the lost children to headquarters? _____
8. Have you shown her the pictures of your trip to Alaska? _____
9. Is it time to go?
10. Our neighbors have gone to Europe. _____
11. What would you like to say? _____
12. Speak directly to the audience. _____
13. Darryl did not want to lend Freddie any money. _____
14. Jane gave her favorite sweater to Pam. _____
15. When she grows up, Isabel plans to teach. _____

21.1 Infinitives and Infinitive Phrases (Infinitive Phrases) • Practice 1

Infinitive Phrases   An infinitive phrase is an infinitive with modifiers, complements, or a subject, all acting together as a single part of speech. Notice that the infinitives in the first two chart examples do not include the word *to*. When an infinitive or infinitive phrase is used as the direct object of certain verbs, *to* is often omitted.

INFINITIVE PHRASES
Please help *set the table*.
I watched Pam *prepare the salad*.
To plan carefully is a good beginning.
That job is hard *to do without help*.

▶ **Exercise 1**   **Recognizing Infinitive Phrases.**   Underline the infinitive phrase in each sentence below. Then write the part of speech it is used as on the line to the right.

EXAMPLE: Dana's desire to help people led to her career in medicine.   _adjective_

1. Elise is a good person to ask for directions. _____
2. Did you get the message to call home? _____
3. The new law requires infants to ride in special seats. _____
4. The whole family was eager to see the new car. _____
5. Pam wants to invite her to the party. _____
6. The carpenters were unable to finish the job in time. _____
7. The troops found the fort impossible to defend against the enemy. _____
8. Do you need a volunteer to help with refreshments? _____
9. Who is the candidate to vote for? _____
10. I helped Phil to rake the yard. _____

▶ **Exercise 2**   **More Work with Infinitive Phrases.**   Underline the infinitive phrase in each sentence. On the line at the right, write the infinitive itself. If *to* has been omitted, add it in parentheses.

EXAMPLE: Let me help you with that.   _(to) help_

1. We saw the Olympic torch bearer pass by. _____
2. The teacher offered to give me extra help. _____
3. I heard him sing in person at the coliseum. _____
4. We watched the sun rise over the ocean. _____
5. The owner allows visitors to tour the house during the week. _____
6. We wouldn't dare ask for another piece of pie. _____
7. No one can make Linda change her mind. _____
8. I warned you to read the directions carefully. _____
9. Alice arranged for Clare to visit for the weekend. _____
10. Let's find a good place for dinner. _____

21.1 Infinitives and Infinitive Phrases (Infinitive Phrases) • Practice 2

▶ **Exercise 1**   **Identifying Infinitive Phrases.**   Underline the infinitive phrase or infinitive phrases in each sentence. Label each one as a *subject*, *direct object*, *predicate nominative*, *object of a preposition*, *adjective*, or *adverb*.

EXAMPLE: To become an astronaut requires special training. ___*subject*___

(1) To carry out their missions, astronauts undergo years of preparation. (2) At first only experienced pilots were able to become astronauts. (3) They needed to have a degree in engineering, physical science, or mathematics. (4) Since 1965 "mission specialists" have been recruited to perform scientific experiments. (5) They also needed to complete flight training. (6) To prepare for missions, astronauts study subjects ranging from rocket engines to geology. (7) Astronauts use full-size spacecraft models and simulators (devices that reproduce conditions of space flight) to train for missions. (8) Astronauts have no choice but to work hard. (9) We admire their ability to succeed at difficult tasks. (10) They make us feel proud of their accomplishments.

1. _____   6. _____
2. _____   7. _____
3. _____   8. _____
4. _____   9. _____
5. _____   10. _____

▶ **Writing Application**   **Writing Sentences with Infinitive Phrases.**   Use the following instructions to write ten sentences with infinitive phrases. Then underline the infinitive phrase in each.

EXAMPLE: Use *to help* as a direct object.   *He wanted to help the lost child.*

1. Use *to change* as a predicate nominative.

   _____

2. Use *to build* as an adjective.

   _____

3. Use *to paint* as a subject.

   _____

4. Use *to refuse* as an adjective.

   _____

5. Use *to leap* as a direct object.

   _____

6. Use *to know* as a predicate nominative.

   _____

7. Use *to send* as an adjective.

   _____

8. Use *to spoil* as a subject.

   _____

9. Use *to meet* as a direct object.

   _____

10. Use *to advise* as a subject.

   _____

21.2 # Adjective Clauses • Practice 1

The Adjective Clause   A clause is a group of words containing its own subject and verb. A clause that can stand by itself as a sentence is an independent clause. A clause that can only be part of a sentence is a subordinate clause. An adjective clause is a subordinate clause that modifies a noun or pronoun, telling what kind or which one. Adjective clauses usually begin with a relative pronoun — *that, which, who, whom,* or *whose.*

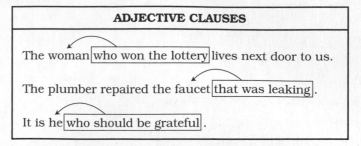

ADJECTIVE CLAUSES

The woman who won the lottery lives next door to us.

The plumber repaired the faucet that was leaking.

It is he who should be grateful.

▶ **Exercise 1**   **Recognizing Adjective Clauses.**   Underline the adjective clause in each sentence.

EXAMPLE: The mayor praised the girl <u>who rescued the drowning child</u>.

1. The candidate who led in the polls became overconfident.
2. Items that are on sale are marked by a red sticker.
3. The contest is open to anyone who lives in this state.
4. The President that was elected four times was Franklin D. Roosevelt.
5. My uncle has a parrot that can say several sentences.
6. The person whom the police arrested turned out to be innocent.
7. The mill that once stood here was torn down long ago.
8. The treasure map, which was crumpled and torn, was hard to make out.
9. Fleetfoot, who was favored to win the race, came in last.
10. Dad needs a secretary who can speak Portuguese.

▶ **Exercise 2**   **Identifying Adjective Clauses and the Words They Modify.**   Underline the adjective clause in each sentence. Then circle the word the clause modifies.

EXAMPLE: The (book) <u>that was missing</u> had turned up at last.

1. Only people who have experience with lions and tigers need apply.
2. The carton that contained the dishes was undamaged.
3. A trapper who knew the woods well led the rescue party.
4. Grandpa still has the first dollar that he ever earned.
5. The author dedicated the book to his uncle, who had been kind to him.
6. The beggar whom the poor farmer helped was really the king.
7. We need a treasurer who can add and subtract.
8. The judges awarded the prize to the girl who made the dragon kite.
9. The page that has the brownie recipe on it is too smudged to read.
10. Alicia finally met the woman whom she had admired for so long.

21.2 Adjective Clauses • Practice 2

▶ **Exercise 1**   **Identifying Adjective Clauses.**   Underline the adjective clause in each sentence. Then circle the relative pronoun or relative adverb in each.

EXAMPLE: The town (where) I live is peaceful.

1. I met a woman who works with your mother.
2. Have you thought of a place where we can meet?
3. Is this the person whom you saw in the library?
4. I found the book that I needed.
5. She remembers the days when there were trolley cars.
6. Did Harriet tell you the reason why she left?
7. I lost the sweater that Aunt Sue made me.
8. Have they found the girl who was lost?
9. Most people who visit the museum are impressed.
10. The pictures that I took are not ready yet.
11. James Fenimore Cooper, who wrote *The Last of the Mohicans*, died in 1851.
12. The baseball cards that Peter bought last year have increased in value.
13. My aunt, whom you met last week, is on vacation now.
14. The restaurant, which is near the river, has an outdoor patio.
15. Carol grows vegetables in the backyard, where she also grows flowers.

▶ **Exercise 2**   **Identifying Adjective Clauses and the Words They Modify.**   Underline the adjective clause in each sentence. Then write the word the adjective clause modifies.

EXAMPLE: The town where she lives is hectic. _____*town*_____

1. Crocuses are usually the first flowers that bloom. _____
2. She works in the town where the movie was filmed. _____
3. The boys who play handball with me go to Central. _____
4. Is this the weekend that you are leaving? _____
5. The scene that reveals the hero's secret is the best. _____
6. The dessert that I ordered never came. _____
7. Did you find all of the tools that you needed? _____
8. They can subpoena anyone who refuses to testify. _____
9. The books that you ordered will be in next week. _____
10. Is he the one who told you about the meeting? _____
11. The advice that my dad gave me could apply to you as well. _____
12. The poem, which is written in iambic pentameter, is quite lovely. _____
13. The three girls who tried out for the team all made it. _____
14. The space under the porch, where the dog rests during the day, is very cool. _____
15. The yarn that the cat is playing with is made of fine wool. _____

21.2 Adjective Clauses (Relative Pronouns and Relative Adverbs) • Practice 1

Relative Pronouns   Relative pronouns connect adjective clauses to the words the clauses modify. Relative pronouns act as subjects, direct objects, adjectives, or objects of prepositions within the clause. Putting the clause in normal word order can help you see how the word acts within the clause.

RELATIVE PRONOUNS
I bought the dictionary *which* was recommended. (*which* was recommended)
This is the house *that* Jack built. (Jack built *that*)
She is a poet *whose* work I greatly admire. (I greatly admire *whose* work)
The person with *whom* I spoke was the boss. (I spoke with *whom*)

Relative Adverbs   Adjective clauses are sometimes introduced by a relative adverb such as *where*, *when*, *why*, *before*, or *since*. The relative adverb connects the clause to the word the clause modifies and acts as an adverb within the clause.

RELATIVE ADVERBS
This is the spot *where* we stopped to rest. (we stopped to rest *where*)
We will come again another time *when* we can stay. (we can stay *when*)

▶ **Exercise 1**   **Recognizing the Use of Relative Pronouns.**   Underline the adjective clause in each sentence. Circle the relative pronoun. On each line at the right, write the use of the pronoun within the clause.

EXAMPLE: The person (who) called you has hung up. _____*subject*_____

1. The book that I wanted to read had been checked out. _____
2. Betsy wrote to the man who returned her lost dog. _____
3. The play in which those lines appear is *Hamlet*. _____
4. The player who has the fewest points wins. _____
5. Columbus is a person whose name everyone knows. _____
6. The page that should follow this one is missing. _____
7. The plane in which the President flies is *Air Force One*. _____
8. Dorris is a critic whose opinions are usually sound. _____
9. The book that I am reading now is about mountain climbing. _____
10. Nick is the partner with whom I usually play doubles. _____

▶ **Exercise 2**   **Recognizing Adjective Clauses with Relative Adverbs.**   Underline the adjective clause in each sentence. Circle the relative adverb.

EXAMPLE: Those were the days (when) every city had trolley cars.

1. Areas where flooding was severe have been evacuated.
2. We couldn't imagine the reason why Laura was so late.
3. An *x* marks the spot where the treasure is buried.
4. In the days before the telegraph was invented, news traveled slowly.
5. No one was in the building at the time when the fire occurred.

21.2 Adjective Clauses (Relative Pronouns and Relative Adverbs) • Practice 2

▶ **Exercise 1** **Recognizing the Uses of Relative Pronouns.** Underline the adjective clause in each sentence, circling the relative pronoun. Then label the use of the relative pronoun within the clause as *subject, direct object, object of a preposition*, or *adjective*.

EXAMPLE: Leonardo, (who) is greatly admired, was an artist. _____*subject*_____

(1) Leonardo da Vinci, whose paintings are among the most famous in the world, was born in 1452 in Italy. (2) As a teenager Leonardo was apprenticed to a painter, with whom he worked for several years. (3) Later, Leonardo moved to Milan to work for a duke who needed the services of an artist. (4) There he designed artillery and planned ways to change the course of rivers, tasks that were usually the jobs of an engineer. (5) Leonardo also designed revolving stages, on which plays were performed.

1. _____ 4. _____
2. _____ 5. _____
3. _____

▶ **Exercise 2** **Recognizing the Use of Relative Adverbs.** Underline the adjective clause in each sentence, circling the relative adverb. Then draw an arrow from the relative adverb to the word or words it modifies.

EXAMPLE: The street (where) Joyce lives is near the library.

1. Anna wouldn't tell us the reason why she quit.
2. In the week since the report was filed, many of the facts have been changed.
3. It was a day when we all enjoyed every minute.
4. The stands where the dignitaries would sit were draped with bunting.
5. In the twelve years since I visited Greece, I have learned to speak German.

▶ **Writing Application** **Using Adjective Clauses to Combine Sentences.** Turn each pair of sentences into one with an adjective clause. Then underline each adjective clause and draw an arrow from it to the word it modifies.

EXAMPLE: The letter will be mailed today. I wrote the letter.

We arrived at the airport as our plane was taking off.

1. Give this package to the person. The person is at the door.

_____

2. Tomorrow is the day. School starts then.

_____

3. The player struck out. He is everyone's favorite.

_____

4. The book is about Africa. I got the book from the library.

_____

5. The candidate has withdrawn for some reason. No one knows the reason.

_____

21.2 Adverb Clauses • Practice 1

The Adverb Clause   An adverb clause is a subordinate clause that modifies a verb, adjective, adverb, or verbal. An adverb clause always begins with a subordinating conjunction. Adverb clauses tell *when, where, how,* or *why.*

ADVERB CLAUSES
We arrived at the airport as our plane was taking off.
Because we had to be up at five, we went to bed early.

Elliptical Adverb Clauses   An elliptical adverb clause is one in which the verb or the subject and verb are understood but not actually stated.

ELLIPTICAL CLAUSES
My brother is taller *than I (am).*
Please send your payment as early as *(it is) possible.*

► Exercise 1   **Identifying Adverb Clauses.**   Underline the adverb clause in each sentence. Then circle the subordinating conjunction in each.

EXAMPLE: The movie had already started (when) we arrived.

1. The elevator will not move unless both doors are closed.
2. You will find the almanacs where the other reference books are shelved.
3. Betsy plays golf whenever she gets the chance.
4. After you have beaten the eggs, slowly add the dry ingredients.
5. The washer will stop if the door is opened.
6. Residents are urged to conserve water until the shortage ends.
7. The pictures came out badly because the lighting was poor.
8. We had a good time at the picnic even though it rained off and on.
9. No one may enter the studio while the red light is on.
10. A tire blew out as the jet taxied to the runway.

► Exercise 2   **Completing Elliptical Clauses.**   Write each adverb clause, adding any understood words that have been left out.

EXAMPLE: Wherever possible, the guide planted trees.   _____*Wherever it was possible*_____

1. When younger, Edison worked for the railroad. _____
2. The contestants valued the honor more than the prize money. _____
3. They walked unsteadily, as if dazed. _____
4. The Penguins are a better all-round team than the Seals. _____
5. I would like to see Dr. Richard this afternoon, if possible. _____
6. An adverb clause is a subordinate clause that acts as an adverb. _____
7. We believe our climate is much better than theirs. _____
8. George goes surfing as often as Glenda. _____
9. If ready, the new chairs will be delivered on Tuesday. _____
10. Julie's dog is more aggressive than Van Winkle. _____

21.2 Adverb Clauses • Practice 2

Exercise 1   **Identifying Adverb Clauses.**   Underline the adverb clause in each sentence. Then circle the subordinating conjunction in each.

EXAMPLE: We arrived (after) the band had left.

1. Will you move the couch when you have time?

2. Because the music was so loud, I got a headache.

3. No one came since I forgot to mail the invitations.

4. Did you see Alex when you were in Bloomington?

5. My ride came before I had finished breakfast.

6. Even though it was raining, we enjoyed the day.

7. Mimi takes her dog wherever she goes.

8. Have you heard from James since I saw you last?

9. She stayed there until the report was finished.

10. Before you leave, please stop by my office.

Exercise 2   **Identifying Adverb Clauses and the Words They Modify.**   Underline the adverb clause in each sentence. Then circle the word or words the adverb clause modifies.

EXAMPLE: When I was three, I (lived) in Dallas.

1. I called you before I fell asleep.

2. I will not be able to finish while you are here.

3. Will you wait until I get a sweater?

4. Mom likes skating when the ice is thick.

5. Put those books where the others are.

6. The old house was quiet after the guests had left.

7. Though it was still early, many of the picnickers were leaving.

8. I feel better than I did yesterday.

9. Jay stood in the wings while he waited for his cue.

10. Daisy plans to work as soon as we leave.

Exercise 3   **Recognizing Elliptical Adverb Clauses.**   Write each adverb clause, adding the missing words in any elliptical clause. Then circle any words you have added.

EXAMPLE: I like cake more than candy.

_____ than (I like) candy._____

1. The other members were more restless than I. _____

2. We found our backpacks where we had left them. _____

3. The thieves acted as if no one knew their whereabouts. _____

4. The San Mateo Matadors are ranked higher in football than our team. _____

5. The actors wanted the new spotlights more than a videotape machine. _____

Name _____ Date _____

The Noun Clause   A noun clause is a subordinate clause that acts as a noun. It can be used in any of the functions common to single-word nouns.

NOUN CLAUSES

Subject: What she said was worth remembering.
Direct Object: I don't know *where the library is.*
Indirect Object: The judges will award *whoever finishes last* a prize.
Predicate Nominative: His problem was *how he could earn a living.*
Object of a Preposition: The pirates quarreled over *why they were lost.*

Introductory Words   Some of the words that introduce noun clauses function as the subject, direct object, or some other important part of their clause. Other introductory words have no function in the clause.

USE OF INTRODUCTORY WORDS WITHIN NOUN CLAUSES

Subject: The police officer asked *who had witnessed the accident.*
Adverb: We argued about *where* we should eat.
Adjective: Jody couldn't decide *which* job she should take.
Direct Object: You are *what* you eat.
No function in clause: Do you know *whether* the train has gone?

▶ **Exercise 1**   **Identifying Noun Clauses.**   Underline the noun clause in each sentence. In the space provided, indicate the function of the clause within the sentence.

EXAMPLE: We wondered what we should do next.   *direct object*

1. When the next meeting will be held has not been announced. _____

2. We have to do our best with what we have. _____

3. Aaron modestly admitted that he had driven in the winning run. _____

4. All of Elaine's friends believed what she said. _____

5. Angie's dream was that she could have a horse of her own. _____

6. The witnesses disagreed about how tall the robber had been. _____

7. What happened next surprised us all. _____

8. The economist predicted that the cost of living would keep rising. _____

9. The real surprise is how the movie ends. _____

10. Do you know if the Penguins won this afternoon? _____

▶ **Exercise 2**   **Recognizing the Use of Introductory Words.**   Underline the noun clause in each sentence. Circle the introductory word. Then in the space provided, write the use of the introductory word within the clause.

EXAMPLE: Do you remember (where) we parked the car?   *adverb*

1. "Whose woods these are, I think I know,"—Robert Frost _____

2. The *x* shows where the treasure is buried. _____

3. Betsy doesn't know who will be playing tennis next week. _____

4. Whoever leaves last should turn off the lights. _____

5. We will never forget what she said next. _____

21.2 Noun Clauses • Practice 2

Exercise 1 **Identifying Noun Clauses.** Underline the noun clause in each sentence. Then label the clause as a *subject, direct object, predicate nominative,* or *object of a preposition.*

EXAMPLE: Andy wished that they would leave. ___direct object___

1. No one understands why Tim is afraid of the dark. _____
2. Jean chose to write about how bees communicate. _____
3. Where the treasure is buried remains a mystery. _____
4. He wrote to whoever promised to write back. _____
5. Our biggest worry was where we would end up. _____
6. My sister has not decided what she wants to study. _____
7. That he didn't ask his neighbors to the party suggests his dislike of them. _____
8. The most difficult question was whether the land should be re-zoned. _____
9. He gave whoever flattered him his friendship. _____
10. They consulted about who would do the job. _____
11. We wondered which route was shorter. _____
12. Her excuse was that she had lost the assignment. _____
13. Why he dropped the class isn't clear. _____
14. Whoever you hire must speak French. _____
15. They worried about how they would cross Death Valley. _____

Exercise 2 **Recognizing the Uses of Introductory Words.** Underline the noun clause in each sentence, circling the introductory word. Then label the use of the introductory word in the clause as *subject, direct object, object of a preposition, adjective, adverb,* or a word with *no function.*

EXAMPLE: Ellen knew (that) she would be late. ___no function___

1. Do you know whether Ms. Hall will be in today? _____
2. What she wanted to speak about was Judy's decision. _____
3. Just leave a message with whoever answers the phone. _____
4. Pete feared that he would forget his lines. _____
5. The university catalog lists which professor gives each course. _____
6. Whether you go or stay makes no difference. _____
7. Do you know whose keys these are? _____
8. The governor said that she would not run again. _____
9. The real issue is who would do a better job. _____
10. We began without knowing where we were headed. _____
11. Whoever draws the short straw must do the dishes. _____
12. No one told us what we were looking for. _____
13. The rumor is that the house is haunted. _____
14. Someone should have told us how he would react. _____
15. No one could remember where the keys were. _____

© Prentice-Hall, Inc.

21.2 Sentences Classified by Structure
• Practice 1

The Four Structures of Sentences   Sentences can be classified by the number and kind of clauses they contain.

Kind of Sentence	Number and Kind of Clauses	Examples (subjects underlined once, verbs twice)
Simple	One independent clause (subject or verb or both may be compound)	Hawks hunt mice. Hawks and owls hunt mice. Owls catch mice and eat them.
Compound	Two or more independent clauses	Football is a good game, but I prefer soccer.
Complex	One independent clause and one or more subordinate clauses	⌐ IND. CL. ⌐ ⌐ SUBORD. CL. ⌐ The train whistled as it neared the tunnel.
Compound-Complex	Two or more independent clauses and one or more subordinate clauses	⌐ IND. CL. ⌐⌐ SUBORD. CL. ⌐ Paul ate a sandwich when he got home, ⌐ IND. CL. ⌐ but he still felt hungry.

▶ **Exercise 1**   **Distinguishing Between Simple and Compound Sentences.**   In the space provided, identify each sentence as *simple* or *compound*.

EXAMPLE: The ball hit the foul pole and bounced into the stands.   *simple*

1. The detour was clearly marked, but we still missed it. _____
2. Rangers and volunteers fought the forest fire together. _____
3. The bull pawed the ground, lowered his head, and charged. _____
4. Whales and porpoises are mammals, but sharks are not. _____
5. The surface should be clean, or the paint will not stick. _____

▶ **Exercise 2**   **Identifying the Structure of Sentences.**   Identify each sentence as (*1*) simple, (*2*) compound, (*3*) complex, or (*4*) compound-complex by writing the proper number on the line.

EXAMPLE: The bolt that holds the handlebar in place is loose.   *3*

1. The club has not decided when the picnic will take place. _____
2. Coach Gaudioso warned his team against overconfidence. _____
3. The runners were on their marks, and the race was about to begin. _____
4. Members must give the password, or they will not be admitted. _____
5. Algebra and biology are my favorite subjects. _____
6. Alicia took an earlier bus than she needed to, for she didn't want to be late. _____
7. Jenny raised herself from the chair and took a tentative step. _____
8. Although it is old and battered, Uncle Jack's car runs well. _____
9. A driver who is entering traffic should yield. _____
10. The ripcord that opens the chute must be strong, or it could break. _____

21.2 Sentences Classified by Structure
• Practice 2

▶ **Exercise 1** **Identifying the Structure of Sentences.** Identify each sentence as *simple*, *compound*, *complex*, or *compound-complex*.

EXAMPLE: I got the one that I wanted. _____*complex*_____

1. We chose one way; they chose another. _____

2. They learned a dance with a variety of steps. _____

3. Whenever Angelo gets to school early, he talks to his friends. _____

4. The vibrations from the jet caused the vase to fall and crack. _____

5. The gum stuck to his face; it looked like glue. _____

6. Stuck to his face, the gum looked like glue. _____

7. The gum that stuck to his face looked like glue. _____

8. My uncle planned to drive to work, but he couldn't until the snowplows cleared the roads. _____

9. She wanted to go on the study tour, yet she could not bring herself to spend all of her savings. _____

10. Because Kelly forgot to water her plants, they wilted. _____

▶ **Writing Application** **Writing Application: Writing Sentences with Different Structures.** Use the following instructions to write ten sentences of your own.

EXAMPLE: Write a compound sentence about hiking.

_____*Sara wore good hiking shoes, but her socks were not heavy enough.*_____

1. Write a simple sentence about a story you have read.

_____

2. Write a compound sentence about dancing.

_____

3. Write a complex sentence about snow.

_____

4. Write a compound-complex sentence about photography.

_____

5. Write a simple sentence about computers.

_____

6. Write a compound sentence about a dog.

_____

7. Write a complex sentence about a cat.

_____

8. Write a compound-complex sentence about traveling.

_____

9. Write a simple sentence about a family get-together.

_____

10. Write a compound-complex sentence about the area in which you live.

_____

22.1 Sentences Classified by Function • Practice 1

The Four Functions of Sentences   Sentences can also be classified by their function.

Kind of Sentence	Function	Examples	End Mark
Declarative	States an idea	Water freezes at 0 C.	period (.)
Interrogative	Asks a question	What is the longest day of the year?	question mark (?)
Imperative	Gives an order or a direction	Abandon ship! Please close the window.	period or exclamation mark (. or !)
Exclamatory	Conveys strong emotion	How wrong you are! You must be joking!	exclamation mark (!)

▶ **Exercise 1**   **Identifying the Function of Sentences.**   Identify each sentence as *declarative,* *interrogative,* *imperative,* or *exclamatory.*

EXAMPLE: Sauté the onions until they are soft. _____*imperative*_____

1. Be sure to enclose a stamped, self-addressed envelope. _____
2. Has anyone ever photographed the Loch Ness monster? _____
3. Which is longer, a meter or a yard? _____
4. The phoenix and the unicorn are mythical creatures. _____
5. Sand the surface lightly before applying the second coat. _____
6. What a dreadful sight that was! _____
7. Go directly to JAIL. _____
8. Natives in Borneo once used human skulls as money. _____
9. The eggs laid in a single nest are called a clutch. _____
10. Is it bigger than a breadbox? _____

▶ **Exercise 2**   **Choosing the Correct End Mark by Function.**   Supply an appropriate end mark for each sentence on the line provided. When you are through, you should have four periods, two question marks, and four exclamation marks.

EXAMPLE: Arabian camels have one hump; Bactrian camels have two ____.

1. Stop in the name of the law_____
2. Did the caller leave a number_____
3. What a weird coincidence that was_____
4. Run for your lives_____
5. Currents are fast-flowing streams within larger bodies of water_____
6. Who won the Oscar for best actor last year_____
7. Now that's what I call hot chili_____
8. Penguins keep their eggs warm by holding them next to their bodies_____
9. Be sure to let us know what you decide_____
10. Americans spend a great deal of money on pet food_____

22.1 Sentences Classified by Function • Practice 2

▶ **Exercise 1** **Identifying the Function of Sentences.** Write the end mark for each sentence. Then, identify each sentence as *declarative, interrogative, imperative,* or *exclamatory.*

EXAMPLE: I decided to run for class president (.) _____declarative_____

(1) When my friends asked how they could help me campaign for class president, the answer was simple (2) "Make some posters for me" (3) Having little artistic talent, I needed all the help with posters that I could get (4) The next challenge I had to face really worried me—making a campaign speech (5) Should I talk about my previous experience as secretary of the Spanish Club (6) Perhaps I should talk about my ability to get along with my classmates (7) The day of the speech was I nervous (8) I knew what I had to do, and I repeated my task to myself again and again (9) "Go out there and convince them" (10) I guess I succeeded because when the results were announced, I was the new class president.

1. _____
2. _____
3. _____
4. _____
5. _____

6. _____
7. _____
8. _____
9. _____
10. _____

▶ **Writing Application** **Writing Sentences with Different Structures and Functions.** Use the following instructions to write ten sentences of your own.

EXAMPLE: Write a compound interrogative sentence about dogs.

_____*Should we get a poodle, or should we get a dachshund?*_____

1. Write a simple declarative sentence about food.

_____

2. Write a compound declarative sentence about music.

_____

3. Write a complex declarative sentence about homework.

_____

4. Write a compound-complex declarative sentence about politics.

_____

5. Write a simple interrogative sentence about next weekend.

_____

6. Write a compound interrogative sentence about a friend.

_____

7. Write a complex interrogative sentence about a friend.

_____

8. Write a compound-complex interrogative sentence about a sports event.

_____

9. Write a simple imperative sentence about something that needs cleaning.

_____

10. Write a simple exclamatory sentence about the results of the action in Sentence 9.

_____

22.2 Sentence Combining • Practice 1

Combining Ideas   Combine short sentences by using compound subjects or verbs, phrase modifiers, compound sentences, complex sentences, or compound-complex sentences.

Separate Sentences	Combined Sentences
The tide came up. It washed away our sand castle.	The tide came up and washed away our sand castle.
It was a huge sand castle. It had a moat around it.	It was a huge sand castle with a moat around it.
We had hoped to visit the rock. The Pilgrims had landed there. The area was blocked off.	We had hoped to visit the rock where the Pilgrims had landed, but the area was blocked off.

▶ **Exercise 1**   **Combining Sentences.**   Combine the sentences in each item into a single, longer sentence.

EXAMPLE: Our neighbor was the first one on the scene. She is a paramedic.

_____ *Our neighbor, a paramedic, was the first one on the scene.* _____

1. Arthur asked a question. The teacher couldn't answer it.

_____

2. We visited the house. Abraham Lincoln had lived there.

_____

3. Did you see the exam schedule? It is on the bulletin board.

_____

4. Several students requested a class newspaper. They are good writers. No advisor was available.

_____

5. The cake is easy to make. Follow the recipe.

_____

▶ **Exercise 2**   **More Work with Combining Sentences.**   Follow the directions for Exercise 1.

1. We tried to make a gingerbread house. We had seen it in a magazine. The walls collapsed.

_____

2. Alvin entered the competition. His coach advised against it.

_____

3. He is a very popular musician. Thousands of people showed up to buy tickets for one of his concerts.

_____

4. Marc Chagall created those stained-glass windows. Chagall is a famous painter. The windows are in a chapel. The chapel is in the south of France.

_____

5. I need that book for my report. The librarian ordered it for me. She said it has not come in yet.

_____

22.2 Sentence Combining • Practice 2

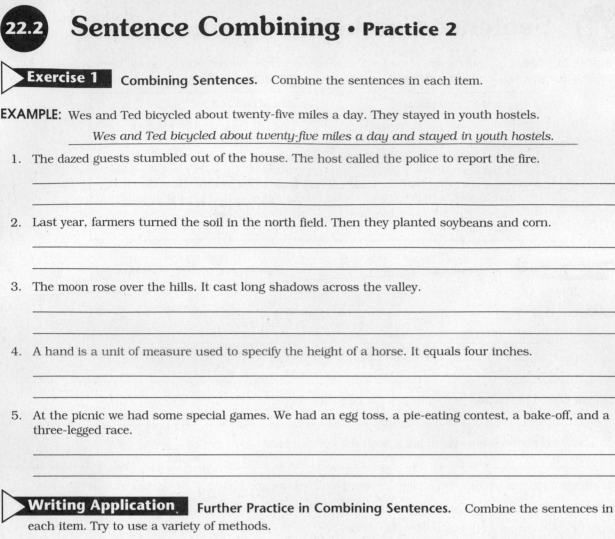

▷ **Exercise 1** **Combining Sentences.** Combine the sentences in each item.

EXAMPLE: Wes and Ted bicycled about twenty-five miles a day. They stayed in youth hostels.

_____Wes and Ted bicycled about twenty-five miles a day and stayed in youth hostels._____

1. The dazed guests stumbled out of the house. The host called the police to report the fire.

_____

_____

2. Last year, farmers turned the soil in the north field. Then they planted soybeans and corn.

_____

_____

3. The moon rose over the hills. It cast long shadows across the valley.

_____

_____

4. A hand is a unit of measure used to specify the height of a horse. It equals four inches.

_____

_____

5. At the picnic we had some special games. We had an egg toss, a pie-eating contest, a bake-off, and a three-legged race.

_____

_____

▷ **Writing Application** **Further Practice in Combining Sentences.** Combine the sentences in each item. Try to use a variety of methods.

EXAMPLE: The goalie darted to the left. He almost blocked the goal.

_____Darting to the left, the goalie almost blocked the goal._____

1. The eruption of a volcano can be destructive. Volcanic eruptions also enrich the soil and bring water up to the surface.

_____

_____

2. Mount Pelée is in Martinique. Kilhauea is in Hawaii. They are both active volcanoes.

_____

_____

3. Snow began to fall in the morning. Six inches had accumulated by evening.

_____

_____

4. A reporter for a newspaper is very busy. However, the city desk editor is even busier.

_____

_____

5. A reporter tracks down the details of a story and then writes an article. The editor must be familiar with all of the developing stories to choose which ones to print.

_____

_____

22.3 Varying Your Sentences (Expanding Short Sentences, Shortening Long Sentences) • Practice 1

Expanding Short Sentences   Short sentences can be expanded by adding details that develop the subject, verb, or complement.

Short Sentences	Expanded Sentences
The woman addressed the convention.	The woman, *a lawyer from Chicago*, addressed the convention.
The delegates applauded her remarks.	The delegates *loudly and enthusiastically* applauded her remarks.
She nominated a candidate.	She nominated a *popular presidential* candidate *from her home state.*

Shortening Long Sentences   Long, involved sentences can be broken into shorter, simpler sentences.

Long, Involved Sentence	Shorter, Clearer Sentences
The puppy, which was a honey-colored cocker spaniel, was frisky and loved to romp around the living room, which caused problems such as a broken antique vase, tears in the slipcovers, and scratches on the table legs.	The frisky puppy, a honey-colored cocker spaniel, loved to romp around the living room. The results included a broken antique vase, tears in the slipcovers, and scratches on the table legs.

▶ **Exercise 1**   **Adding Details to Short Sentences.**   Add details to improve each sentence.

EXAMPLE: Len had but one dream.

Len had but one dream, to win the marathon.

1. That plant has magnificent flowers.

   _____

2. The same menu is served every New Year's Eve.

   _____

3. The athletes prepared well.

   _____

4. The story aroused her curiosity.

   _____

5. They learned more about chess.

   _____

▶ **Exercise 2**   **Shortening Sentences.**   Divide each long sentence into two or more sentences.

1. A whole group of us had arranged to work together on a huge banner which we would carry to the pep rally, but it didn't take long for us to begin to disagree about how to design it.

   _____

   _____

2. Having rehearsed several weeks both in the classroom and on the stage, we felt quite confident when the day of the dress rehearsal finally came and were firmly convinced that all would go well.

   _____

   _____

22.3 Varying Your Sentences (Expanding Short Sentences, Shortening Long Sentences) • Practice 2

▷ **Exercise 1** **Adding Details to Short Sentences.** Improve each sentence by adding the phrase in parentheses.

EXAMPLE: The river flooded the streets. (swollen by rain)

The river, swollen by rain, flooded the streets.

1. We must develop new sources of energy. (to provide for the future as well as the present)

_____

2. The teller counted one-dollar bills. (slowly and tediously)

_____

3. The bicycle rider crossed the finish line. (followed closely by an enthusiastically cheering crowd)

_____

4. The noise came from beneath the water. (of the scuba divers salvaging the downed submarine)

_____

5. The hikers returned. (eager to tell about their adventure)

_____

▷ **Exercise 2** **Shortening Long Sentences.** Divide each long sentence into two or more shorter, clear sentences.

EXAMPLE: When Jerry turned the ignition key in the car, it made a clicking noise, but the motor did not start because, as the mechanic later explained, the battery was dead.

When Jerry turned the ignition key in the car, he heard a clicking noise, but the motor did not start. As the mechanic later explained, the car's battery was dead.

1. Ants are warlike creatures, and they are natural empire builders, so they attack weaker insects to increase the numbers of their slaves and the size of their territory.

_____

_____

_____

2. The boat's crew located the sound and used radar to track its course through the harbor but could not identify the sound, and whatever lurked beneath the surface circled the area for almost thirty minutes.

_____

_____

_____

3. Gale-force winds buffeted the tiny seacoast village, including Judd Beere's old, single-masted sloop, which was tied to the rotting town dock, and the sloop's lines strained against rusty cleats until first one and then another gave way.

_____

_____

_____

4. Helen was determined to compete in the marathon and had been training for the race for several months by exercising and running one mile each morning and five miles each afternoon.

_____

_____

22.3 Varying Your Sentences (Using Different Sentence Openers, Using Different Sentence Structures)
• Practice 1

Using Different Sentence Openers   Vary sentence openers, using one-word modifiers, phrases, and clauses.

WAYS TO BEGIN SENTENCES
Subject First: The whole *family* drove Grandma to the station.
Modifier First: Eventually, we found a parking place.
Phrase First: Peering through the train window, Grandma waved good-bye.
Clause First: Although we hated to see Grandma leave, we knew she would come for another visit soon.

Using Different Sentence Structures   Use a variety of sentence structures in your writing.

Monotonous Sentences	Varied Sentence Structures
My cousin enjoys her job. She is a counselor at a summer camp. She teaches crafts during the day. She sleeps in a cabin with the ten-year-olds. She says that some of them are homesick at first. They usually get over it after a couple of days.	My cousin enjoys her job as a counselor at a summer camp. During the day, she teaches crafts, and at night she sleeps in a cabin with the ten-year-olds. Many of the youngsters, she says, are homesick at first but usually recover after a couple of days.

▶ **Exercise 1**   **Using Different Sentence Openers.**   Rewrite each sentence to make it begin with a one-word modifier, a phrase, or a clause.

EXAMPLE: We will meet you at the library as soon as school is over.

_____*As soon as school is over, we will meet you at the library.*_____

1. The train occasionally makes whistle stops to discharge passengers.

_____

2. We allowed plenty of time to be sure of seeing the kick-off.

_____

3. My parents ask us to serve and clean up when they entertain.

_____

4. I usually have no problem with math.

_____

5. We watched fireflies in the backyard at night.

_____

▶ **Exercise 2**   **Using Different Sentence Structures.**   On separate paper, rewrite the following paragraph, combining sentences and using a variety of sentence structures.

(1) Thomas Jefferson was a great public leader. (2) He was an architect and an inventor, too. (3) He bought land on a small mountain. (4) He named the place Monticello. (5) That means "little mountain." (6) Jefferson built a home there. (7) He was his own architect and builder. (8) He invented the dumbwaiter. (9) It was used in Monticello. (10) He invented revolving bookshelves for his library. too.

22.3 Varying Your Sentences (Using Different Sentence Openers, Using Different Sentence Structures) • Practice 2

Exercise 1 Identifying Sentence Openers. Label each sentence opener as a *subject*, a *one-word modifier*, a *phrase*, or a *clause*.

EXAMPLE: Like a carefree seagull, the hang glider hovered over the waves. _____*phrase*_____

1. When the storm ended, we inspected the barn for damage. _____
2. Proudly, the marchers strutted down the boulevard waving their flags. _____
3. The mayor feared a drop in the city's mass transit income. _____
4. To do somersaults on a trampoline, you need good balance. _____
5. Hissing loudly, the cat backed away from the curious puppy. _____
6. Lost, the three-year-old sat down on the curb and cried. _____
7. Pedro earned letters in three varsity sports. _____
8. In the street eight floors below, the taxis darted to and fro like yellow bugs. _____
9. While Angie entertained the guests, Karl made dinner. _____
10. Usually, the local bus runs on schedule on weekdays. _____

Exercise 2 Using Different Sentence Openers. Rewrite each sentence to make it begin with a one-word modifier, a phrase, or a clause.

EXAMPLE: You should pass the test if you review your notes.

_____*If you review your notes, you should pass the test.*_____

1. You should read the instructions carefully before you assemble a model.

_____

2. Carol, insulted, turned on her heel and stalked out.

_____

3. The cars on the highway were backed up for miles because of a jackknifed tractor-trailer.

_____

4. The auditorium was filled with the sound of cheering at the end of the graduation ceremony.

_____

5. The spacecraft encountered the other ship at 1300 hours.

_____

6. The governess happily waved to Meg on the Ferris wheel.

_____

7. See the dentist at least twice a year to check for cavities and other problems.

_____

8. A mid-afternoon solar eclipse predictably drew hundreds of onlookers into the street.

_____

9. Chicago was a thriving young city when the great fire erupted.

_____

10. The actor enthusiastically campaigned for the senator.

_____

Name _____ Date _____

 22.4 **Fragments** (Recognizing Fragments) • **Practice 1**

Fragments   A fragment is a group of words that does not express a complete thought. Part of a sentence should not be presented as a full sentence ending with a period or other end mark.

Fragments	Sentences
Because we missed the train	We were late *because we missed the train.*
After the rainfall	*After the rainfall,* the river rose.
Without looking back	Sue got on the train *without looking back.*
The boy wearing the green shirt	*The boy wearing the green shirt* is Tim.
Hope to return to New York someday	They *hope to return to New York someday.*

▶ **Exercise 1**   **Identifying Sentence Fragments.**   Write whether each group of words is a *sentence* or a *fragment.*

EXAMPLE: Riding on the *Orient Express*. _____*fragment*_____

1. To see the new muscum was a real thrill. _____
2. Which Cindy got for her birthday. _____
3. Who won? _____
4. The player with the lowest score. _____
5. Enjoys working out at the gym. _____
6. Stop. _____
7. The smell of buttery popcorn. _____
8. The most amazing thing about Andrew. _____
9. Playing musical chairs. _____
10. My bikc is missing. _____
11. What timc is it? _____
12. After searching high and low. _____
13. The combination of diet, rest, and exercise. _____
14. Surrounded by a line of poplars. _____
15. The movie is hilarious. _____
16. Bagels used to be found only in the East. _____
17. Whoever you want. _____
18. After the circus had come to our town. _____
19. Beyond the ridge lay another valley. _____
20. Known for good service, the restaurant prospered. _____

▶ **Exercise 2**   **Identifying Fragments in a Paragraph.**   Underline each sentence fragment in the paragraph below.

EXAMPLE: We gathered all our equipment. <u>Before setting out on our camping trip.</u>

(1) We each had a sleeping bag and backpack. (2) Which we would carry ourselves. (3) Dad would drag the tent behind him on poles. (4) As some Indians had dragged their tepees. (5) The day before the expedition. (6) We had done our food shopping. (7) Our main purchases had been lightweight, dried foods. (8) Including rice, nuts and dried fruit, and beans. (9) After one last check of our list. (10) We were ready to start out on our adventure.

© Prentice-Hall, Inc.   Fragments (Recognizing Fragments) • 101

22.4 Fragments (Recognizing Fragments) • Practice 2

▷ **Exercise 1**   **Identifying Sentence Fragments.**   Identify each item as a *fragment* or *sentence*.

EXAMPLE: Leaving early in the morning. _____*fragment*_____

1. A bouquet of freshly cut flowers. _____
2. Will arrive between one and two o'clock. _____
3. In the jar on top of the refrigerator. _____
4. Swimming, skiing, or boating on the lake. _____
5. That hurts. _____
6. Wanting to write to you. _____
7. To know her is to admire her. _____
8. Broke all speed records in the last race. _____
9. After you sit down, I will begin. _____
10. A doctor of great skill and devotion to her patients. _____
11. While we were swimming. _____
12. Please be seated. _____
13. Seeing my friend at the concert. _____
14. If the train is not late. _____
15. John was angry with us. _____
16. Because the rain has stopped. _____
17. Someone left a mess behind. _____
18. Everyone had voted. _____
19. Which hangs on the wall. _____
20. Until the next time we meet. _____

▷ **Exercise 2**   **Identifying Fragments in a Paragraph.**   Underline each sentence fragment in the paragraph below.

EXAMPLE: (1) The football game would begin in less than five minutes. (2) <u>Weren't in our seats yet.</u>

(1) Basketball is the only major sport that originated in the United States. (2) Invented by a Canadian, James Naismith, who was teaching at the Y.M.C.A. in Springfield, Massachusetts, at the time. (3) The students there were studying to become secretaries and physical education instructors. (4) Bored with the marching, calisthenics, and gymnastics that made up their gym classes. (5) The head of the department had a talk with Naismith. (6) In the fall of 1891. (7) Asking the Canadian teacher to develop a game that could be played in a gym. (8) Had no physical contact. (9) Lightweight ball. (10) to make it safe for the students and also for the school's gym. (11) Each player was to have an equal chance to handle the ball. (12) And to make plays. (13) By December, Naismith had developed what he called "the game." (14) Intended to nail up some boxes to serve as targets. (15) No boxes being available, they nailed up some half-bushel peach baskets instead. (16) The game was soon called *basket ball.* (17) By 1902 the word was often hyphenated. (18) Becoming *basket-ball.* (19) It wasn't until about 1912 that the name of the game was written as one word. (20) It's interesting to note that if the school had had some boxes, we might be playing boxball today.

22.4 Fragments (Correcting Fragments) • Practice 1

Correcting Fragments   A phrase should not be capitalized and punctuated as if it were a sentence.

Phrase Fragments	Completed Sentences
a person with great integrity	*A person with great integrity* is needed.
followed us home	A stray dog *followed us home*.
throughout the house	We searched *throughout the house*.
fed by the spring	The river *fed by the spring* is cold.

A subordinate clause should not be capitalized and punctuated as if it were a sentence.

Clause Fragments	Completed Sentences
whom I greatly respect	Lee is someone *whom I greatly respect*.
just as we began our picnic	The rain started *just as we began our picnic*.
what I asked	*What I asked* was impossible to do.

Words in a series should not be capitalized and punctuated as if they were a sentence.

Series Fragment	Completed Sentence
blueberry pie, strawberry shortcake, and cherry cheesecake	The dessert choices include *blueberry pie, strawberry shortcake, and cherry cheesecake*.

▶ **Exercise 1**   **Identifying Kinds of Sentence Fragments.**   After each item below, write *phrase*, *clause*, *series*, or *sentence* to describe the word group.

EXAMPLE: Wherever you want them. _____*clause*_____

1. To make friends in a new place. _____
2. A wide meadow, a babbling brook, and bright sunshine. _____
3. Please wait for me. _____
4. That you invited to the party. _____
5. You succeeded. _____
6. Without a second thought. _____
7. Whenever you are ready. _____
8. Offered by the dog's owner. _____
9. Take your mark. _____
10. The action during the first scene. _____

▶ **Exercise 2**   **Correcting Fragments.**   Turn five of the fragments in Exercise A into sentences.

EXAMPLE: _____*I will put these boxes wherever you want them.*_____

1. _____
2. _____
3. _____
4. _____
5. _____

22.4 Fragments (Correcting Fragments) • Practice 2

Exercise 1   **Using Phrase Fragments to Write Sentences.**   Use each fragment in a complete sentence.

EXAMPLE: Among the clouds.

    Our hot-air balloon rose higher and higher until it floated among the clouds.

1. on the front page

    _____

2. to sing folk songs professionally

    _____

3. many beautiful birds

    _____

4. drinking from a green glass

    _____

5. a dark, menacing cloud

    _____

Exercise 2   **Using Clause Fragments to Write Sentences.**   Use each fragment in a complete sentence.

1. when I awoke this morning

    _____

2. that my class likes best

    _____

3. unless you practice each day

    _____

4. if it is cold tomorrow

    _____

5. who waited in line

    _____

Exercise 3   **Using Series Fragments to Write Sentences.**   Use each of the following fragments in a complete sentence.

1. calico kittens, green parakeets, and dachshund puppies

    _____

2. ran, skipped, and jumped

    _____

3. in the drawer, on the top shelf of the closet, or under the sink

    _____

4. deep orange, yellow, or red

    _____

5. slowly, methodically, and quite gracefully

    _____

22.4 Run-ons (Recognizing Run-ons) • Practice 1

Recognizing Run-ons A run-on sentence is two or more complete sentences that are not properly joined or separated; that is, they are not separated by an end mark, or they are separated only by a comma.

RUN-ONS
The coals are ready now we can begin cooking.
The lettuce is thriving, the broccoli is straggly.

▶ **Exercise 1** **Identifying Run-ons.** Identify each item as a *run-on* or a *sentence* in each space to the right.

EXAMPLE: David has a new camera, but he forgot to bring it. _____ *sentence* _____

1. Emily Dickinson wrote most of her poems without leaving her room. _____

2. The children played in the back yard, the swings and sandbox amused them. _____

3. We got three easy outs our team was up. _____

4. Louise did a wonderful job, we knew she would. _____

5. Amanda stepped through the gate and into a beautiful garden. _____

6. The TV series was excellent, but it never found its audience. _____

7. Billy wanted to be an actor, jobs were hard to get. _____

8. Languages are not easy for me I do better in math. _____

9. Several new families live on our block, we have been here longer. _____

10. Lisa left early, but no one knew why. _____

11. Although we all were hungry, we waited patiently. _____

12. The architects have worked hard the lowest bid will get the job. _____

13. The cove is quite pretty, it is rocky at low tide. _____

14. The audience applauded when the curtain fell. _____

15. The boat docked, all the passengers got off. _____

16. The family reunion was a much greater success than we had expected. _____

17. No one liked our new neighbors, they made incredible noises. _____

18. Jack listens to the radio all the time except when Laura turns it off. _____

19. Kurt didn't know what he wanted to do; however, Carla had plans. _____

20. She loved science, nevertheless she failed the test. _____

▶ **Exercise 2** **Identifying Run-ons in a Paragraph.** Underline each run-on in the paragraph below.

EXAMPLE: Our new house is finally finished, we moved in last week. There is still much to be done.

(1) Some rooms still need painting not all the light fixtures are in. (2) However, even more work needs to be done outside. (3) In clearing the lot, the builders razed all the trees. (4) We have ordered new trees and shrubs, they will be delivered this weekend. (5) After the nursery has planted them, we can begin thinking about flowers. (6) Rick and I have picked out a perfect spot for a vegetable garden, Dad has other ideas. (7) Mom plans a flower bed in front there is a perfect sunny spot for it. (8) We have already put in grass seed, it needs to be watered every day. (9) Soon we will have a beautiful yard. (10) It is hard work every bit is worth it.

22.4 **Run-ons** (Recognizing Run-ons) • **Practice 2**

▶ **Exercise 1**   **Identifying Run-ons.**   Identify each item as a *run-on* or a *sentence*.

EXAMPLE: Although he disliked her, he was polite. _____*sentence*_____

1. Queen Mary slowly entered the huge hall in silence the crowd gathered there gazed at the woman who was about to be executed. _____

2. Forced onto the sidelines by his torn ligament, Jack was restless and unhappy. _____

3. Keats came into the house from the garden and casually threw down some paper, on it was written "Ode on a Grecian Urn." _____

4. Lord Rosse built a telescope in Ireland in 1845, it was often inactive because of poor Irish weather. _____

5. Though billions of comets circle beyond the edges of our solar system, few come close to the earth. _____

6. Wind and water are major causes of erosion of the soil, they constantly change the appearance of the Earth's surface. _____

7. Shrimp eggs can survive for over one year in the desert sands, rainwater brings them to life. _____

8. March is the month when huge blocks of ice in the Arctic begin to melt and break up. _____

9. In drawings by young children, sizes and shapes of objects often look wrong. _____

10. Deserts turn cold at night, there is nothing to stop the heat from escaping into the atmosphere. _____

11. My grandmother loved *Gone with the Wind* she read it years ago. _____

12. Lightning turns nitrogen in the air into an oxide, it then falls with the rain and fertilizes the soil. _____

13. The famous Irish writer James Joyce left his native land in 1902 at various times he lived in the cities of Paris, Trieste, and Zurich. _____

14. For the last fifty years of his life, the poet Robinson Jeffers lived in a tower on the California coast. _____

15. When the bases are loaded and two players are already out, baseball is at its most exciting. _____

16. National parks in this country were established to protect wildlife, preserve natural resources, and provide recreational areas. _____

17. Crater Lake in the state of Oregon is a unique tourist attraction, it fills a crater on top of an inactive volcano. _____

18. The typical sonnet has fourteen lines, ten syllables make up each line. _____

19. The sun's rays striking raindrops can produce a rainbow you can see it if the sun is behind you and the rain is ahead of you. _____

20. Roosters begin to crow at dawn, they seem to bring the farm to life. _____

22.4 Run-ons (Correcting Run-ons) • Practice 1

Correcting Run-ons   Use one of the following methods to correct run-ons.

END MARK	
What do you think will we win?	What do you think? Will we win?
COMMA AND COORDINATING CONJUNCTION	
Kelly came with us, Sue stayed home.	Kelly came with us, but Sue stayed home.
SEMICOLON	
The food was delicious the service was excellent.	The food was delicious; the service was excellent.
ONE SIMPLE SENTENCE	
The jet was a 747 it landed gracefully.	The jet, a 747, landed gracefully.
ONE COMPLEX SENTENCE	
We lost the game we had played our best.	Although we lost the game, we had played our best.

▶ **Exercise 1**   **Preparing to Correct Run-ons.**   If a word group below is a run-on sentence, insert a caret (^) between the two sentences or independent clauses. If a sentence is correct, write *C* after it.

EXAMPLE: The trick amazed the group ^ they had never seen anything like it. _____

1. Senator Hill was the graduation speaker he talked about responsibility. _____
2. The base of the Statue of Liberty is granite which came from Stony Creek, Connecticut. _____
3. Several council members opposed the tax, they voted against it. _____
4. Many cactuses are odd-looking plants they have beautiful blossoms. _____
5. The owner offered a handsome reward no trace of the show dog was found. _____
6. The troops had no defense they were completely surrounded. _____
7. Without saying a word, the messenger handed me an envelope. _____
8. Lighthouse keepers have a lonely life they do important work. _____
9. We rounded the bend, the castle came into view. _____
10. Judy recognized the bike at once it was the one she had sold last week. _____

▶ **Exercise 2**   **Correcting Run-ons.**   Rewrite five run-ons from Exercise 1. Use each method of rewriting noted in the chart.

EXAMPLE: _____*The trick amazed the crowd, who had never seen anything like it.*_____

1. _____
2. _____
3. _____
4. _____
5. _____

22.4 Run-ons (Correcting Run-ons) • Practice 2

▶ **Exercise 1**   **Using Punctuation and Conjunctions to Correct Run-ons.**   Use an end mark, a comma and a coordinating conjunction, or a semicolon to correct each run-on. Use each method at least once.

EXAMPLE: The cash was hidden in a rusty tin can nobody thought to look inside it.

The cash was hidden in a rusty tin can, but nobody thought to look inside it.

1. I could hardly wait to jump in the water looked so inviting.

_____

2. They seemed to expect me to babysit again, I wouldn't do it for any price.

_____

3. A stray dog wandered onto the field, the outfielder tried to catch it.

_____

4. We spent hours searching for the car keys we never found them.

_____

5. Would you care for French dressing on your salad, would you prefer it unseasoned?

_____

▶ **Exercise 2**   **Forming Simple and Complex Sentences to Correct Run-ons.**   Form a simple or complex sentence to correct each run-on. Use each method at least two times.

EXAMPLE: The sun set, the forest was quiet.

When the sun set, the forest was quiet.

1. Mr. Adams was a candidate for mayor, he spoke to many community organizations.

_____

2. The iguana raced across the yard it was a family pet.

_____

3. The snow was piled around the parked cars, it made it impossible for us to leave.

_____

4. The child was delighted with the gift, he began to play with it right away.

_____

5. I couldn't handle the luggage alone I had three suitcases and a small trunk.

_____

▶ **Writing Application**   **Correcting Run-ons.**   Rewrite the following paragraphs, correcting all run-ons.

(1) After flying through a dense, seemingly endless cloud bank, the shuttle plane with its pilot, co-pilot, and three nervous passengers was lost. (2) The pilot could not recognize any landmarks, the co-pilot could not recognize any either. (3) One of the passengers, a young girl, entered the pilot's cabin and asked if she could help. (4) Although worried, the pilot smiled, he was very good-natured.

(5) The girl explained that she recognized the terrain her father had taken her camping in these hills just last summer. (6) "If you turn slightly and fly over that far ridge," explained the girl, "you will see a highway. (7) Follow it west it will lead toward Pescadora."

(8) The pilot and co-pilot thanked the girl and complimented her on her keen sense of direction. (9) Their praises pleased the girl, they also gave her an idea. (10) As soon as she finished school, she would take flying lessons.

22.4 Misplaced Modifiers • Practice 1

Recognizing Misplaced Modifiers A modifier should be placed as close as possible to the word it modifies. A misplaced modifier appears to modify the wrong word in a sentence.

MISPLACED MODIFIERS

Joan went to meet the President wearing her new white suit.

We found an old olive grove hiking up the mountain.

Correcting Misplaced Modifiers Correct a misplaced modifier by moving the phrase or clause closer to the word it should logically modify.

Misplaced Modifiers	Corrected Sentences
Joan went to meet the president wearing her new white suit.	Wearing her new white suit, Joan went to meet the President.
We found an old olive grove hiking up the mountain.	Hiking up the mountain, we found an old olive grove.

Exercise 1 **Recognizing Misplaced Modifiers.** Underline each misplaced modifier. If a sentence is correct as written, leave it unmarked.

EXAMPLE: Uncle Al shot the tiger that sprang at him with his rifle.

1. The sale at Bowen's features shirts for men with minor flaws.

2. Aground on some rocks, the freighter was slowly breaking apart.

3. My sister dropped in while I was scrubbing the floor with her new baby.

4. Clare opened the package brought by the letter carrier with a cry of delight.

5. Charlie squandered all the money on new records that his uncle left him.

6. Dad had been looking for a mechanic who can repair our car without success.

7. Paul had a tomato that he had grown himself in his lunchbox.

8. Trying to stretch a single into a double, the runner was thrown out easily.

9. Ms. Dove threatened to keep the class after school many times that day.

10. In 1700, the first practical umbrella was invented by an anonymous Englishman with whalebone ribs.

Exercise 2 **Correcting Misplaced Modifiers.** Rewrite five incorrect sentences from Exercise 1, correcting the misplaced modifier. Then underline the corrected modifier and draw an arrow from it to the word it modifies.

EXAMPLE: With his rifle, Uncle Al shot the tiger that sprang at him.

1. _____

2. _____

3. _____

4. _____

5. _____

22.4 Misplaced Modifiers • Practice 2

Exercise 1 **Recognizing Misplaced Modifiers.**   Underline each misplaced modifier. If a sentence is correct, write *correct*.

EXAMPLE: The baby crawled on the floor <u>with blue overalls</u>.

1. The messenger spoke to the receptionist who delivered the package. _____

2. The golfer won the trophy wearing green golf shoes. _____

3. Our desire grew smaller to win the prize. _____

4. Reading the menu, Hugh decided to have steak again. _____

5. Finishing the dishes, we were ready to relax. _____

6. The kitten drank the milk that was hungry. _____

7. I hurried to open the gift happily surprised. _____

8. Sailing into port, my grandfather stood at the wheel of his beautiful new boat. _____

9. Soaring gracefully over the treetops, I watched the hawk disappear from view. _____

10. Badly frightened, the puppy cowered under the porch. _____

Exercise 2 **Correcting Misplaced Modifiers.**   Rewrite each of the following sentences, correcting each misplaced modifier. Then underline the correct modifier and draw an arrow from it to the word it modifies.

EXAMPLE: The child ran into the house crying loudly. *Crying loudly, the child ran into the house.*

1. A sundae was served to each guest, dripping with chocolate sauce.

_____

2. Wilkins realized the mistake he had made after a few minutes.

_____

3. The dean spoke to the boys about loitering in the principal's office.

_____

4. We gave the scraps of meat to the dog that had been left on our plates.

_____

5. Michelle bought an umbrella after shopping carefully with red and yellow stripes.

_____

6. The ballad singer heard most of the songs he later sang wandering through the hill country.

_____

7. The hunter crouched behind a tree waiting for a bear to come along with a bow and arrow.

_____

8. The bloodhound picked up the fugitive's scent sniffing in the bushes.

_____

9. We saw many beautiful homes driving through the South.

_____

10. Wilma put the trophies into a glass cabinet that she had won in golf tournaments.

_____

© Prentice-Hall, Inc.

22.4 Dangling Modifiers • Practice 1

Recognizing Dangling Modifiers   A dangling modifier seems to modify the wrong word or no word at all because the word it should logically modify is missing.

DANGLING MODIFIERS
Flying over the Alps, the view was breathtaking.
Sailing out into the ocean, a tropical island appeared.

Correcting Dangling Modifiers   Correct a dangling modifier by rewriting the sentence to include the missing word.

Dangling Modifiers	Corrected Sentences
Flying over the Alps, the view was breathtaking.	*Flying over the Alps*, we found the view breathtaking.
Sailing out into the ocean, a tropical island appeared.	*Sailing out into the ocean*, they saw a tropical island.

▶ **Exercise 1**   **Recognizing Dangling Modifiers.**   Underline each dangling modifier. If a sentence has no dangling modifier, leave it unmarked.

EXAMPLE: <u>Rowing through the swamp at night</u>, many weird sounds were heard.

1. Born into a poor family, college seemed an impossible dream.

2. Speeding through a red light, the cyclist nearly hit an old man.

3. Taking the stairs two at a time, the bell rang.

4. After stepping into the shower, the telephone rang.

5. Descending by a different trail, the hazardous slope was avoided.

6. After walking across the hot sand, the clump of trees offered welcome relief.

7. Practicing for weeks, the difficult sonata was finally mastered.

8. While Mary was greeting her guests, her dog was eating the sandwiches.

9. Sympathizing with the flood victims, donations flowed in from all over.

10. Arriving a day late, the tickets were worthless.

▶ **Exercise 2**   **Correcting Dangling Modifiers.**   Rewrite five incorrect sentences from Exercise 1, correcting the dangling modifiers. Underline the modifier in the corrected sentence and draw an arrow from it to the word it modifies.

EXAMPLE: <u>Rowing through the swamp at night</u>, we heard many weird sounds.

1. _____

2. _____

3. _____

4. _____

5. _____

22.4 Dangling Modifiers • Practice 2

▶ **Exercise 1** **Recognizing Dangling Modifiers.** Underline each dangling modifier. If a sentence is correct, write *correct*.

EXAMPLE: <u>Carrying so many packages</u>, the path was hard to follow.

1. Skating across the pond, the ice was very slick. _____

2. Studying for weeks, the test was easy. _____

3. Considering my small allowance, the tickets were expensive. _____

4. Writing letters at camp all afternoon, home seemed far away. _____

5. Finishing the dishes, we were ready to relax. _____

▶ **Exercise 2** **Correcting Dangling Modifiers.** Rewrite each sentence, correcting the dangling modifier. Then underline the correct modifier and draw an arrow from it to the word it modifies.

EXAMPLE: Losing hope, the mountains rose in the distance.

<u>Losing hope,</u> *we saw the mountains rise in the distance.*

1. Trying to get to town quickly, the highway seemed best.

_____

2. Jogging one morning, the solution to the problem was obvious.

_____

3. When she was five, Paula's mother graduated from the university.

_____

4. Wandering aimlessly in the woods, the first sight of camp was welcome.

_____

5. Hearing of the refugees' plight, emergency funds were made available.

_____

6. Getting up much earlier than usual, the house seemed strangely quiet.

_____

7. When he developed measles, Dan's father called the school.

_____

8. Absorbed in the crossword puzzle, the time passed quickly.

_____

9. Waiting for a ride, the rain pounded down all around.

_____

10. Sailing far from shore, a squall suddenly arose.

_____

▶ **Writing Application** **Correcting Misplaced and Dangling Modifiers.** Rewrite the following paragraph, correcting all misplaced or dangling modifiers.

(1) Washington Irving's stories often contain elements of fantasy. (2) In one story, Rip van Winkle slept through the whole American Revolution that Irving wrote. (3) Waking up, his rusted musket should have indicated that something unusual had happened. (4) Rip was greeted by other puzzling things strolling into town. (5) The faces of the people were all strange that he met. (6) Hanging over the door of the inn, Rip noticed George Washington's portrait. (7) King George's portrait had always hung there before. (8) Rip then looked for his old friend, the innkeeper. (9) Rip questioned an old man trying to find the innkeeper. (10) The old man replied, "He is dead these eighteen years."

23.1 Verb Tenses (Six Tenses of Verbs, Four Principal Parts of Verbs) • Practice 1

The Six Tenses of Verbs A tense is a form of a verb that shows the time of an action or a condition. Each tense has a basic and a progressive form.

Tenses	Basic Forms	Progressive Forms
Present	I *work.*	I *am working.*
Past	I *worked.*	I *was working.*
Future	I *will work.*	I *will be working.*
Present Perfect	I *have worked.*	I *have been working.*
Past Perfect	I *had worked.*	I *had been working.*
Future Perfect	I *will have worked.*	I *will have been working.*

The Four Principal Parts of Verbs A verb has four principal parts: the present, the present participle, the past, and the past participle.

THE FOUR PRINCIPAL PARTS			
Present	**Present Participle**	**Past**	**Past Participle**
cook	cooking	cooked	(have) cooked
steal	stealing	stole	(have) stolen
make	making	made	(have) made

▶ **Exercise 1** **Recognizing Tenses and Forms of Verbs.** Underline the verb or verb phrase in each sentence below. Then write the tense on each line to the right. If the form is progressive, write the word *progressive* after the tense.

EXAMPLE: Vinnie will be working on Saturday night. ___*future progressive*___

1. Caroline arranged the flowers for the centerpiece. _____

2. The TV was working fine last night. _____

3. I have ordered the pizza already. _____

4. In December Dad will have been working there thirty years. _____

5. We often stay in that cottage on vacation. _____

6. Grandma will visit us next week. _____

7. Someone has been snooping through my things. _____

8. The fans had hoped for a win. _____

9. The chemist had been experimenting with a new formula. _____

10. The train will have left without us. _____

▶ **Exercise 2** **Identifying Principal Parts.** On the lines below, write the principal part of the main verb used in each sentence above. Then write the name of that principal part.

EXAMPLE: ___*working, present participle*___

1. _____   6. _____

2. _____   7. _____

3. _____   8. _____

4. _____   9. _____

5. _____   10. _____

23.1 Verb Tenses (Six Tenses of Verbs, Four Principal Parts of Verbs) • Practice 2

▶ Exercise 1 **Recognizing Basic and Progressive Forms.** Identify the form of each verb as *basic* or *progressive*.

EXAMPLE: He has been swimming. _____*progressive*_____

1. He is leaving. _____
2. I was singing. _____
3. She has rested. _____
4. They had tried. _____
5. He has been waiting. _____
6. I will have been working. _____
7. He spoke. _____
8. They will help. _____
9. He had been sleeping. _____
10. You will have gone. _____

▶ Exercise 2 **Recognizing the Six Tenses.** Write the tense of each verb in Exercise 1. If the tense is a progressive form, add the word *progressive*.

EXAMPLE: He has been swimming. _____*present perfect progressive*_____

1. _____ 6. _____
2. _____ 7. _____
3. _____ 8. _____
4. _____ 9. _____
5. _____ 10. _____

▶ Exercise 3 **Recognizing Principal Parts.** Identify the principal part used to form each verb in Exercise 1.

EXAMPLE: He has been swimming. _____*present participle*_____

1. _____ 6. _____
2. _____ 7. _____
3. _____ 8. _____
4. _____ 9. _____
5. _____ 10. _____

23.1 Verb Tenses (Regular and Irregular Verbs)
• Practice 1

Regular and Irregular Verbs   A regular verb is one whose past and past participle are formed by adding *-ed* or *-d* to the present form.

PRINCIPAL PARTS OF REGULAR VERBS			
Present	**Present Participle**	**Past**	**Past Participle**
learn	learning	learned	(have) learned
carry	carrying	carried	(have) carried
promise	promising	promised	(have) promised
drip	dripping	dripped	(have) dripped

An irregular verb is one whose past and past participle are not formed by adding *-ed* or *-d* to the present form.

PRINCIPAL PARTS OF IRREGULAR VERBS			
Present	**Present Participle**	**Past**	**Past Participle**
cost	costing	cost	(have) cost
put	putting	put	(have) put
bring	bringing	brought	(have) brought
sleep	sleeping	slept	(have) slept
draw	drawing	drew	(have) drawn
freeze	freezing	froze	(have) frozen
rise	rising	rose	(have) risen

▶**Exercise 1**   **Writing the Principal Parts of Irregular Verbs.**   Add the missing principal parts.

EXAMPLE: speak ____*speaking*____ ____*spoke*____ ____*(have) spoken*____

1. _____ writing _____ _____
2. _____ _____ flew _____
3. see _____ _____ _____
4. _____ _____ _____ (have) spun
5. _____ _____ hurt _____
6. _____ fighting _____ _____
7. _____ _____ _____ (have) driven
8. spend _____ _____ _____
9. _____ _____ wound _____
10. _____ eating _____ _____

▶**Exercise 2**   **Recognizing Principal Parts of Verbs.**   Fill in each blank with the correct verb form from those given in parentheses.

EXAMPLE: Sasha never had ____*sung*____ in public before. (sang, sung)

1. The balloon _____ suddenly. (burst, busted)
2. The sweater _____ in the wash. (shrank, shrinked)
3. They _____ all of their money out of the bank. (drew, drawed)
4. Aunt Mary _____ she would help us. (sayed, said)
5. Jack _____ up the beanstalk. (climbed, clumb)

23.1 Verb Tenses (Regular and Irregular Verbs)
• Practice 2

▶ **Exercise 1** **Learning the Principal Parts of Irregular Verbs.** Write the present participle, the past, and the past participle of each verb.

EXAMPLE: throw ___*throwing, threw, thrown*___

1. build _____
2. find _____
3. get _____
4. hold _____
5. drink _____
6. do _____
7. bring _____
8. burst _____
9. fly _____
10. teach _____

▶ **Exercise 2** **Recognizing Principal Parts in Sentences.** Fill in each blank with the correct verb form from those given in parentheses.

EXAMPLE: He ___*brought*___ the wrong book to class. (bring, brought)

1. The batter _____ hard but missed the ball. (swang, swung)
2. Steve _____ me home. (drived, drove)
3. Rachel _____ the cabin in the woods in only two and a half months. (built, builded)
4. We _____ the rent a week early. (payed, paid)
5. All around us fire crackers were _____. (busting, bursting)
6. The used car _____ me only a little more than two hundred dollars. (costed, cost)
7. The campers _____ on the ground. (sleeped, slept)
8. I _____ the money on the table. (layed, laid)
9. Our guide _____ us to a waterfall. (leaded, led)
10. She _____ the package with string. (binded, bound)

▶ **Exercise 3** **Correcting Principal Parts.** The paragraph below contains five errors in the choice between the past and the past participle. Cross out the errors and write corrections on the lines that follow the paragraph.

EXAMPLE: Dorothea Dix fighted for the mentally ill. *Dorothea Dix fought for the mentally ill.*

(1) Dorothea Dix played a crucial role in helping the mentally ill. (2) After visiting a jail in Massachusetts in the 1840s, she seen that they led the same life as criminals. (3) Until her visit, she had not knew that the mentally ill led such miserable lives. (4) Often, they lived in unheated housing. (5) Dix knew that she had not took enough responsibility in the past. (6) She begun to visit each place in the state where the mentally ill lived. (7) After her visits, she wrote a detailed report. (8) She convinced the state to improve the treatment of the mentally ill. (9) She also fighted in other states. (10) In all, fifteen states passed laws to help the mentally ill.

1. _____
2. _____
3. _____
4. _____
5. _____
6. _____
7. _____
8. _____
9. _____
10. _____

23.1 # Verb Tenses (Conjugating the Tenses) • Practice 1

Conjugating the Tenses   A conjugation is a complete list of the singular and plural forms of a verb. A short conjugation lists just the forms that are used with a single pronoun. As you study the following short conjugations, note that the verbs used with *you* are also used with *we* and *they*. The verbs used with *she*, likewise, are also used with *he* and *it*.

SHORT CONJUGATIONS			
Basic and Progressive Forms	do (with *I*)	do (with *you*)	do (with *she*)
Present	I do	you do	she does
Past	I did	you did	she did
Future	I will do	you will do	she will do
Present Perfect	I have done	you have done	she has done
Past Perfect	I had done	you had done	she had done
Future Perfect	I will have done	you will have done	she will have done
Present Progressive	I am doing	you are doing	she is doing
Past Progressive	I was doing	you were doing	she was doing
Future Progressive	I will be doing	you will be doing	she will be doing
Present Perfect Progressive	I have been doing	you have been doing	she has been doing
Past Perfect Progressive	I had been doing	you had been doing	she had been doing
Future Perfect Progressive	I will have been doing	you will have been doing	she will have been doing

▶**Exercise 1**   **Conjugating Basic and Progressive Forms.**   Complete each of the following short conjugations.

1. use (with *I*) _____

_____

2. take (with *he*) _____

_____

3. go (with *we*) _____

_____

4. see (with *they*) _____

_____

▶**Exercise 2**   **Supplying the Correct Verb.**   Fill in each blank with the form of each verb given in parentheses.

EXAMPLE: The train _____*will be arriving*_____ soon. (*arrive*, future progressive)

1. We _____ here for ten years. (*live*, present perfect progressive)

2. Palmer _____ his way in the jungle. (*lose*, past perfect)

3. Mom _____ just the car she wants. (*find*, present perfect)

4. Aunt Betty _____ us next week. (*visit*, future progressive)

5. The owner _____ a large reward. (*offer*, present progressive)

23.1 **Verb Tenses** (Conjugating the Tenses) • Practice 2

▶ **Exercise 1** **Conjugating the Basic Forms of Verbs.** Conjugate the basic forms of the verbs below in the manner shown in the example.

EXAMPLE: spend (conjugated with *we*)

Present: we spend   Present Perfect: we have spent
Past: we spent   Past Perfect: we had spent
Future: we will spend   Future Perfect: we will have spent

1. open (conjugated with *I*)

_____   _____
_____   _____
_____   _____

2. move (conjugated with *you*)

_____   _____
_____   _____
_____   _____

3. know (conjugated with *he*

_____   _____
_____   _____
_____   _____

▶ **Exercise 2** **Conjugating the Progressive Forms of Verbs.** Conjugate the progressive forms of the verbs below in the manner shown in the example.

EXAMPLE: spend (conjugated with *we*)

Present Progressive: we are spending   Present Perfect Progressive: we have been spending
Past Progressive: we were spending   Past Perfect Progressive: we had been spending
Future Progressive: we will be spending   Future Perfect Progressive: we will have been
                                              spending

1. walk (conjugated with *you*)

_____   _____
_____   _____
_____   _____

2. jump (conjugated with *she*)

_____   _____
_____   _____
_____   _____

3. say (conjugated with *they*)

_____   _____
_____   _____
_____   _____

Expressing Time Through Tense (Uses of Tense in Present Time) • **Practice 1**

Uses of Tense in Present Time   The present and the present progressive show present actions or conditions as well as various continuing actions or conditions.

USES OF TENSE IN PRESENT TIME		
Verb Forms	**Uses**	**Examples**
Present	Present action	Here *comes* Elsie.
	Present condition	Those tomatoes *are* ripe.
	Reoccurring action	I *exercise* daily.
	Reoccurring condition	Ernie *is* often late.
	Constant action	Water *freezes* at 0°C.
	Constant condition	The sun *is* our nearest star.
Present Progressive	Continuing action	Dad *is cooking* dinner.
	Continuing condition	Laura *is feeling* better.

▶ **Exercise 1**   **Identifying the Uses of Tenses in Present Time.**   On each line to the right, identify the use of the verb in each sentence, using the labels in the chart above.

EXAMPLE: The baby is learning to walk. _____*continuing action*_____

1. Paula studies in the library. _____
2. The Nile River flows from south to north. _____
3. Tasha baby-sits for the Logans every Friday night. _____
4. The new chef is here now. _____
5. I smell something sweet. _____
6. Bruce is cutting the lawn. _____
7. Cactuses grow in deserts. _____
8. Grandpa is teaching me chess. _____
9. My sister writes home once a week. _____
10. The Martins live in Virginia now. _____

▶ **Exercise 2**   **Using Present Tense Forms in Sentences.**   Complete each sentence by filling in an appropriate verb in the present time.

EXAMPLE: Mom _____*is talking*_____ on the phone at the moment.

1. The baby _____ for two hours every afternoon.
2. Those plants _____ well in the shade.
3. Aunt Janet _____ the baby a bath now.
4. Harold _____ unusually stubborn today.
5. Many people _____ to eat in restaurants.
6. The people next door _____ their house.
7. Sometimes my sister _____ my clothes.
8. Someone _____ on the door.
9. This cheese _____ strong.
10. The sun _____ at last.

23.1 Expressing Time Through Tense (Uses of Tense in Present Time) • Practice 2

USES OF THE PRESENT

Present action: There he *goes.*
Present condition: The apples *are* rotten.
Regularly occurring action: My sister *chews* her nails.
Regularly occurring condition: They *are* never ready.
Constant action: The sun *radiates* energy.
Constant condition: Human blood *is* red.

USES OF THE PRESENT PROGRESSIVE

Continuing action: He *is working* on a novel.
Continuing condition: The baby *is being* very difficult this week.

▶ **Exercise 1** **Identifying the Uses of Tense in Present Time.** Identify the use of the underlined verb in each sentence, using the labels in the charts above.

EXAMPLE: Greg <u>plays</u> tennis every Saturday. _____regularly occurring action_____

1. I <u>leave</u> for school at 7:30 each morning. _____

2. Gasoline <u>is</u> a flammable liquid. _____

3. My friends and I <u>race</u> home from school every afternoon. _____

4. This entire meal <u>is</u> delicious. _____

5. I <u>hear</u> a television in the other room. _____

6. My brother <u>is doing</u> his homework now. _____

7. Gravity <u>pulls</u> all objects downward. _____

8. My father <u>is building</u> stereo speaker cabinets. _____

9. He <u>reads</u> mostly biographies. _____

10. My sister Judy generally <u>travels</u> to work on the train. _____

11. The birds <u>fascinate</u> the cats in our yard. _____

12. The peaches <u>are</u> ready to fall from the tree. _____

13. The sun <u>sets</u> in the west. _____

14. The coach <u>starts</u> class at two o'clock sharp. _____

15. Sandra <u>is studying</u> violin with Mr. Stevenson. _____

16. The twins <u>are</u> always cheerful. _____

17. Barbara <u>is being</u> helpful around the house. _____

18. The United States <u>is</u> part of the continent of North America. _____

19. Gina <u>is acting</u> like a fool. _____

20. Patrice <u>annoys</u> people with her whining. _____

23.1 Expressing Time Through Tense (Uses of Tense in Past Time) • Practice 1

Uses of Tense in Past Time   The six forms that express past time show actions and conditions beginning in the past.

Verb Forms	USES OF TENSES IN PAST TIME	
	Uses	Examples
Past	Indefinite past time	Eleanor *studied* hard.
	Definite past time	The sunset *was* brief tonight.
Present Perfect	Indefinite past time continuing to present	I *have seen* that movie. The baby *has been* very quiet.
Past Perfect	Completed before another past event	Some guests *had arrived* before we did.
Past Progressive	Continuous past event	Ed *was acting* strangely last night.
Present Perfect Progressive	Event continuing to present	Pan *has been looking* for a job all summer.
Past Perfect Progressive	Continuous past event before another	Before you called, we *had been planning* for a quiet evening.

▶ **Exercise 1**   **Identifying the Uses of Tense in Past Time.**   Identify the use of the verb in each sentence, using the labels in the chart above.

EXAMPLE: I have been studying for that test all week. ____*event continuing to present*____

1. Up to this inning we had hoped for a win. _____
2. Grandpa was waiting for us at the station. _____
3. Dana worked for the same company for twenty years. _____
4. The realtor has shown us this same house before. _____
5. We were uncomfortable because of the heat. _____
6. That store has been offering double coupons for several weeks. _____
7. Those youngsters have waited here for hours. _____
8. Audrey had been trying to reach you earlier. _____
9. I finished the test at three o'clock. _____
10. We were painting the house last weekend. _____

▶ **Exercise 2**   **Using Tenses in Past Time.**   Write the correct form of the verb in parentheses.

EXAMPLE: I ____*had finished*____ when the bell rang. (have finished, had finished)

1. Before he retired, Uncle Al _____ cattle on his ranch. (raised, has raised)
2. For the last two years, Sue _____ our class president. (has been, was being)
3. Last night's storm _____ with the TV. (interfered, had interfered)
4. The horse _____ before we knew it. (has escaped, had escaped)
5. Joshua certainly _____ more agreeable lately. (has grown, was growing)
6. When I saw it last, my book _____ on the table. (has lain, was lying)
7. Jan _____ oddly today. (has been acting, had been acting)
8. Lou _____ me three times yesterday. (phoned, has phoned)
9. I _____ you a note when you came in. (wrote, was writing)
10. Pat _____ for you since lunch. (has been waiting, was waiting)

23.1 Expressing Time Through Tense (Uses of Tense in Past Time) • Practice 2

USES OF THE PROGRESSIVE FORMS THAT EXPRESS PAST TIME	
Past Progressive	*Continuous completed action:* He *was working* on a ranch that summer.
	Continuous completed condition: Mimi *was being* agreeable last week.
Present Perfect Progressive	*Action continuing to present:* Louisa *has been reading* mysteries for a month now.
Past Perfect Progressive	*Continuing action interrupted by another:* I *had been sleeping* when you called.

▶ **Exercise 1** **Using Past, Present Perfect, and Past Perfect.** Write the correct form of the verb in parentheses.

EXAMPLE: Mary _____*bought*_____ a new dress yesterday. (bought, has bought)

1. Father _____ tomatoes in our yard last year. (grew, has grown)

2. I _____ her three times on Tuesday. (called, have called)

3. Carol _____ an hour before she left. (has waited, had waited)

4. We _____ our trip yesterday. (postponed, have postponed)

5. Ken _____ the bus to work since he moved. (rode, has ridden)

6. Sue _____ her sister at college last week. (visited, has visited)

7. I _____ terribly sleepy lately. (was, have been)

8. My sister _____ before I did. (has arrived, had arrived)

9. I _____ my report at three o'clock. (finished, have finished)

10. He _____ across the river before I started. (has swum, had swum)

▶ **Exercise 2** **Identifying the Uses of the Progressive Forms in the Past.** Identify the use of the underlined verb in each sentence, using the labels in the chart above.

EXAMPLE: I was writing my book report last night. _____*continuous completed action*_____

1. Father has been building a porch behind the house.

_____

2. My brother had been going to college until his accident.

_____

3. After lunch I was writing my report on Walt Whitman.

_____

4. Our fruit trees have been growing at an amazing rate.

_____

5. I was painting my bicycle when the rain started.

_____

6. Jan was being unusually generous last night.

_____

7. They were eating when we arrived.

_____

8. I had been working nights until I inherited the money.

_____

9. Mary has been studying French for two years now.

_____

10. Linda was rehearsing her speech this morning.

_____

23.1 # Expressing Time Through Tense (Uses of

Tense in Future Time) • Practice 1

Uses of Tense in Future Time The four forms that express future time show future actions or conditions.

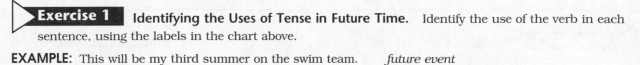

USES OF TENSES IN FUTURE TIME		
Verb Forms	**Uses**	**Examples**
Future	Future event	The storm *will arrive* soon.
Future Perfect	Future event before another future event	We *will have finished* the book by next Tuesday.
Future Progressive	Continuing future event	That group *will be performing* here for two nights.
Future Perfect Progressive	Continuing future event before another	By then, we *will have been waiting* here for two hours.

▶ **Exercise 1** **Identifying the Uses of Tense in Future Time.** Identify the use of the verb in each sentence, using the labels in the chart above.

EXAMPLE: This will be my third summer on the swim team. ____*future event*____

1. The Bergers will be traveling in Europe this summer. _____

2. The crew will have paved the road by tomorrow. _____

3. The manager will be interviewing the candidates next week. _____

4. By Tuesday, we will have been traveling for a week. _____

5. Dr. Kelsey will see you now. _____

6. Your invitation will be arriving in the mail. _____

7. I will have finished my rough draft by Monday. _____

8. At his retirement, Mr. Poli will have been teaching for years. _____

9. I will be looking for a job next summer. _____

10. In another hour the cement will have dried. _____

▶ **Exercise 2** **Using Tenses in Future Time.** Fill in each blank with the indicated form of the verb in parentheses.

EXAMPLE: All the networks ____*will carry*____ the speech live. (*carry*, future)

1. I _____ French this year. (*study*, future progressive)

2. Your teacher _____ you the necessary forms. (*give*, future progressive)

3. All told, we _____ on this for forty hours. (*work*, future perfect progressive)

4. The books I ordered _____ soon. (*come*, future progressive)

5. I _____ you at the library. (*meet*, future)

6. After the party, you _____ all my friends. (*meet*, future perfect)

7. Alicia _____ my favorite piece in the recital. (*play*, future progressive)

8. If the police don't hurry, the accomplice _____ the evidence. (*destroy*, future perfect)

9. The team _____ every Saturday afternoon. (*practice*, future progressive)

10. I _____ for you after the last class. (*wait*, future)

23.1 Expressing Time Through Tense (Uses of Tense in Future Time) • Practice 2

USES OF THE FUTURE AND THE FUTURE PERFECT	
Future	*Future action:* A frost *will damage* the crop. *Future condition:* I *will be* home tomorrow.
Future Perfect	*Future action completed before another:* I *will have left* by the time you arrive. *Future condition completed before another:* I *will have been* up for hours before you call.

USES OF THE PROGRESSIVE FORMS THAT EXPRESS FUTURE TIME	
Future Progressive Future Perfect Progressive	*Continuing future action:* They *will be visiting* New York this fall. *Continuing future action completed before another:* When we meet next week, I *will have been practicing* tennis for a month.

▶ **Exercise 1**   **Identifying the Uses of Tense in Future Time.**   Identify the use of each underlined verb, using the labels in the charts above.

EXAMPLE: She will have been traveling a full year when she comes home tomorrow.

_____*continuing future action completed before another*_____

1. The President will deliver a speech tonight.

   _____

2. The Kramers will be vacationing for two weeks.

   _____

3. Fred will move to California next summer.

   _____

4. Fred will be transferring to Oregon in two years.

   _____

5. By the time you reach Chicago, you will have been driving for eight hours.

   _____

▶ **Exercise 2**   **Using Tenses in Future Time.**   Write the indicated form of each verb in parentheses.

EXAMPLE: By the time we reach the summit, we _____*will have been climbing*_____ for four hours. (climb—*future perfect progressive*)

1. My aunt _____ in Brazil for a month. (travel—*future progressive*)

2. The department store _____ in an hour. (open—*future*)

3. By tomorrow, we _____ our grades. (receive—*future perfect*)

4. I _____ for Toronto at noon. (leave—*future*)

5. When I return from Puerto Rico in August, I _____ Spanish for two months. (speak—*future perfect progressive*)

23.1

Expressing Time Through Tense (Shifts in Tense) • Practice 1

Shifts in Tense   When showing a sequence of events, do not shift tenses unnecessarily.

Unnecessary (Incorrect Shifts)	Correct Sequence
I *had meant* to get up early but accidentally *oversleep.* (shift from past perfect to present)	I *had meant* to get up early but accidentally *overslept.* (two past actions, one completed before another)
Jed *takes* the bus to school. I *rode* my bike. (shift from present to past)	Jed *takes* the bus to school. I *ride* my bike. (two regularly occurring actions)
If the car *breaks* down, we *were* late. (shift from present to past)	If the car *breaks* down, we *will be* late. (present condition leading to future outcome)

▶ **Exercise 1**   **Recognizing Unnecessary Shifts in Tense.**   Write *P* after each sentence below that has a problem in tense. If the sentence is correct as written, label it *C*.

EXAMPLE: We will leave after you finished the dishes. _____*P*_____

1. We never have dinner before Dad got home from work. _____

2. My sister will miss the twins when they were away. _____

3. Marcia began writing her paper before she reads any sources. _____

4. The owner offers a reward to anyone who found the dog. _____

5. Most likely we will be happier after we started our trip. _____

6. If Jason wins the election, he revised the dress code. _____

7. Erica has lost a lot of weight since I saw her last. _____

8. Whenever you are ready, we left. _____

9. Hugo barks loudly if he heard anything unusual. _____

10. When we got to the pier, the boat is already leaving _____

▶ **Exercise 2**   **Correcting Errors in Tense.**   Rewrite five of the sentences labeled *P* above, correcting the error by changing the tense of the second verb.

EXAMPLE: _____*We will leave after you finish the dishes.*_____

1. _____

2. _____

3. _____

4. _____

5. _____

23.1 Expressing Time Through Tense (Shifts in Tense) • Practice 2

▶ **Exercise 1** **Avoiding Unnecessary Shifts in Tense.** Correct tense problems by crossing out the second verb and writing a correction in the blank.

EXAMPLE: Bill goes fishing whenever he ~~got~~ a day off.

_____gets_____

1. I sit in the hall all day and answered the phone. _____
2. The class had read *Hamlet* before it reads *Macbeth*. _____
3. Eric talked to the newcomers before I do. _____
4. When Grandfather arrived, the whole family greets him at the airport. _____
5. As soon as you find a pleasing color, I help you. _____
6. By the time you phoned, I will have gone to bed. _____
7. Stella had eaten by the time I get there. _____
8. He will reach his goal when he got ten more orders. _____
9. I will be lonely when you will be away. _____
10. By the time I found him, he has mailed the letter already. _____
11. It has been months since the day I have seen you. _____
12. He went below deck and cleans his bunk. _____
13. Sally opens the door whenever the dog barked. _____
14. He sailed for Paris and has arrived there two weeks later. _____
15. If he goes to the rally, I joined him later. _____
16. The game was over when we leave. _____
17. Our team never wins the championship, nor did our rival from across town. _____
18. If I am elected secretary, I will have done many things. _____
19. My little sister smiled at the doctor and says hello. _____
20. He shook my hand and asks me to sit down. _____

▶ **Exercise 2** **Correcting Errors in Tense.** In the following paragraph, cross out unnecessary shifts in tense and write corrections in the blanks that follow.

(1) An unusual feature of Quincy Market in Boston is Faneuil Hall. (2) It was built in 1742 by Peter Faneuil, who later gives it to the city. (3) Nineteen years later, it burns. (4) Soon after, however, it was rebuilt. (5) Before the Revolutionary War, it is a theater. (6) Later, it was called "The Cradle of Liberty." (7) The name was given to it because it is the scene of many important meetings during the Revolutionary War. (8) For years the first floor was a produce market. (9) The second floor is the place for meetings. (10) It now has contained many historical paintings and is exciting to visit.

1. _____   4. _____
2. _____   5. _____
3. _____   6. _____

Name _____ Date _____

23.2 Active and Passive Voice (Differences Between Active and Passive Voice, Forms of Passive Verbs)
• Practice 1

Differences Between Active and Passive Voice   Voice is the form of a verb that shows whether or not the subject is performing the action. A verb is active if its subject performs the action. A verb is passive if its action is performed upon the subject.

Active Voice	Passive Voice
Alice *left* a message.	A message *was left* by Alice.
We *called* the doctor.	The doctor *was called*.

The Forms of Passive Verbs
A passive verb is made from a form of *be* plus the past participle of a transitive verb.

THE VERB *FOLLOW* IN THE PASSIVE VOICE		
Tense	Basic Forms	Progressive Forms
Present	I am followed.	I am being followed.
Past	I was followed.	I was being followed.
Future	I will be followed.	
Present Perfect	I have been followed.	
Past Perfect	I had been followed.	
Future Perfect	I will have been followed	

▶ **Exercise 1**   **Distinguishing Between the Active and Passive Voice.**   After each sentence, write *active* or *passive* to describe the verb.

EXAMPLE: That book was autographed by the author. ___*passive*___

1. The authorities have been notified. _____
2. This lettuce was grown in our own garden. _____
3. Mom added fresh mushrooms just before serving the salad. _____
4. Delegates to the convention have already been selected. _____
5. Every scrap of food was eaten during the party. _____
6. The team will elect a new captain tomorrow. _____
7. That car was stolen from the municipal parking lot. _____
8. Lydia has been visiting us this week. _____
9. Damian has already chosen his courses. _____
10. The governor has been asked to speak. _____

▶ **Exercise 2**   **Forming the Tenses of Passive Verbs.**   Write the basic forms of each of the following verbs in the passive voice.

1. say (with *it*)   2. drive (with *they*)   3. tell (with *you*)   4. praise (with *we*)

_____ _____ _____ _____
_____ _____ _____ _____
_____ _____ _____ _____
_____ _____ _____ _____
_____ _____ _____ _____
_____ _____ _____ _____

23.2 Active and Passive Voice (Differences Between Active and Passive Voice, Forms of Passive Verbs)
• Practice 2

▶ **Exercise 1** **Distinguishing Between the Active and Passive Voice.** Identify each verb as *active* or *passive*.

EXAMPLE: The letter was signed by the President. _____*passive*_____

1. The bitter medicine was taken by my sister. _____
2. Delegates to the convention have been chosen by the voters. _____
3. We each purchased several new outfits for spring. _____
4. Later, the speaker wrote a letter of apology. _____
5. Bread crumbs were then sprinkled on the fish. _____
6. Many wild animals live in the forest. _____
7. Surgery was performed by a team of specialists. _____
8. Ellen grew her own fresh vegetables this summer. _____
9. In the winter snow covers the mountains. _____
10. The bad news was then given to Brad by the coach. _____
11. Representatives had been selected earlier by Congress. _____
12. Kansas City was reached by the convoy in two hours. _____
13. I always read the evening newspaper after dinner. _____
14. After a debate the report was accepted by the chairperson. _____
15. The President has appointed a new ambassador. _____

THE VERB *CALL* IN THE PASSIVE VOICE	
Present	she is called
Past	she was called
Future	she will be called
Present Perfect	she has been called
Past Perfect	she had been called
Future Perfect	she will have been called
Present Progressive	she is being called
Past Progressive	she was being called

▶ **Exercise 2** **Forming the Tenses of Passive Verbs.** Conjugate each verb in the passive voice, using the chart above as your model.

1. type (with *it*)   2. forgive (with *we*)   3. sell (with *it*)   4. alert (with *they*)

_____   _____   _____   _____

_____   _____   _____   _____

_____   _____   _____   _____

_____   _____   _____   _____

_____   _____   _____   _____

_____   _____   _____   _____

23.2 Active and Passive Voice (Using Voice Correctly)
• Practice 1

Using Voice Correctly   Use the active voice whenever possible. Use the passive voice to emphasize the receiver of the action rather than the performer of the action. Use the passive voice to point out the receiver of an action whenever the performer is not important or not easily identified.

THE VERB IN THE PASSIVE VOICE

My term paper *was typed* by my sister.
    (Unnecessary passive; better: My sister typed my term
    paper.)
 The accident victims *were rushed* to the hospital by ambulance.
    (Emphasizes the victims rather than the ambulance.)
 The library *is closed* on Saturdays during the summer.
    (Performer is not important and unknown.)

▶ **Exercise 1**   **Distinguishing Between Appropriate and Inappropriate Uses of Passive Voice.**   Label the three necessary uses of the passive voice in the sentences below as *A* (appropriate). Label the other uses as *U* (unnecessary).

EXAMPLE: Jason was asked by his mother to answer the phone. ____*U*____

1. A grand slam home run was hit by the catcher. _____

2. Lincoln was elected to his first term in 1860. _____

3. This sweater was knitted for me by my favorite aunt. _____

4. In 1983 the America's Cup races were won by Australia. _____

5. Many restaurants are closed on Mondays. _____

6. That model airplane was made by Paul. _____

7. Federal income tax returns must be postmarked by midnight on April 15. _____

8. Candidates will be judged by the voters on their merits, not on their

   speeches. _____

9. I have been being followed by that dog for three blocks. _____

10. Dinner is being fixed by Mom right now. _____

▶ **Exercise 2**   **Using the Active Voice.**   Rewrite five of the sentences that you labeled *U* in Exercise 1. Change or add words as necessary to put each verb into the active voice.

EXAMPLE: *Jason's mother asked him to answer the phone.*

1. _____

2. _____

3. _____

4. _____

5. _____

23.2 Active and Passive Voice (Using Voice Correctly)
• Practice 2

▶ **Exercise 1** **Correcting Unnecessary Use of the Passive Voice.** Rewrite the following paragraph, changing at least five uses of the passive voice to active.

EXAMPLE: Loch Ness *is being studied* by many scientists.

_____*Many scientists are studying Loch Ness*_____ .

(1) For years a so-called monster has been spotted by visitors to Loch Ness in Scotland. (2) The large creature has been reported by many witnesses. (3) Do lake monsters really exist? (4) These reports have been questioned by scientists. (5) According to some Canadian scientists, the sightings may be explained by temperature inversions. (6) A temperature inversion occurs when the temperature of a body of water is much lower than the temperature of the air above it. (7) Experiments were conducted by scientists on Lake Winnipeg, Canada, during a temperature inversion. (8) Two photos of an ordinary stick floating on the lake were taken only three minutes apart. (9) The bending, or refraction, of light caused by the inversion made the stick appear to be a strangely shaped "monster." (10) These photos have been accepted by some scientists as proof that the lake monsters are really ordinary objects that appear distorted because of a temperature inversion.

_____

_____

_____

_____

_____

_____

_____

_____

_____

_____

_____

_____

_____

_____

_____

▶ **Writing Application** **Using the Active and Passive Voice in Writing.** Write five sentences describing the events that happened on your way to school this morning. Include one sentence using the passive voice. Make sure all the other sentences use the active voice.

_____

_____

_____

_____

_____

24.1 The Cases of Pronouns (The Three Cases)
• Practice 1

The Three Cases Case is the form of a noun or pronoun that indicates its use in a sentence. The three cases are the nominative, the objective, and the possessive.

CASE FORMS OF PRONOUNS		
Case	**Use in Sentence**	**Forms**
Nominative	subject, predicate nominative	I; you; he, she, it; we; they
Objective	direct object, indirect object, object of preposition	me; you; him, her, it; us; them
Possessive	to show ownership	my, mine; you, yours; his, her, hers, its; our, ours; their, theirs

Exercise 1 **Identifying Case.** Write the case of each underlined pronoun on each line to the right.

EXAMPLE: Soon after starting out, we had a flat tire. ____nominative____

1. The doctor cannot see you until next week. _____
2. Gail has misplaced her keys again. _____
3. Foster broke his bat on that hit. _____
4. The Jacksons took the dog with them on vacation. _____
5. Surely this bike is yours. _____
6. Occasionally I enjoy a horror movie. _____
7. Edison returned to his laboratory. _____
8. Louise said that someone invited her. _____
9. The boat was turned over on its side. _____
10. Kevin asked us for directions. _____

Exercise 2 **Identifying Pronoun Case and Use.** Write the case of each underlined pronoun. Then write the number that describes how the pronoun is used in the sentence: 1 (subject), 2 (predicate nominative), 3 (direct object), 4 (indirect object), 5 (object of a preposition), 6 (to show ownership).

EXAMPLE: The first guests were Donna and I. ____nominative, 2____

1. Ms. Parker read us students the directions. _____
2. Louie and he are bringing the dessert. _____
3. Did you get a postcard from Dawn or me? _____
4. Every house in this neighborhood has its own well. _____
5. They promised to be here in time for lunch. _____
6. Because of all the other noise, no one heard us. _____
7. Grace described her plan in detail. _____
8. The best choice would be Don or you. _____
9. The judges have not explained their choice. _____
10. Mom divided the pie among us. _____

24.1 The Cases of Pronouns (The Three Cases)
• Practice 2

▶ **Exercise 1**   **Identifying Pronoun Case.**   Write the case of each underlined pronoun on the line to the right of each sentence.

EXAMPLE: It was clearly a case of mistaken identity. _____nominative_____

1. The antique doll with the lace dress belonged to her. _____
2. The two brothers took their responsibilities seriously. _____
3. Our doubts about getting there on time began to grow. _____
4. Until the age of thirteen, she was afraid of dogs. _____
5. His relationship with Elizabeth kept him going. _____
6. Oscar handed me the tastefully wrapped package. _____
7. We had a garage sale last weekend. _____
8. You never know what might happen. _____
9. Do not pay any attention to them. _____
10. Is this cake yours or mine? _____

▶ **Exercise 2**   **Identifying Case.**   Write the case of each underlined pronoun. Then write its use: subject, predicate nominative, direct object, indirect object, object of a preposition, to show ownership.

EXAMPLE: The doctor gave her the good news. _____*objective, indirect object*_____

1. After waiting an hour, we finally spoke to the coach. _____
2. Give them the present. _____
3. Their reply surprised the judge. _____
4. Betty will see you on Friday. _____
5. John waved to us on the way to the game. _____
6. There is no question that this is my wallet. _____
7. They accepted our explanation completely. _____
8. Your mother phoned from her office. _____
9. Much to my delight, Phil asked me to dance. _____
10. My mother asked for her help with the children. _____
11. General Smith gave his word to the troops. _____
12. My sister and I agreed to perform. _____
13. The chairperson is she. _____
14. The principal gave us a broad smile. _____
15. Does Father want to hear our reasons? _____
16. Their science project is the best in the class. _____
17. The winners are Joan and I. _____
18. Give your answer to him. _____
19. Dr. Smith gave us debaters a small pin. _____
20. I really want to visit the campus. _____

24.1 The Cases of Pronouns (Nominative Case, Objective Case) • Practice 1

The Nominative Case   Use the nominative case for the subject of a verb or for a predicate nominative. When a pronoun used as a subject or predicate nominative is followed by an appositive, the nominative case is still used.

USES OF NOMINATIVE CASE	
Subject	James and *I* went to summer camp.
	They were the winners.
	We members voted on the project.
Predicate Nominative	The one who answered the phone was *she*.
	The winners were *we* Howlers.

The Objective Case   Use the objective case for a direct object, for an indirect object, or for the object of a preposition—even if the pronoun has an appositive.

USES OF OBJECTIVE CASE	
Direct Object	David met *us* at the library.
	Grandma treated Jim and *me* to a movie.
	The theater uses *us* students as ushers.
Indirect Object	The sitter read *him* a bedtime story.
	The guide showed Jim and *me* the map.
	The teacher read *us* students the directions.
Object of a Preposition	I got a postcard from *her*.
	This letter is addressed to Jan and *him*.
	Move the microphone closer to *us* speakers.

> **Exercise 1**   **Identifying Pronouns in the Nominative Case.**   Circle the nominative pronoun form in parentheses. Then write *S* (subject) or *PN* (predicate nominative) to describe its use.

EXAMPLE: Florence and ((he), him) enjoyed the lobster. ___S___

1. Ed and (I, me) came early. _____
2. The late one was (he, him). _____
3. The winners are (them, they). _____
4. (Her, She) is the coach. _____
5. Kim or (he, him) can help. _____

> **Exercise 2**   **Identifying Pronouns in the Objective Case.**   Circle the objective pronoun form in parentheses. Then write *DO* (direct object), *IO* (indirect object), or *OP* (object of a preposition) to describe its use.

EXAMPLE: The director told (we, (us)) campers the rules. ___IO___

1. No one saw (she, her). _____
2. I left this for (him, he). _____
3. Leave (we, us) kids alone. _____
4. Please show (I, me) that. _____
5. Tell (we, us) a story. _____

24.1 The Cases of Pronouns (Nominative Case, Objective Case) • Practice 2

▷ **Exercise 1** Using Pronouns in the Nominative Case. Write a nominative pronoun to complete each sentence. Then, in the blank after the sentence, write the use of the pronoun.

EXAMPLE: Jane and ___I___ worked late. ___subject___

1. _____ are waiting for us at the station. _____
2. _____ is a cold and damp morning. _____
3. Are _____ serious about that offer? _____
4. The key to victory is _____ delegates from Boston. _____
5. _____ are hoping for an invitation to the party. _____
6. _____ is the uncle I love most. _____
7. You know that _____ is ill today. _____
8. I hope that _____ will go with me. _____
9. _____ is my oldest sister. _____
10. Surely _____ will accept your offer. _____

▷ **Exercise 2** Using Pronouns in the Objective Case. Write an objective pronoun to complete each sentence. Then, in the blank after the sentence, write the use of the pronoun.

EXAMPLE: George gave ___me___ his old catcher's mitt. ___indirect object___

1. Brenda gave _____ lots of unwanted advice. _____
2. The disc jockey smiled at _____ girls. _____
3. My father lent _____ his car. _____
4. Our teacher gave _____ two new baseball bats after our surprise victory. _____
5. With his record, can we really trust _____? _____
6. He gave _____ Little Leaguers tickets to the big game next Saturday. _____
7. That experience gave _____ boys a real scare. _____
8. Call for Elizabeth and _____ in about an hour. _____
9. I gave _____ different eye makeup to try. _____
10. I congratulated _____ and the other swimmers. _____

24.1 The Cases of Pronouns (Possessive Case)
• Practice 1

The Possessive Case   Use the possessive case before nouns to show ownership and before gerunds. Use certain possessive pronouns by themselves to indicate possession.

USES OF POSSESSIVE CASE	
Before Nouns	*My* bicycle chain needs oil.
	Joan showed us *her* new camera.
Before Gerunds	*Our* playing the music disturbed Mr. Hayes.
	Max is a darling baby, but *his* crying sometimes gets on my nerves.
Alone	Are these keys *yours*?
	Mine is the third locker from the end.

▷ **Exercise 1**   **Using Pronouns in the Possessive Case.**   Write the correct word from the parentheses to complete each sentence.

EXAMPLE: The cat has ____*its*____ own basket to sleep in. (it's, its)

1. _____ constant whining is very annoying. (Him, His)

2. None of the books on this table are _____. (mine, my)

3. I'm sure Mr. Lawson appreciated _____ helping him. (our, us)

4. These are June's sneakers, but where are _____? (your's, yours)

5. Carol forgot _____ lunch. (her, hers)

6. Did you ask Peter about _____ playing the piano at the party? (him, his)

7. The Holts claim this picnic table is _____. (their's, theirs)

8. _____ learning magic tricks cost the family a lot of eggs. (Me, My, Mine)

9. After you have looked it over, put the radio back in _____ original packing carton. (it's, its)

10. Everyone enjoyed _____ singing. (them, their)

▷ **Exercise 2**   **Using All Three Cases.**   Complete each sentence with the appropriate pronoun form. The code number in parentheses indicates which group of pronouns to choose from:

(1) I, me, my, mine   (3) he, him, his; it, its; she,   (4) we, us, our, ours
(2) you, your, yours   her, hers   (5) they, them, their, theirs

EXAMPLE: The first one to volunteer was ____*I*____. (1)

1. Surely this house must be _____. (5)

2. Next summer _____ older campers can help the younger ones. (4)

3. When I saw Rhona, I told _____ about the party. (3)

4. _____ practicing the drums sometimes disturbs the neighbors. (1)

5. Which of these duffel bags is _____? (2)

6. Bobby asked the sitter to sing _____ a song. (3)

7. Happily the argument between Don and _____ didn't last very long. (1)

8. The coach urged _____ players to do our best. (4)

9. The boat slipped loose from _____ moorings. (3)

10. Several customers mentioned _____ finding flaws in the product. (5)

24.1 The Cases of Pronouns (Possessive Case)
• Practice 2

▶ **Exercise 1**   **Using Pronouns in the Possessive Case.**   Write the correct word from the parentheses to complete each sentence.

EXAMPLE: We must give them ____*theirs*____ . (theirs, their's)

1. I spoke to Ralph about _____ chewing gum in class. (his, him)
2. There is no question that this is _____ . (yours, your's)
3. Our kitten hurt _____ front paw. (it's, its)
4. The president asked for _____ resignation. (his, his's)
5. _____ speeding finally got him into trouble. (His, Him)
6. We told him that this is _____ . (our's, ours)
7. They want _____ cutting to stop immediately. (his, him)
8. _____ winnings will be divided equally. (They're, Their)
9. May I borrow _____ ? (your's, yours)
10. I feel that _____ too expensive. (its, it's)
11. _____ singing leaves much to be desired. (Our, Us)
12. I finally said that it was _____ . (mine's, mine)
13. _____ leaving will cause much embarrassment. (Your, You)
14. Is it really _____ ? (hers, her's)
15. _____ constant smiling cheers us all up. (Him, His)
16. _____ not really prepared to dance. (Your, You're)
17. I thought he would understand _____ joking. (our, us)
18. Mother was worried about _____ growing. (me, my)
19. _____ really none of your business. (Its, It's)
20. The ship veered off _____ course. (its, it's)

▶ **Exercise 2**   **Using All Three Cases.**   Write the correct word from the parentheses to complete each sentence.

1. My neighbor helped _____ with the model. (he, him)
2. _____ policy is very strict. (Their, They're)
3. The professor said that it was _____ . (she, her, her's)
4. _____ girls will decorate the gym. (We, Us)
5. Dr. Stevenson gave _____ and _____ his blessing. (she, her) (he, him)
6. Our puppy wagged _____ tail. (its, it's)
7. I waited for _____ while _____ changed clothes. (they, them) (they, them)
8. Can _____ work on _____ projects now? (we, us) (our, our's)
9. Your costume is the best of all of _____ . (them, their's)
10. Why were _____ and _____ late to class? (he, him) (she, her)

24.2 Special Problems with Pronouns (Who and Whom, Elliptical Clauses) • Practice 1

Using Who and Whom Correctly   *Who* is nominative and should be used for a subject or a predicate nominative. *Whom* is objective and should be used for a direct object or the object of a preposition. *Whose*, not *who's*, is possessive.

CASE FORMS OF WHO	
Nominative	*Who* told you that story?
	Who will be the winner?
	I wonder *who* will play.
	Jed asked *who* the leader was.
Objective	*Whom* shall we choose?
	Whom have you written to?
	That is the girl *whom* I met at the party.
	Those are the people *whom* we had dinner with.
Possessive	*Whose* jacket is this?
	That is a poet *whose* work I admire.

Using Pronouns Correctly in Elliptical Clauses   In elliptical clauses beginning with *than* or *as*, use the form of the pronoun that you would use if the clauses were fully stated.

PRONOUNS IN ELLIPTICAL CLAUSES	
Elliptical Clauses	**Completed Clauses**
Ellie studies harder than (*I* or *me*).	Ellie studies harder than *I* [do].
The teacher gave Jon a higher mark than (*I* or *me*).	The teacher gave Jon a higher mark than [she gave] *me*.
Mom gives Carl more attention than (*I* or *me*).	Mom gives Carl more attention than [she gives] *me*.
	Mom gives Carl more attention than *I* [give him].

▶ **Exercise 1**   **Using Who and Whom Correctly.**   Write *who* or *whom* to complete each sentence.

EXAMPLE: Jake is someone _____*whom*_____ I greatly respect.

1. _____ shall we choose as chairman?

2. Mr. Zimmerman is a teacher _____ inspires his students.

3. The owner offered a reward to anyone _____ finds the dog.

4. _____ is your favorite poet?

5. We must choose someone _____ can do a good job.

▶ **Exercise 2**   **Using Pronouns in Elliptical Clauses.**   Complete each sentence with the correct form of the pronoun in parentheses.

EXAMPLE: Sue has more clothes than ___*I*___. (I, me)

1. My parents give my brother more allowance than _____. (I, me)

2. Surely none of the other guests were as late as _____. (they, them)

3. Jim is not as busy as _____. (he, him)

4. The movie upset Mom more than _____. (I, me)

5. All of a sudden, my younger brother is taller than _____. (I, me)

24.2 Special Problems with Pronouns (*Who* and *Whom*, Elliptical Clauses) • Practice 2

▶ **Exercise 1**   Using *Who* and *Whom* in Questions and Clauses.   Complete each sentence with the correct form of the pronoun in parentheses.

EXAMPLE: She is the candidate for ____whom____ I voted. (who, whom)

1. I know _____ the culprit is. (who, whom)

2. Can you tell us _____ they really want? (who, whom)

3. Fritz is the only barber _____ I trust. (who, whom)

4. We accept contributions from all _____ will give. (who, whom)

5. The girl _____ you like is a friend of mine. (who, whom)

6. Into _____ classroom have they gone? (whose, who's)

7. I met the man _____, all the polls said, will win. (who, whom)

8. To _____ were you writing? (who, whom)

9. It is he with _____ you should speak. (who, whom)

10. Take these roses to the man _____ lives next door. (who, whom)

11. The lieutenant _____ won was later promoted. (who, whom)

12. My father is the man _____ prepared the schedule for the volunteer fire department. (who, whom)

13. _____ the student with the highest score? (Who's, Whose)

14. Ask all _____ are concerned to aid our cause. (who, whom)

15. With _____ were you visiting? (who, whom)

16. Is she the saleswoman to _____ you spoke? (who, whom)

17. The shortstop _____ you saw at today's game is having a poor season. (who, whom)

18. To _____ will you give the job? (who, whom)

19. _____ is the teacher you want us to meet? (Who, Whom)

20. We are the ones _____ are to blame. (who, whom)

▶ **Exercise 2**   Identifying the Correct Pronoun in Elliptical Clauses.   Rewrite each sentence by choosing one pronoun in parentheses and correctly completing the elliptical clause.

EXAMPLE: She is as short as ____I am____. (I, me)

1. Beth has more experience than _____. (I, me)

2. She writes better than _____. (I, me)

3. He feels that he is as skilled as _____. (she, her)

4. I have better manners than _____. (he, him)

5. He was more seriously injured than _____. (she, her)

6. My brother is as advanced in chemistry as _____. (she, her)

7. Helen can type as fast as _____. (I, me)

8. Mrs. Pratt gave me a higher grade than _____. (he, him)

9. I worked longer last night than _____. (he, him)

10. Find out if he earned more money than _____. (she, her)

25.1 Subject and Verb Agreement (Number, Singular and Plural Subjects) • Practice 1

Number: Singular and Plural   Number refers to the two forms of a word: singular and plural. Singular words indicate one; plural words indicate more than one.

NUMBER OF WORDS			
Part of Speech	**Singular**	**Plural**	**Singular or Plural**
Nouns	baby	babies	fish
	toy	toys	deer
	child	children	moose
Pronouns	I, he, she, it	we, they	you
Verbs	travels		(I, you, we, they) travel
	has gone		(I, you, we, they) have gone
	am, is, was		(you, we, they) are, were

Singular and Plural Subjects   A singular subject must have a singular verb. A plural subject must have a plural verb. A phrase or clause that interrupts a subject and its verb does not affect subject-verb agreement.

SUBJECT-VERB AGREEMENT	
Singular	**Plural**
She enjoys reading mysteries.	We have just missed the bus.
A box of cookies is in the cupboard.	Two boxes of books are missing.
That fish has unusual colors.	These fish have long whiskers.

▶ **Exercise 1**   **Determining the Number of Words.**   Label each word below as *sing.* (singular), *plur.* (plural), or *both.*

EXAMPLE: should _____*both*_____

1. potatoes _____
2. are _____
3. reindeer _____
4. defendants _____
5. puts _____

6. like _____
7. women _____
8. digit _____
9. amuses _____
10. were given _____

▶ **Exercise 2**   **Making Subjects and Verbs Agree.**   Complete each sentence by writing the verb form from parentheses that agrees with the subject. Then label each sentence *S* if the subject is singular or *P* if it is plural.

EXAMPLE: Some players on that team _____*have*_____ been disqualified. (has, have) ____*P*____

1. That song by the Weavers _____ become a classic (has, have)_____
2. The students in Mr. Long's class _____ going to the opera. (is, are)_____
3. Both the trout that Dana caught _____ quite large. (was, were)_____
4. The carton of Christmas decorations _____ in the basement. (is, are)_____
5. The team with the most wins _____ the league. (lead, leads)_____

25.1 Subject and Verb Agreement (Number, Singular and Plural Subjects) • Practice 2

▶ **Exercise 1** **Determining the Number of Nouns, Pronouns, and Verbs.** Identify each item as *singular*, *plural*, or *both*.

EXAMPLE: speaks _____*singular*_____

1. car _____
2. lifeguards _____
3. tomatoes _____
4. woman _____
5. he _____
6. lizard _____
7. demonstrators _____
8. writes _____
9. soldiers _____
10. she _____
11. helps _____
12. is _____
13. was _____
14. was plotting _____
15. grow _____
16. seeks _____
17. loses _____
18. has been watching _____
19. choose _____
20. you _____

▶ **Exercise 2** **Making Subjects Agree With Their Verbs.** Write the verb from parentheses that agrees with the subject of each sentence.

EXAMPLE: He _____*jogs*_____ two miles every day. (jog, jogs)

1. A tall tree _____ in our front yard. (stands, stand)
2. The ships _____ passing the island. (was, were)
3. It seems that the baby _____ an inch every day. (grows, grow)
4. Our blackboards _____ all scratched. (was, were)
5. Candles _____ quite expensive. (is, are)
6. Yesterday the newspaper _____ not delivered. (was, were)
7. His pictures _____ in the gallery. (belongs, belong)
8. Mr. Cody _____ reading poems in a dramatic voice. (was were)
9. At sunrise the ships _____ from the harbor. (sails, sail)
10. At the quarry the noises _____ deafening. (is, are)

25.1 Subject and Verb Agreement (Compound Subjects) • Practice 1

Compound Subjects A singular subject after *or* takes a singular verb. A plural subject after *or* takes a plural verb. Compound subjects joined by *and* take a plural verb unless they are thought of as one thing or modified by *every* or *each*.

AGREEMENT WITH COMPOUND SUBJECTS	
Joined by *or* or *nor*	Ed, Sue, or Pam *has* a good chance of winning. Neither the cats nor the dogs *eat* table scraps. Either the servants or the owner *shows* tourists around. Either the owner or the servants *show* tourists around.
Joined by *and*	Hot dogs and hamburgers *are* traditional picnic foods. Ian and Pete *are* on the same team. Bacon, lettuce, and tomato *is* my favorite sandwich. Every man, woman, and child *has* a separate seat.

▶ **Exercise 1** **Compound Subjects Joined by *Or* or *Nor*.** Write the verb form from parentheses that agrees with the subject in each sentence.

EXAMPLE: Louise or her sisters ____*are*____ usually home in the evening. (is, are)

1. Neither Elmer nor his children _____ fried chicken. (like, likes)

2. Pat, Dana, or Tony _____ a good person to ask for directions. (is, are)

3. The twins or their sister _____ for the Harpers. (baby-sit, baby-sits)

4. Either Dad or Mom _____ bought corn for dinner. (has, have)

5. Nelly, Dobbin, or Prince _____ a good name for the horse. (is, are)

6. Erik or the twins _____ always welcome here. (is, are)

7. Neither Dawn nor her mother _____ faddish clothes. (buy, buys)

8. Either the magician himself or his assistants _____ up the audience. (warm, warms)

9. Mom or my brothers _____ sweet rolls on Sunday morning. (get, gets)

10. Kim or Kelly _____ the daily paper. (deliver, delivers)

▶ **Exercise 2** **Compound Subjects Joined by *And*.** Write the verb form from parentheses that agrees with the subject in each sentence.

EXAMPLE: Peanut butter and jelly ____*is*____ a favorite sandwich with children. (is, are)

1. My brother and sister _____ been very cooperative lately. (has, have)

2. Every glass and plate in the house _____ dirty after the party. (was, were)

3. Both the painter and the carpenter _____ coming today. (is, are)

4. The chairs and table _____ made of oak. (is, are)

5. The Stars and Stripes _____ the United States. (represent, represents)

25.1 Subject and Verb Agreement (Compound Subjects) • Practice 2

▶ **Exercise 1** **Making Compound Subjects Agree With Their Verbs.** Write the verb form from parentheses that agrees with the subject in each sentence.

EXAMPLE: Either Kelly or Jim _____*plays*_____ the lead role. (play, plays)

1. The door and the window _____ stuck. (is, are)

2. Neither Mother nor Father _____ phoned. (has, have)

3. The dog or the cats _____ always howling. (is, are)

4. Apples and bananas _____ been my favorite fruits for years. (has, have)

5. Mary or Louise _____ to the bridge club. (belongs, belong)

6. Each morning Tom or the children _____ fresh rolls at the bakery. (buys, buy)

7. Both the man with the appliances and the plumber _____ arrived. (has, have)

8. My son and daughter _____ never been so cooperative. (has, have)

9. Mark and David _____ in the office yet. (isn't, aren't)

10. Two large packages and a letter _____ delivered. (was, were)

11. Either the children or I _____ into town for the mail. (walks, walk)

12. Joan and Ellen _____ called in a month. (hasn't, haven't)

13. My car or Ted's _____ always available. (is, are)

14. His messiness and my chattering _____ Mother. (annoys, annoy)

15. Every cup and saucer _____ broken in the move. (was, were)

▶ **Exercise 2** **Making Compound Subjects Agree With Their Verbs in Sentences.** Write a sentence for each compound subject, making sure that the compound subject and verb agree.

EXAMPLE: time and temperature

_____*The time and temperature are displayed on the sign in front of the bank.*_____

1. neither Jason nor Julie

_____

2. radio and television

_____

3. computers and the Internet

_____

4. beets, carrots, or celery

_____

5. an apple or a banana

_____

25.1 Subject and Verb Agreement (Confusing Subjects) • Practice 1

Confusing Subjects Always check certain kinds of subjects carefully to make sure they agree with their verbs.

AGREEMENT WITH CONFUSING SUBJECTS	
Subject After Verb	In the middle of the second act *appear* two *elves.* Beyond the pasture *lies* a dense *forest.*
Subject Versus Predicate Nominative	These two *socks are* a pair. A *pair is* two objects of the same kind.
Collective Nouns	The *family makes* decisions together. (as a group) The *family share* their feelings. (as individuals)
Plural Form with Singular Meaning	*Mumps was* once a common illness. *Sports is* the only thing I ever watch on television.
Amounts	Two *weeks is* never enough vacation. Three *cups* of sugar *is* a lot for that recipe.
Titles	*A Tale of Two Cities* is a classic novel.
Indefinite Pronouns	*One* of the cups *is* missing. (always singular) *Both* of the cups *are* missing. (always plural) *Some* of the soup *is* still simmering. *Some* of the cookies *have* been eaten.

▶ **Exercise 1** **Deciding on the Number of Subjects.** Assume that each item below is to be the subject of a sentence. Label each one S if it needs a singular verb or P if it needs a plural verb.

EXAMPLE: *All the King's Men* ____S____

1. Some of the students _____
2. Econometrics _____
3. Aesop's *Fables* _____
4. Half of the students _____
5. German measles _____
6. Each of the men _____
7. *Pride and Prejudice* _____
8. Six months _____
9. Both of the cars _____
10. All of the pie _____

▶ **Exercise 2** **Choosing Verbs to Agree With Difficult Subjects.** Write the correct verb form from parentheses to complete each sentence.

EXAMPLE: Here ____are____ the books you ordered. (is, are)

1. The news on the front page _____ often distressing. (is, are)
2. The committee sometimes _____ among themselves. (disagree, disagrees)
3. High winds _____ a major threat to coastal property. (is, are)
4. Half of the students _____ chicken pox. (has, have)
5. The whole group _____ the same schedule. (follow, follows)

25.1 Subject and Verb Agreement (Confusing Subjects) • Practice 2

▷ Exercise 1 **Making Confusing Subjects Agree With Their Verbs.** Write the verb form from parentheses that agrees with the subject of each sentence.

EXAMPLE: All of the apples ____are____ rotten. (is, are)

1. Near the top of the closet _____ an old electric fan. (is, are)
2. The committee _____ been unable to reach an agreement. (has, have)
3. Rich foods _____ one cause of oily skin. (is, are)
4. Economics _____ my sister's major in college. (was, were)
5. _____ exotic plants thrive in this climate? (Do, Does)
6. The group of tourists _____ left on the bus. (has, have)
7. The jury _____ left their seats but will soon return. (has, have)
8. He said that civics _____ his favorite subject. (was, were)
9. _____ some of the soup still available? (Is, Are)
10. _____ more volunteers for the clean-up crew. (Here's, Here are)
11. The problem at the picnic _____ bees. (was, were)
12. There _____ two excellent reasons for his choice. (is, are)
13. Politics _____ one of his major interests. (was, were)
14. The entire faculty _____ voiced their opinions. (has, have)
15. _____ the captains of both teams. (There's, There are)
16. *Green Mansions* _____ her favorite novel. (is, are)
17. There _____ only one possible explanation. (is, are)
18. Another example of the area's underdevelopment _____ the narrow dirt roads. (is, are)
19. Mumps _____ a dangerous disease for adults. (is, are)
20. The team _____ has been squabbling with each other again. (has, have)

▷ Exercise 2 **More Work With Confusing Subjects.** Write the verb form from parentheses that agrees with the subject of each sentence.

1. One of the girls _____ hurt on the soccer field. (was, were)
2. Few _____ volunteered for the assignment. (has, have)
3. Somebody in the room above _____ to be quite ill. (seems, seem)
4. Several of the contestants _____ arrived. (has, have)
5. Some of the food _____ not cooked thoroughly. (was, were)
6. Ten dollars _____ an outrageous price for the book. (is, are)
7. Each of the guards _____ sworn allegiance. (has, have)
8. Why _____ everyone so unhappy? (is, are)
9. None of the cakes _____ thrown away. (was, were)
10. Three fourths of the fence _____ installed. (was, were)

Name _____   Date _____

25.2 Pronoun and Antecedent Agreement
(Between Personal Pronouns and Antecedents) • Practice 1

Agreement Between Personal Pronouns and Antecedents A personal pronoun must agree with its antecedent in person, number, and gender. Use a singular personal pronoun with two or more singular antecedents joined by *or* or *nor*. Use a plural personal pronoun with two or more antecedents joined by *and*. When gender is not specified, use the masculine or rewrite the sentence.

PRONOUN-ANTECEDENT AGREEMENT

My uncle likes *his* new job.

The cat has *its* own basket.

Alicia says this is *hers*.

Dawn or Sue will give you *her* notes.

Ed, Jon, and Bob brought *their* gloves.

Each player has *his* own uniform.

All the players have *their* own uniforms.

▶ **Exercise 1** **Choosing Personal Pronouns to Agree With Antecedents.** Assume that each item below is an antecedent for a personal pronoun. After each, write *his*, *her*, *its*, or *their* to show which pronoun you would use.

EXAMPLE: Eloise or Mary _____*her*_____

1. several students _____
2. the toy train _____
3. either Kevin or Bruce _____
4. Lucy, Cindy, or Karen _____
5. only one girl _____
6. Paul and Harry _____
7. each boy _____
8. many inventions _____
9. our neighbor's dog _____
10. the famous actress _____

▶ **Exercise 2** **Pronoun-Antecedent Agreement in Sentences.** Write an appropriate personal pronoun to complete each sentence.

EXAMPLE: My sister and I visited ____*our*____ grandparents last weekend.

1. Henry called loudly from the cave, but no one heard _____.
2. The second-hand table has only a few scratches on _____ surface.
3. Neither Linda nor Carol had a pencil with _____.
4. The mayor and the city council announced _____ new proposal.
5. Grandpa likes to have us visit _____.

25.2 Pronoun and Antecedent Agreement
(Between Personal Pronouns and Antecedents) • Practice 2

▶ **Exercise 1** **Making Personal Pronouns Agree With Their Antecedents.** Write an appropriate personal pronoun to complete each sentence.

EXAMPLE: Either Mark or Bill will drive _____*his*_____ car.

1. Mrs. Berger described _____ plans for the new store.
2. Carol will read _____ own report.
3. The goat shook _____ head in confusion.
4. My father gave us _____ secret recipe for muffins.
5. The city officials explained _____ reasons for the curfew.
6. Marie sealed the letter; then _____ tore it open again.
7. Neither Nancy nor Carol explained _____ position.
8. Uncle Roy sent us a package, but _____ never arrived.
9. I told John and Irene that _____ should be here by noon.
10. The nurse asked us about _____ eating habits.

▶ **Exercise 2** **Making Personal Pronouns Agree With Their Antecedents.** Write an appropriate personal pronoun to complete each sentence in the paragraph.

EXAMPLE: Neither Jill nor Suzy wore (1) *her* coat in the mall.

Joel and Henry ran along the path, each one wondering how much longer

(1) _____ could last. It was a cool day, and (2) _____ both were

in good shape. Still, (3) _____ had been running for about forty minutes, and for each

of (4) _____, this was a sufficient amount of exercise. Joel looked over at

(5) _____ best friend and saw that (6) _____ did not even seem

tired. Henry looked over at Joel and felt that (7) _____ was not even out of breath.

"Say, Joel," said Henry. "Are (8) _____ about ready to stop?"

"Not yet," said Joel. "Why? Is this too much for (9) _____?"

"Not at all," said Henry. "My mom just told (10) _____ this morning that she

thought (11) _____ was getting stronger every day. Since you and

(12) _____ started this program, I've been improving. I just thought that

(13) _____ might be getting tired."

"No," said Joel. "(14) _____ stamina has increased during the past few weeks.

Let's keep running."

As the two friends continued (15) _____ run, each one hoped that the other

would stop soon.

25.2 Pronoun and Antecedent Agreement (With Indefinite Pronouns and With Reflexive Pronouns)

• Practice 1

Agreement with Indefinite Pronouns Use a singular personal pronoun when the antecedent is a singular indefinite pronoun. Use a plural personal pronoun when the antecedent is a plural indefinite pronoun. With an indefinite pronoun that can be either singular or plural, agreement depends on the antecedent of the indefinite pronoun.

AGREEMENT WITH INDEFINITE PRONOUNS
Each of the girls has *her* own room.
Both of the boys rode *their* bikes.
All of the cake has icing on *it*. (cake = singular antecedent)
All of the boys wore *their* ties. (boys = plural antecedent)

Agreement with Reflexive Pronouns A reflexive pronoun must agree with an antecedent that is clearly stated.

REFLEXIVE PRONOUN AGREEMENT	
Incorrect	Correct
The trouble between Sue and *myself* arose over jealousy.	The trouble between Sue and *me* arose over jealousy.

▶ **Exercise 1** **Making Personal Pronouns Agree With Indefinite Pronouns.** Write an appropriate personal pronoun to complete each sentence.

EXAMPLE: Each of the houses must have a street number on _____*it*_____.

1. Some of the wood has insects in _____.

2. Several of the players have purchased extra uniforms on _____ own.

3. Most of the coins have mold on _____.

4. Neither of those books has much useful information in _____.

5. Somebody from the League of Women Voters said _____ would speak to us.

6. Most of my friends get along well with _____ families.

7. Little of the yard has grass growing in _____.

8. Anybody from that Boy Scout troop will gladly show you _____ catalog.

9. Do all of the brownies have nuts in _____ ?

10. Many of those homes have alarm systems in _____.

▶ **Exercise 2** **Using Reflexive Pronouns Correctly.** Underline the misused reflexive pronoun in each sentence. Write the correct pronoun on the line.

EXAMPLE: Both Jim and yourself should come. _____*you*_____

1. Give that to myself when you're finished with it. _____

2. The Palmers invited the Youngs and ourselves for dinner. _____

3. Trudy and herself share a room. _____

4. Luis and myself will take the dog for a walk. _____

5. We hope Alice and yourself can go on the picnic. _____

25.2 Pronoun and Antecedent Agreement (With Indefinite Pronouns and With Reflexive Pronouns)
• Practice 2

▷ **Exercise 1** **Making Personal Pronouns Agree With Indefinite Pronouns.** Write the correct pronoun to complete each sentence.

EXAMPLE: All of the boys lost _____*their*_____ money. (his, their)

1. Few at the conference gave _____ approval. (its, their)
2. Every one of the boys has _____ instructions. (his, their)
3. Each of the girls is responsible for _____ own room. (her, their)
4. Neither of the boys agreed to ask _____ parents. (his, their)
5. Every one of the girls agreed to ask _____ opinion. (her, their)
6. One of the fellows will have to volunteer _____ time. (his, their)
7. Both of my aunts sent _____ congratulations. (her, their)
8. Several of the men volunteered _____ service. (his, their)
9. Each of the women was given _____ lieutenant bars. (her, their)
10. Neither of the men could remember _____ number. (his, their)
11. Each of the ballerinas gave us _____ autograph. (her, their)
12. All of the women refused to give _____ consent. (her, their)
13. Several of the ships had _____ sails destroyed. (its, their)
14. Each of the boys must pay _____ dues soon. (his, their)
15. Some of the foods had lost _____ flavor. (its, their)
16. Neither of the girls brought _____ new records. (her, their)
17. Most soldiers in the battalion admired _____ lieutenant. (his, their)
18. Nobody in the boys' group brought _____ radio. (his, their)
19. Each of the sales women announced _____ results. (her, their)
20. Only one of the committees gave _____ consent. (its, their)

▷ **Exercise 2** **Using Reflexive Pronouns Correctly.** Rewrite each sentence, correcting the misused reflexive pronoun.

EXAMPLE: Both Todd and myself are going to the game.

_____*Both Todd and I are going to the game.*_____

1. Bob and I think the best person for this job is yourself.

_____

2. The Parkinsons and ourselves went to the opera together.

_____

3. Neither Francine nor myself knew who left the package.

_____

4. A guard directed the teacher and ourselves to the entrance.

_____

5. Sal was worried that he would hurt himself or myself.

_____

25.2 Pronoun and Antecedent Agreement (Four Special Problems) • Practice 1

Four Special Problems in Pronoun Agreement   A personal pronoun should have a clear, single, close, and logical antecedent, stated or understood.

Problems	Corrections
They make a lot of mistakes in the paper.	Newspaper stories are not always accurate. That paper has many typographical errors.
Bruce told Danny *his* mother was sick.	Bruce told Danny that Danny's mother was sick. Bruce told Danny that Bruce's mother was sick.
When Joyce invited Anna and her family to come for the weekend, *she* forgot to check the date.	When she invited Anna ..., Joyce forgot ... Joyce forgot to check the date when she invited Anna and ...
In English literature *you* will read Shakespeare and Milton.	A student of English literature will read Shakespeare and Milton.

▶ **Exercise 1**   **Solving Special Problems in Pronoun Agreement.**   Write the word or words from parentheses that best complete each sentence.

EXAMPLE: I thought ____the forecasters____ said it would rain today. (they, the forecasters)

1. The form says _____ must mail the entries by June 1. (you, contestants)
2. Mike spoke to Danny as soon as _____ got home. (he, Mike)
3. Take the dishes out of the cartons and put _____ downstairs. (them, the cartons)
4. It was rude for _____ to boo the opposing pitcher. (them, the fans)
5. The children and their parents agreed that _____ would be home before dark. (they, the children)
6. After dinner _____ can enjoy dessert on the lakeside patio. (you, guests)
7. The winner was stunned when _____ gave her the news. (they, the judges)
8. Aunt Helen told Mom what _____ had been doing. (her children, our cousins)
9. In the last year _____ may choose more electives. (you, students)
10. Why do _____ always demonstrate oxygen masks? (they, flight attendants)

▶ **Exercise 2**   **Correcting Special Problems in Pronoun Agreement.**   Rewrite each sentence below to correct any problems in pronoun agreement.

EXAMPLE: Tasha told Annie that she must not be late for the party.
Tasha told Annie that Annie must not be late for the party.

1. Why do they always make tests so hard?

_____

2. Sandy left the car in the garage without locking it.

_____

3. In that program, they expect you to do a lot of independent work.

_____

4. Paul told Steve that his bicycle had a flat tire.

_____

5. How do they make that product look so attractive?

_____

25.2 Pronoun and Antecedent Agreement (Four Special Problems) • Practice 2

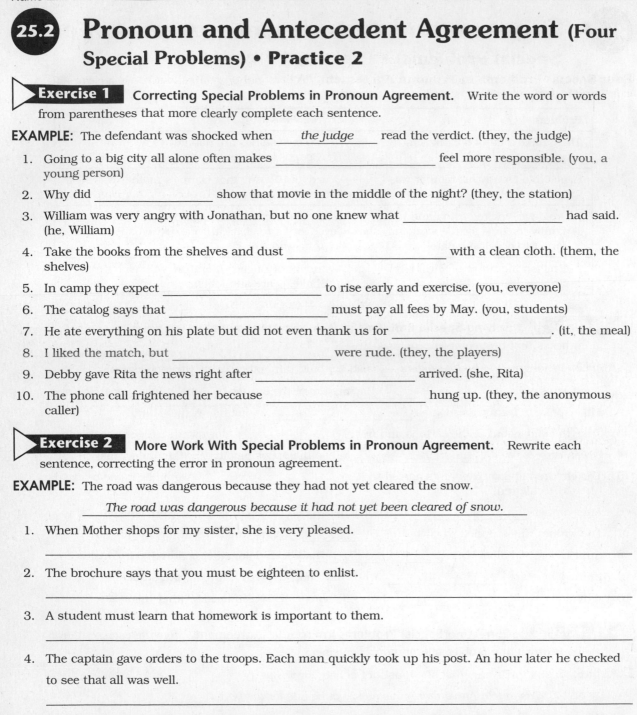

▶ **Exercise 1**   **Correcting Special Problems in Pronoun Agreement.**   Write the word or words from parentheses that more clearly complete each sentence.

EXAMPLE: The defendant was shocked when _____*the judge*_____ read the verdict. (they, the judge)

1. Going to a big city all alone often makes _____ feel more responsible. (you, a young person)

2. Why did _____ show that movie in the middle of the night? (they, the station)

3. William was very angry with Jonathan, but no one knew what _____ had said. (he, William)

4. Take the books from the shelves and dust _____ with a clean cloth. (them, the shelves)

5. In camp they expect _____ to rise early and exercise. (you, everyone)

6. The catalog says that _____ must pay all fees by May. (you, students)

7. He ate everything on his plate but did not even thank us for _____. (it, the meal)

8. I liked the match, but _____ were rude. (they, the players)

9. Debby gave Rita the news right after _____ arrived. (she, Rita)

10. The phone call frightened her because _____ hung up. (they, the anonymous caller)

▶ **Exercise 2**   **More Work With Special Problems in Pronoun Agreement.**   Rewrite each sentence, correcting the error in pronoun agreement.

EXAMPLE: The road was dangerous because they had not yet cleared the snow.

   The road was dangerous because it had not yet been cleared of snow.

1. When Mother shops for my sister, she is very pleased.

   _____

2. The brochure says that you must be eighteen to enlist.

   _____

3. A student must learn that homework is important to them.

   _____

4. The captain gave orders to the troops. Each man quickly took up his post. An hour later he checked to see that all was well.

   _____

5. After forgetting her lines in the show, my sister did not want to try it again.

   _____

26.1 Degrees of Comparison (Recognizing Degrees of Comparison, Regular Forms) • Practice 1

Recognizing Degrees of Comparison Most adjectives and adverbs have different forms to show degrees of comparison.

DEGREES OF COMPARISON			
	Positive	**Comparative**	**Superlative**
Adjectives	few	fewer	fewest
	recent	more recent	most recent
	bad	worse	worst
Adverbs	soon	sooner	soonest
	recently	more recently	most recently
	badly	worse	worst

Regular Forms Use—*er* or *more* to form the comparative degree and—*est* or *most* to form the superlative degree.

REGULAR FORMS OF COMPARISON			
One- and two-syllable modifiers	large	larger	largest
	pretty	prettier	prettiest
	helpless	more helpless	most helpless
Three or more syllables	beautiful	more beautiful	most beautiful
	comfortable	more comfortable	most comfortable

▶ **Exercise 1** **Recognizing Degrees of Comparison.** Identify the degree of comparison of the underlined word in each sentence by writing *pos.* (positive), *comp.* (comparative), or *sup.* (superlative).

EXAMPLE: Andrew sleeps on the <u>lower</u> bunk. _____*comp.*_____

1. We are hoping for <u>better</u> weather tomorrow. _____
2. Lucy interviewed a <u>famous</u> movie star. _____
3. Jesse is the <u>strongest</u> pitcher in the bull pen. _____
4. This is the <u>juiciest</u> orange I ever ate. _____
5. Garlic is the <u>most strongly</u> flavored monocotyledon. _____
6. Cheetahs run <u>more swiftly</u> than any other animal. _____
7. The dancers moved <u>gracefully</u> across the stage. _____
8. That is the <u>largest</u> pizza I have ever seen. _____
9. The patient seems somewhat <u>better</u> today. _____
10. That singer has a <u>loyal</u> fan club. _____

▶ **Exercise 2** **Comparing Adjectives and Adverbs.** Write the missing forms of each modifier.

EXAMPLE: narrow _____*narrower*_____ _____*narrowest*_____

1. amazing _____ _____
2. _____ _____ fastest
3. _____ more rapidly _____
4. modern _____ _____
5. oddly _____ _____

26.1 Degrees of Comparison (Recognizing Degrees of Comparison, Regular Forms) • Practice 2

▷ **Exercise 1** **Recognizing Positive, Comparative, and Superlative Degrees.** Identify the degree of comparison of the underlined word in each sentence by writing *pos.* (positive), *comp.* (comparative), or *sup.* (superlative).

EXAMPLE: Today's test was the <u>hardest</u> one of all. ____*sup.*____

1. This is the <u>largest</u> room in the house. _____
2. Dad's health is <u>more robust</u> than it has been in years. _____
3. Your memory is <u>better</u> than mine. _____
4. The tractor moved <u>slowly</u> across the field. _____
5. Our house is the <u>farthest</u> one from the corner. _____
6. Getting medicine to the victims is <u>more urgent</u> than getting food to them. _____
7. Tim is the <u>shortest</u> player on the team. _____
8. A poet would describe the scene <u>more lyrically</u> than I. _____
9. His mother is <u>stricter</u> with him than mine is with me. _____
10. Greenwald was the <u>best-known</u> painter in the exhibition. _____
11. Marilyn is <u>happiest</u> when she is dancing. _____
12. We reminded him of his <u>important</u> responsibility. _____
13. My sister has been <u>more successful</u> than I. _____
14. The <u>finest</u> piece of jade sold for $25,000. _____
15. I thought the movie was <u>more interesting</u> than the book. _____
16. This behavior is <u>typical</u> of him. _____
17. She is <u>better</u> in biology than she is in math. _____
18. The <u>sunniest</u> day all week was Tuesday. _____
19. Copland's <u>most famous</u> piece is *Fanfare for the Common Man.* _____
20. You will feel <u>warmer</u> by the fire. _____

▷ **Exercise 2** **Forming Regular Comparative and Superlative Degrees.** Write the comparative and the superlative form of each modifier.

EXAMPLE: large ____*larger*____ ____*largest*____

1. tough _____ _____
2. heavy _____ _____
3. strong _____ _____
4. comfortable _____ _____
5. interesting _____ _____
6. pretty _____ _____
7. popular _____ _____
8. confusing _____ _____
9. frightening _____ _____
10. clearly _____ _____

26.1 Degrees of Comparison (Irregular Forms)
• Practice 1

Irregular Forms   The irregular comparative and superlative forms of certain adjectives and adverbs must be memorized.

IRREGULAR MODIFIERS		
Positive	Comparative	Superlative
bad	worse	worst
badly	worse	worst
far (distance)	farther	farthest
far (extent)	further	furthest
good	better	best
ill	worse	worst
late	later	last *or* latest
little (amount)	less	least
many	more	most
much	more	most
well	better	best

▷ **Exercise 1**   **Forming Irregular Comparative and Superlative Degrees.**   Write the appropriate form of the modifier in parentheses to complete each sentence.

EXAMPLE: Tanya is a _____*better*_____ athlete than her twin sister. (good)

1. Soccer is the sport Eddy plays _____ of all. (well)

2. We hiked until we could go no _____. (far)

3. Hillary felt _____ about the unkind remark than about anything else. (bad)

4. Phil ate the _____ amount of food of anyone at the party. (little)

5. Elsa was the _____ guest to leave. (late)

6. Jed needed no _____ explanation. (far)

7. This is the _____ meal I ever ate. (good)

8. Suddenly the patient became _____ than before. (ill)

9. I did _____ of all on Part IV of the test. (badly)

10. This week's winner won the _____ money ever in a sweepstakes. (much)

▷ **Exercise 2**   **Using Adjectives and Adverbs to Make Comparisons.**   Use each modifier in a sentence of your own that shows a clear comparison. Use three comparative forms and two superlatives.

EXAMPLE: (many) _____*Jenny ate more cookies than I did.*_____

1. (bad) _____

2. (badly) _____

3. (good) _____

4. (little) _____

5. (well) _____

26.1 Degrees of Comparison (Irregular Forms)
• Practice 2

▶ **Exercise 1**   **Forming Irregular Comparative and Superlative Degrees.**   Write the appropriate form of the underlined modifier to complete each sentence.

EXAMPLE: I may have little money, but you have ___*less*___ than I.

1. Cod is a good fish, but Boston scrod is even _____.

2. Grandmother is well today, but she felt even _____ yesterday.

3. Utica is farther from New York City than Albany, but Ithaca is the _____ from New York City of the three.

4. Trissy did badly on the first three tests of the term, but her performance on the final test was the _____ of all.

5. Terry is still ill, but she was _____ two hours ago.

6. Billy's house is far from the center of town, but Tom's house is even _____ away.

7. Michael danced very well in the contest, but Karyn danced even _____.

8. Although my mother's chocolate cake tastes very good, my grandmother's tastes much _____.

9. Jonathan arrived late for the party, and Tina and Jim arrived even _____.

10. There has been much talk of a tax break, but during the campaign there will be even _____.

11. There were not many visitors this morning, but there will be _____ this evening.

12. I thought *The Empire Strikes Back* was better than *Return of the Jedi*, but *Star Wars* was the _____ of the three movies.

13. Cynthia was late for class; Carol was _____.

14. The singer's first song during the concert was quite good, but his second was much _____.

15. The rehearsal went well today, but it went _____ yesterday.

▶ **Writing Application**   **Using Adjectives and Adverbs to Make Comparisons.**   Use each item in a sentence of your own.

EXAMPLE: most frightening ___*That was the most frightening movie I've ever seen.*___

1. hungrier _____
2. proudest _____
3. farther _____
4. more quickly _____
5. fastest _____
6. most foolish _____
7. worst _____
8. good _____
9. well (as adjective) _____
10. well (as adverb) _____

© Prentice-Hall, Inc.

26.2 Clear Comparisons (Using Comparative and Superlative Degrees) • Practice 1

Using Comparative and Superlative Degrees   Use the comparative degree to compare two people, places, or things. Use the superlative degree to compare three or more people, places, or things.

Comparative (comparing two)	Superlative (comparing three or more)
I often get *higher* grades than my brother.	Of all the students in my class, Liz usually gets the *highest* grades.
One of these shoes feels *tighter* than the other.	This car can maneuver into even the *tightest* parking spaces.
If you had called *more promptly*, we could have been *more helpful*.	Ali responded the *most promptly* of everyone we invited.

▷ **Exercise 1**   **Using the Comparative and Superlative Degrees Correctly.**   Write the form from parentheses that correctly completes each sentence.

EXAMPLE: Paul plays the piano _____*better*_____ than Andrew. (better, best)

1. Waldo is often grumpy, but he is _____ agreeable when tired. (less, least)

2. Christine is the _____ of my five cousins. (older, oldest)

3. In this weather, the basement is the _____ place in the house (cooler, coolest)

4. Mickey Mouse is probably the _____ famous of all cartoon characters. (more, most)

5. Which of Shakespeare's plays is _____ ? (longer, longest)

6. I have never seen anyone move_____ gracefully than Margot. (more, most)

7. That fan cools the room _____ effectively than we thought it would. (more, most)

8. Which has _____ calories, the cheesecake or the chocolate mousse? (fewer, fewest)

9. At present, the _____ trains in the world are in Japan. (faster, fastest)

10. Of the three candidates, Elkins answered the questions _____ honestly. (more, most)

▷ **Exercise 2**   **Recognizing Inappropriate Comparisons.**   In the sentences below, underline any problems that exist in comparisons. On the line below, rewrite each sentence correctly. If a sentence contains no problem, write *correct* on the line.

EXAMPLE: Portia is one of Shakespeare's <u>famousest</u> heroines.

_____*Portia is one of Shakespeare's most famous heroines.*_____

1. Lenore studies more harder than the rest of us.

_____

2. The oldest of my two sisters is a doctor.

_____

3. Tom's problem sounds worser than it really is.

_____

4. Parents usually want what seems best for their children.

_____

5. That restaurant has the more carefully prepared food in town.

_____

26.2 Clear Comparisons (Using Comparative and Superlative Degrees) • Practice 2

▶ **Exercise 1** **Using the Comparative and Superlative Degrees Correctly.** Write the correct comparative or superlative form from parentheses to complete each sentence.

EXAMPLE: He is _____more_____ patient than his sister. (more, most)

1. Which of the twins swims _____? (better, best)
2. She is the _____ talented actress in The Thespians. (more, most)
3. My sister is _____ than I. (hungrier, hungriest)
4. Are you the _____ in your family? (stronger, strongest)
5. He is _____ responsible than his older brother. (less, least)
6. She was the _____ beautiful child I've ever seen. (more, most)
7. My health is _____ today than it was yesterday. (worse, worst)
8. Of the two, Copenhagen is the _____ city. (cleaner, cleanest)
9. That actor is _____ than he appears on television. (smaller, smallest)
10. Tim is _____ willing to cooperate than his friend. (less, least)

▶ **Exercise 2** **Supplying the Comparative and Superlative Degrees.** Write the appropriate comparative or superlative degree of the modifier in parentheses.

EXAMPLE: Of the two plays, *Macbeth* is _____shorter_____. (short)

1. This year, June 21 will be the _____ day of the year. (long)
2. The weather is _____ today than it was yesterday. (bad)
3. Ted is the _____ of Uncle John's three sons. (old)
4. This is the _____ train I've ever been on. (fast)
5. Today is the _____ day of my life. (happy)
6. Louise is _____ than the other dentist in town. (capable)
7. Bill is the _____ person I know. (kind)
8. Aunt Sarah is _____ this morning than she was last night. (ill)
9. Edward speaks French _____ than I do. (fluently)
10. Arthur's essay is the _____ in the class. (good)
11. St. Louis is _____ from New Orleans than Memphis is. (far)
12. Alan does _____ on English tests than I do. (well)
13. Kim is the _____ of the three children. (young)
14. This is the _____ meal I've ever eaten. (delicious)
15. Your computer is _____ than mine. (versatile)
16. Faulkner is a _____ novelist than Hemingway is. (difficult)
17. Jill arrived _____ than Joan. (late)
18. The living room is the _____ room in the house. (warm)
19. I'm feeling _____ than I did yesterday. (well)
20. This chair is _____ than that one. (comfortable)

26.2 Clear Comparisons (Balanced Comparisons, *Other* and *Else* in Comparisons) • Practice 1

Balanced Comparisons   Make sure that your sentences compare only items of a similar kind.

Unbalanced Comparisons	Correct
Jon's score was better than *Tom.* *My record collection* is bigger than *my brother.*	*Jon's score* was better than *Tom's.* *My record collection* is bigger than *my brother's.*

***Other* and *Else* in Comparisons**   When comparing one of a group with the rest of the group, use the word *other* or the word *else.*

Illogical	Correct
John Kennedy was *younger than any* American president. Michael bats *better than anyone* on the team.	John Kennedy was *younger than any other* American president. Michael bats *better than anyone else* on the team.

▷ **Exercise 1**   **Making Balanced Comparisons.**   Rewrite each sentence, correcting the comparison.

EXAMPLE: My room is even messier than my brother.

   My room is even messier than my brother's.

1. Carol's clothes are much more elegant than Angie.

   _____

2. My brownies are richer than Aunt Polly.

   _____

3. Judson's essay was harder to understand than Len.

   _____

4. Clare's version of the story sounds even stranger than Pete.

   _____

5. The fish that I caught was even bigger than Dad.

   _____

▷ **Exercise 2**   **Using *Other* and *Else* in Comparisons.**   Rewrite each sentence, correcting the comparison.

EXAMPLE: Dave has a lower ERA than any pitcher in the league.

   Dave has a lower ERA than any other pitcher in the league.

1. Mr. Talbert is a better teacher than anyone on the faculty.

   _____

2. My brother Jason is more trustworthy than anyone in the family.

   _____

3. That chef is better than any cook in town.

   _____

4. I like Emily Dickinson's work better than any poet's.

   _____

5. Our street curves more dangerously than any road in town.

   _____

26.2 Clear Comparisons (Balanced Comparisons, *Other* and *Else* in Comparisons) • **Practice 2**

▶ **Exercise 1** **Making Balanced Comparisons.** Rewrite each sentence, correcting the unbalanced comparison.

EXAMPLE: Valerie's eyes are bluer than Annie.

_____*Valerie's eyes are bluer than Annie's.*_____

1. His swimming record is better than his chief rival.

_____

2. Dad's cooking is better than Mom.

_____

3. The rooms in my dorm are bigger than this hotel.

_____

4. My gloves are in poorer condition than Sandra.

_____

5. I like Cynthia's costume better than her twin.

_____

6. Isn't my haircut more stylish than Joan?

_____

7. My old bike's tires are bigger than my new bike.

_____

8. Her coin collection is more valuable than her brother.

_____

9. Jennifer's grades are higher than Keith.

_____

10. My brother's wardrobe is more varied than my sister.

_____

▶ **Exercise 2** **Using *Other* and *Else* in Comparisons.** Rewrite each sentence, correcting the illogical comparison.

EXAMPLE: Beth is nicer than anyone in class.

_____*Beth is nicer than anyone else in class.*_____

1. This ice cream is better than any I've ever tasted.

_____

2. The guitarist plays better than anyone in the band.

_____

3. Senator Hammer's record is better than any senator's.

_____

4. Ty Cobb hit better than any baseball player.

_____

5. He spends more money on clothing than anyone I know.

_____

27.1 Negative Sentences • Practice 1

Recognizing Double Negatives   Do not write sentences with double negatives.

Double Negatives	Correct Negative Sentences
I *can't* wait *no* longer.	I *can't* wait any longer.
	I can wait *no* longer.
Jack *isn't no* friend of mine.	Jack *isn't* a friend of mine.
	Jack is *no* friend of mine.
Why *doesn't nobody* help me?	Why *doesn't* somebody help me?
	Why does *nobody* help me?

Forming Negative Sentences Correctly   Do not use two negative words in the same clause. Do not use *but* in its negative sense with another negative. Do not use *barely, hardly,* or *scarcely* with another negative.

More Double Negatives	Correct Negative Sentences
There was*n't nothing* to do.	There was*n't* anything to do.
	There was *nothing* to do.
There is*n't but* one cookie left.	There is *but* one cookie left.
	There is *only* one cookie left.
We could*n't hardly* wait.	We could*n't wait.*
	We could hardly *wait.*

▶ **Exercise 1**   **Avoiding Problems With Negatives.**   Write the word from parentheses that makes each sentence negative without creating a double negative.

EXAMPLE: The stranded explorers had not had ____*any*____ food for days. (any, no)

1. You shouldn't have said _____ about our plans. (anything, nothing)

2. Toward the end of the movie, we _____ hardly stand the suspense. (could, couldn't)

3. Are you sure I _____ bring but one suitcase? (can, can't)

4. The missing dog _____ nowhere in sight. (was, wasn't)

5. You can be sure Tim won't eat _____ of those fish eggs. (any, none)

6. Ms. Lawson didn't say _____ about a test. (nothing, anything)

7. We don't need _____ two other players. (but, more than)

8. They can't _____ hope to win that way. (ever, never)

9. By morning, there _____ barely a trace of snow. (was, wasn't)

10. I have hardly _____ seen a more beautiful ballet. (ever, never)

▶ **Exercise 2**   **Using Negatives Correctly.**   Write a sentence of your own, correctly using each negative word given.

EXAMPLE: (barely) _____*I got barely any sleep last night.*_____

1. (nowhere) _____

2. (but) _____

3. (shouldn't) _____

4. (hardly) _____

5. (never) _____

27.1 Negative Sentences • Practice 2

► Exercise 1   **Avoiding Double Negatives.**   Write the word from parentheses that makes each sentence negative without forming a double negative.

EXAMPLE: She couldn't find ____*any*____ of the lost coins. (none, any)

1. He has never done _____ to help us. (anything, nothing)

2. I don't want _____ more spinach. (no, any)

3. We couldn't read _____ of the writing in the letter. (none, any)

4. Don't strike a match _____ near the gasoline. (anywhere, nowhere)

5. I did _____ of the things they accused me of. (none, any)

6. The children didn't eat _____ of their dinner. (any, none)

7. No one at the party ate _____ of the cake. (any, none)

8. Nobody said _____ to me about a meeting. (nothing, anything)

9. We could get _____ out of the burning house. (nothing, anything)

10. I haven't _____ more sentences to write. (no, any)

► Exercise 2   **Avoiding Problems With Negatives.**   Underline the word in parentheses that makes each sentence negative without creating a double negative.

EXAMPLE: John (could, couldn't) hardly believe he'd won.

1. I don't want (anything, nothing).

2. Remember that I have done (anything, nothing) wrong.

3. Lila (could, couldn't) scarcely catch her breath.

4. We haven't (any, no) strong feelings about it.

5. I couldn't have (anything, nothing) for dessert.

6. There (were, weren't) but three choices.

7. I (can, can't) hardly believe my eyes.

8. Don't you have (anything, nothing) more exciting to read?

9. She doesn't write to me (any, no) more.

10. Luke (had, hadn't) but two days of provisions left when he was found.

► Exercise 3   **Correcting Double Negatives.**   Rewrite each sentence, correcting the double negative.

EXAMPLE: Dad would never accept no charity.

       Dad would never accept any charity.

1. I promise that I won't tell nobody.

_____

2. Mary can't hardly read the small print.

_____

3. My father hadn't never been to Athens.

_____

4. I haven't but a few minutes left to work.

_____

5. She didn't have no lunch.

_____

27.2 # Fifty Common Usage Problems • Practice 1

Solving Usage Problems   Study the items in the usage glossary in your textbook, paying particular attention to similar spellings, words that should never be used, pairs that are often misused, and problems with verb forms.

TYPES OF PROBLEMS	
Similar Spellings	*accept* and *except; than* and *then*
Wrong Words	*ain't alright somewheres*
Misused Pairs	*among* and *between; bring* and *take*
Verb Forms	*has done should have*

▶ **Exercise 1**   **Avoiding Some Common Usage Problems.**   Write the word from parentheses that correctly completes each sentence.

EXAMPLE: Free _____*advice*_____ is often worth what it costs. (advice, advise)

1. This lawn mower _____ work as well as it used to. (don't, doesn't)

2. Mom told Paul he had _____ in bed long enough. (laid, lain)

3. I should _____ known he couldn't keep a secret. (have, of)

4. Air pollution _____ elderly people most of all. (affects, effects)

5. The twins and I had only two dollars _____ us. (among, between)

6. Will you _____ this book back to the library when you go? (bring, take)

7. My answer to the last problem is different _____ yours. (from, than)

8. Carrot and celery sticks make a good and _____ snack. (healthful, healthy)

9. Customers with _____ than six items can use the express line. (fewer, less)

10. Who says you can't _____ an old dog new tricks. (learn, teach)

▶ **Exercise 2**   **Avoiding Other Common Usage Problems.**   Write the word from parentheses that correctly completes each sentence.

EXAMPLE: What are your ideas _____*about*_____ the best solution? (about, as to)

1. When are they going to _____ the flag? (rise, raise)

2. I was _____ disappointed in the result. (kind of, somewhat)

3. Let's go _____ the lobby to wait for them. (in, into)

4. A few fans _____ in the bleachers in spite of the rain. (sat, set)

5. This short cut seems _____ than the regular way. (farther, further)

6. _____ the chips fall where they may. (Leave, Let)

7. The player _____ pinch hit for the pitcher struck out. (that, which)

8. The hikers still had a long _____ to go before nightfall. (way, ways)

9. The _____ of the new drug are not fully known. (affects, effects)

10. The prisoner returned to jail that night _____ he said he would. (as, like)

27.2 Fifty Common Usage Problems • Practice 2

Exercise 1 **Avoiding Usage Problems.** Write the correct expression from the parentheses to complete each sentence.

EXAMPLE: The ____effects____ of the experiment startled us. (affects, effects)

1. I can't find my classes _____. (anywhere, anywheres)

2. I hope you can _____ him properly. (advice, advise)

3. Everyone visited the museum _____ my father. (accept, except)

4. There _____ a dry eye in the auditorium. (ain't, isn't)

5. Is everything _____ at home? (all right, alright)

6. The horses were huddled _____. (all together, altogether)

7. Are you _____ to go? (all ready, already)

8. What is the _____ of the new law? (affect, effect)

9. Pete _____ the machine for a particular job. (adapted, adopted)

10. Your _____ was very helpful. (advice, advise)

Exercise 2 **Avoiding Usage Problems.** Write the correct expression from the parentheses to complete each sentence.

1. The old man stood _____ the tree. (beside, besides)

2. _____ you asked, I will tell you the story. (Being that, Since)

3. _____ your empty tray over here. (Bring, Take)

4. The sergeant _____ into the room. (burst, busted)

5. This new pen is much different _____ my old one. (from, than)

6. I can't help _____ to go with you. (but want, wanting)

7. I don't know where _____. (I'm at, I am)

8. They had no suggestions _____ what to do next on our vacation. (as to, about)

9. Practice is canceled _____ the coach is sick. (being as, because)

10. The reason I am not going is _____ I am exhausted from my trip yesterday. (because, that)

Exercise 3 **Avoiding Usage Problems.** Write the correct expression from the parentheses to complete each sentence.

1. My brother _____ care much for rock music. (doesn't, don't)

2. We _____ our French homework already. (done, have done)

3. I have _____ classical records in my collection than my sister does. (fewer, less)

4. My parents _____ to a movie. (gone, have gone)

5. There was _____ damage after the tornado than we had expected at first. (fewer, less)

6. _____ his poor record, he was dropped from the team. (Due to, Because of)

7. _____ your friend care whether you borrow his new bicycle? (Doesn't, Don't)

8. I _____ all that I can for you. (done, have done)

9. His explanation led her to seek _____ answers from other experts in the field. (farther, further)

10. The diver jumped _____ the water from the cliff. (in, into)

Name _____ Date _____

 Capitalization (Sentences) • **Practice 1**

Capitals for Sentences   To capitalize means to begin a word with a capital letter. Capitalize the first word in a sentence. Capitalize the first word in a quotation if the quotation is a complete sentence. Capitalize the first word after a colon if the word begins a complete sentence.

SENTENCES THAT STAND ALONE
Declarative: The trail leads to the river bank. *Interrogative:* What is the name of your favorite novel? *Imperative:* Take a taxi to the airport terminal. *Exclamatory:* What a pleasant surprise!
SENTENCES IN QUOTATIONS
Mother replied, "You'll have to work harder." "You'll have to work harder, " Mother replied.
SENTENCES AFTER COLONS
Everyone asked the same question: How will we raise funds?

▷ **Exercise 1**   **Using Capitals to Begin Sentences.**   Underline the word or words that should be capitalized in each sentence.

EXAMPLE: <u>sally</u> asked, "<u>can</u> I help pack?"

1. after school, I often work on my coin collection.

2. this is the problem: we can't afford a new car.

3. we joined the volleyball team last year.

4. the doctor said, "exercise and get enough rest."

5. how will we get to the ballpark from the station?

6. the treasurer explained our goal: we must raise five hundred dollars.

7. how happy we were to see our cousins!

8. my teacher asked, "who has completed the report?"

9. mark includes radishes and scallions in his salads.

10. have you read a good biography this year?

▷ **Exercise 2**   **Using Capitalized Words.**   Complete each sentence by adding an appropriate capitalized word.

EXAMPLE: Billy replied, " _____*Peaches*_____ are my favorite fruit."

1. _____ are a good source of protein.

2. Father said, " _____ phoned last night."

3. _____ , would you reply to that question?

4. Here is the problem: _____ is too expensive.

5. _____ laughed, "I can't remember her name."

6. _____ the letter in the morning.

7. _____ would make the best treasurer?

8. This is important: _____ follow the directions exactly.

9. _____ teacher said, "Please write the paper over."

10. We agreed, " _____ can't start again."

28 Capitalization (Sentences) • Practice 2

▶ **Exercise 1** **Using Capitalization Correctly in Sentences.** Underline the word or words that should be capitalized in each sentence.

EXAMPLE: what a difficult mountain that was to climb!

1. show me what you are holding in your hand, young man.

2. getting my school schedule worked out for next year is causing problems.

3. "every hero becomes a bore at last, " observed Emerson.

4. when will dinner be ready?

5. my grandmother taught me one important lesson: giving more than 100 percent is the surest way to get ahead.

6. we found a twenty-dollar bill on the sidewalk!

7. at one time Confucius warned, "the cautious seldom err."

8. the store down the street is holding a big sale today.

9. will you go on many weekend ski trips this winter?

10. sit still while the barber finishes cutting your hair.

11. "if you would wish another to keep your secret, " advised Seneca, "first keep it yourself."

12. where did you take the camera to be repaired?

13. we saw quite a feat at the circus: a young man did a high-wire act without any safety nets below him.

14. the company gave us a substantial salary increase today!

15. many people put more salt on their food than is healthful.

16. they spent yesterday buying gifts: a stuffed panda, an electric razor, and a giant rubber plant.

17. "we can stay as long as we want, " she said. "they have given us permission."

18. what in the world were you thinking of?

19. "why not try, " she asked, "to climb a mountain?"

20. he was afraid: he had never climbed a mountain.

▶ **Exercise 2** **Using Capitalization Correctly in Paragraphs.** Underline the words that should be capitalized in the following paragraphs.

karly said, "yesterday i was walking through the woods, and a porcupine crossed my path."

phil answered, "the porcupine is such a strange animal. did you know," he continued, "that people who live in the mountains often call the porcupine a quill-pig?"

"yes, i did know that," answered Karly. "the animal is certainly as clumsy and slow-moving as any pig, but it is not a pig at all. it is actually a rodent, with sharp teeth somewhat like those of a rabbit or a squirrel. even though it is a mere rodent, nearly every other wild creature in the forest is afraid to attack it. do you know why?"

"well, yes, i do," said Phil. "the reason is this: the porcupine's body is thickly sprinkled with stiff, needle-sharp quills. these quills are from half an inch to four inches long. a porcupine might have as many as 20, 000 or 25, 000 of these peculiar weapons. interestingly, when one is lost, a new one grows quickly to replace it. if you were a forest creature, you'd probably be afraid of porcupines, too!"

Name _____ Date _____

 28 # Capitalization (Proper Nouns, Proper Adjectives)
• Practice 1

Capitals for Proper Nouns   Capitalize all proper nouns.

PROPER NOUNS	
Names of people: Jane Eyre	*Geographic names:* Pikes Peak
Specific events: World Series	*Organizations:* Rotary Club
Religious references: God	*Special items:* Pulitzer Prize

Capitals for Proper Adjectives   Capitalize most proper adjectives.

With Capitals	Without Capitals
a Broadway play	Common terms: french fries
a Mexican treaty	Most prefixes: pro-American event
a Franklin stove	Parts of compounds: French-speaking tourists

▶ **Exercise 1**   **Recognizing Proper Nouns and Proper Adjectives.**   Underline the proper nouns and proper adjectives that should be capitalized.

EXAMPLE: I visit <u>canada</u> each summer.

1. In europe she visited france and belgium.
2. I know that william faulkner received a nobel prize.
3. Will ted develop into an all-american?
4. Ask judy whether she wants some french fries.
5. My family always buys the same brand of televisions and radios, electrosonic.
6. The chamber of commerce sponsored the contest.
7. The cuban exiles chanted pro-american slogans.
8. Many people pray to god and read the bible.
9. The fortress of louisbourg is in nova scotia.
10. Have you met any french-speaking canadians?

▶ **Exercise 2**   **Using Proper Nouns and Proper Adjectives.**   Fill in each blank with a proper noun or proper adjective.

EXAMPLE: My favorite two cities are ____*Boston*____ and ____*Chicago*____

1. Frank wants a _____ camera for his birthday.
2. Last summer she traveled to _____ and _____.
3. Nancy is an all- _____ field hockey player.
4. _____ is the writer I like the best.
5. The professional football season ends with the _____.
6. I live in _____.
7. After the meeting, I spoke to _____ and _____.
8. The _____ River passes through several states.
9. Sudan and Nigeria are on the _____ continent.
10. In my religion we study the _____.

28 Capitalization (Proper Nouns, Proper Adjectives)
• Practice 2

▶ **Exercise 1** **Capitalizing Proper Nouns.** Underline the words that should be capitalized.

EXAMPLE: After the sun sets, <u>venus</u> will be visible in the west.

1. To see a play that has been running for twenty-five years, you should go to st. martin's theater in london.
2. One well-known suspension bridge is the golden gate, which spans san francisco bay.
3. Both the shoshone and the arapaho make up a part of the population of wyoming.
4. By checking a perpetual calendar, I found that benjamin franklin was born on sunday, january 17, 1706.
5. In the northeast winters are quite harsh and long.
6. Astronauts will probably visit jupiter some day.
7. The lowest point in all north america is in death valley.
8. thomas mckean, a lawyer from pennsylvania, signed the declaration of independence.
9. Some of the major airline companies that went bankrupt were eastern, national, and people's express.
10. In october 1976, congress repealed the homestead act of 1862 since there was no longer any land available for homesteading.
11. In ancient mythology the goddess athena dispensed wisdom.
12. The kentucky derby is held annually in the spring at churchill downs.
13. A well-known race horse, secretariat, won many races.
14. The torah, the talmud, and the midrash are the sacred writings of judaism.
15. You can find out about the great smoky mountains by writing to the chamber of commerce, 505 fesslers lane, nashville, tennessee 37210.
16. I think arabic is a difficult language to master.
17. The nebula award is presented for outstanding works of science fiction.
18. The nuclear regulatory commission regulates all civilian uses of atomic energy.
19. The white house uses the blue room as its official reception room.
20. About one half of our national leaders have been republicans and the other half have been democrats.

▶ **Exercise 2** **Capitalizing Proper Adjectives.** Underline the words that should be capitalized.

EXAMPLE: I am taking a <u>chinese</u> cooking course.

1. Open-air theaters are often used for the performance of elizabethan plays.
2. Many african american groups have held several conferences during the past few years to discuss their heritage.
3. Large crowds at an american political rally gave the police some crowd-control problems.
4. The anglo-saxon invasion of Britain took place in the fifth and sixth centuries.
5. Some early buddhist monasteries were caves that were elegantly carved and decorated.
6. Her old pictureperfect camera accompanied her on all her travels.
7. A sino-russian pact could have a significant effect on foreign policy.
8. Those who own pre-columbian sculptures have valuable art pieces in their possession.
9. A lovely indian woman in a sari came into the store asking for the manager.
10. The franklin d. roosevelt years were marred by World War II.

Name _____   Date _____

 28 # Capitalization (for Titles, in Letters) • Practice 1

Capitals for Titles   Capitalize titles of people and titles of works.

People	Works
Doctor Vance	*Great Expectations*
Colonel Andrews	*News Review Magazine*
the President	"Gunga Din"
Grandfather Wilkins	"The Cask of Amontillado"
Mr., Ms., Dr., Jr.	*Portrait of a Man with a Red Cap*

Capitals in Letters   Capitalize the first word and all nouns in letter salutations and the first word in letter closings.

Salutations	Closings
Dear Cousin Beth,	Yours truly,
Dear Dr. Stanton:	Sincerely yours,
My dear Friends,	Very truly yours,

> **Exercise 1**   **Using Capitals in Titles.**   Underline the words that should be capitalized.

EXAMPLE: I just read Frost's "at woodward's gardens."

1. I lunched with captain perez yesterday.

2. Susan just finished reading "the most dangerous game."

3. The chief justice of the United States just resigned.

4. What are the symptoms of this disease, doctor gilbert?

5. We saw *portrait of a lady* at the National Gallery.

6. Can I borrow your copy of *the member of the wedding*?

7. Have you been introduced to bishop wilson?

8. I know that ms. greer and mr. kelly will volunteer.

9. Does *nature's beauty magazine* still have great photos?

10. I bought a copy of Grant Wood's *american gothic*.

> **Exercise 2**   **Using Capitals for Salutations and Closings.**   Rewrite each of the following letter parts, adding the missing capitals.

EXAMPLE: dear aunt maria,   _____Dear Aunt Maria,_____

1. dear mr. stevenson, _____

2. respectfully yours, _____

3. my dear uncle, _____

4. very truly yours, _____

5. dear senator brock: _____

6. sincerely yours, _____

7. affectionately, _____

8. dear colonel cobb: _____

9. dear ms. brody: _____

10. with deepest regret, _____

28 Capitalization (for Titles, in Letters) • Practice 2

▷ **Exercise 1** **Capitalizing Titles of People.** Underline the words and abbreviations that should be capitalized.

EXAMPLE: The recruits saluted <u>major general caruthers</u>.

1. Could you direct me, sir, to this address?

2. We invited dr. and mrs. strutner to the play.

3. One of the greatest mystery writers of all time was dame agatha christie.

4. It is my great pleasure to present the president of the United States.

5. The ex-secretary of state is writing his memoirs.

6. Lieutenant governor taylor ran our state last week while governor hull was away on a business trip.

7. We expect colonel green to inspect the troops today.

8. We visited grandmother, who teaches in a small country school.

9. Please tell us, senator, how you expect to vote.

10. The reverend john hyder and father madison met to discuss some of the concerns facing their parishes.

▷ **Exercise 2** **Capitalizing Titles of Things.** Underline the words that should be capitalized.

EXAMPLE: Have you read the novel *<u>the red pony</u>* by Steinbeck?

1. *the financial journal* is a respected newspaper that presents news from the point of view of business people.

2. The only classes they are offering that I want to take are psychology, german, and art.

3. The story "the lottery" by Shirley Jackson makes the reader contemplate some of humanity's baser instincts.

4. When registration opened, english 1A, biology 45, and all the calculus courses filled up immediately.

5. *the making of the past: the egyptian kingdoms* contains some excellent pictures of ancient tomb treasures.

6. Robert Graves based much of his novel *i, claudius* on the Roman historian Suetonius's *the lives of the caesars*.

7. Loren Eisley's *the man who saw through time* is a collection of essays about the Elizabethan scientist Francis Bacon.

8. Edgar Allan Poe once wrote a very fine poem entitled "a dream within a dream."

9. One of Phyllis McGinley's best books for children is *the horse who lived upstairs*.

10. *measure for measure* is one of Shakespeare's lesser-known plays.

Name _____ Date _____

 29.1 # End Marks • Practice 1

Uses of the Period Use a period to end a declarative or imperative sentence, an indirect question, and most abbreviations.

PERIODS
Declarative Sentence: The stone is large and smooth. *Imperative Sentence:* Open the window about six inches. *Indirect Question:* I asked him what he wanted. *Abbreviations:* Conn. (Connecticut) Rd. (Road)

Uses of the Question Mark Use a question mark to end an interrogative sentence.

QUESTION MARKS
Interrogative Sentence: What is your telephone number?

Uses of the Exclamation Mark Use an exclamation mark to end an exclamatory sentence, an urgent imperative sentence, and most interjections.

EXCLAMATION MARKS
Exclamatory Sentence: What a remarkable pass! *Imperative Sentence:* Don't let go of the wheel! *Interjection:* Good grief! She won.

▶ **Exercise 1** **Using End Marks Correctly.** Write the proper end mark at the end of each item.

EXAMPLE: What a wonderful achievement _____!_____

1. How many pairs of shoes do you have _____

2. Beethoven wrote nine symphonies _____

3. I have an interview with Rinaldo and Son, Inc _____

4. June won the first prize. Hurray _____

5. We asked them when they wanted to leave _____

6. Some batteries contain sulfuric acid _____

7. Where is Ethiopia _____

8. What an astounding performance _____

9. Have you read *A Day No Pigs Would Die* _____

10. Choose another uniform _____

▶ **Exercise 2** **Supplying End Marks.** Write a sentence using each of the following end marks.

EXAMPLE: Period _____*She wrote a report on proper manners.*_____

1. Question Mark _____

2. Exclamation Mark _____

3. Period _____

4. Question Mark _____

5. Exclamation Mark _____

29.1 End Marks • Practice 2

> **Exercise 1** **Using the Period Correctly.**   Add the necessary periods to the following sentences.

EXAMPLE: John R Carlson asked you to return his call
   John R. Carlson asked you to return his call.

1. The American humorist S J Perelman was once a scriptwriter for the Marx Brothers
2. My parents wondered what grade I received on the test
3. Address the package to Mr Arthur Grover, Jr
4. I think Elizabeth Bishop is a fine modern American poet
5. She prefers the title Mrs to the title Ms
6. I asked Mrs Ramos to go with us
7. Schedule a certain amount of time for studying every day
8. Elizabeth P Peabody started the first kindergarten in the United States in 1860
9. The son of Efrem Zimbalist, Sr, a violinist, is an actor
10. Dr Elvira M Thackery spoke at the seminar

> **Exercise 2** **Using the Question Mark Correctly.**   Some of the following sentences are direct questions and require question marks. Others are indirect questions and require periods. Add the necessary punctuation.

EXAMPLE: What was comedian Milton Berle's nickname
   What was comedian Milton Berle's nickname?___?___

1. How much money did Lucille Ball make from her television series _____
2. Many have wondered whether more people watched Lucille Ball or President Eisenhower's inauguration _____
3. How did Dinah Shore customarily end her shows _____
4. Who was known as Mr. Television _____
5. What were two of the popular TV shows that children of the 1950's liked to watch _____
6. Before 1951, what percentage of the American public was asleep by midnight _____
7. Some wondered whether shows like the Steve Allen and Jack Paar talk shows were responsible for people staying up later _____
8. In what TV show did Mary Martin fly through the air on wires _____
9. In what show did audiences see Joe Friday _____
10. During the 1953–1954 season, which show was rated first _____

> **Exercise 3** **Using the Exclamation Mark Correctly.**   Add the necessary exclamation marks to the following items. Then identify each use as *exclamatory, imperative,* or *interjection.*

EXAMPLE: What a terrifying movie that was
   What a terrifying movie that was! ___*exclamatory*___

1. Our dog had four puppies last night _____
2. There goes the thief _____
3. Quick hide Mother's birthday present _____
4. Help me _____
5. We have just three minutes before the plane takes off _____

29.2 Commas That Separate Basic Elements
(Compound Sentences, Items in a Series, Adjectives)
• Practice 1

Commas With Compound Sentences   Use a comma before the coordinating conjunction in a compound sentence.

COMPOUND SENTENCES
Jose wanted to attend the game, but he decided to do his report instead. Either we will win tonight, or we will have to face a sad crowd afterward.

Commas Between Items in a Series   Use commas to separate three or more words, phrases, or clauses in a series.

SERIES
Ellen bought new jeans, a plaid skirt, and a pair of gloves. They drove to the post office, parked the car, and unloaded the boxes.

Commas Between Adjectives   Use commas to separate adjectives of equal rank. (Do not use commas to separate adjectives that must stay in a specific order.)

With Commas	Without Commas
A narrow, rough road led to the country market.	Many new books on sports are on display in the library.

▶ **Exercise 1**   Using Commas Correctly.   Add commas where they are required. One sentence needs no commas.

EXAMPLE: During the night it rained but the day was brilliant.
             During the night it rained, but the day was brilliant.

1. Mary Grace lives in a dark wooded area.

2. The crash awoke Father and he jumped out of bed.

3. Buy tomatoes cucumbers scallions and lettuce.

4. An exhausted discouraged team limped into the locker room.

5. Betty must have reached home safely or she would have phoned.

6. I found many old stamps in Grandfather's collection.

7. The rain has stopped but it is still very humid.

8. An angry determined speaker addressed the mayor.

9. Frank planned to read his speech but he lost his notes.

10. I prepared a salad cooked a roast and baked some cookies.

▶ **Exercise 2**   Understanding the Use of Commas.   The sentences below are correctly punctuated. Identify the use of commas by writing the words *compound*, *series*, or *adjectives*.

EXAMPLE: She stared at the horizon lined with old, withered trees. ___*adjectives*___

1. I will take the train, or I will drive to work. _____

2. Steve bought an umbrella, boots, and a rain hat. _____

3. A happy, smiling crowd greeted the contestants. _____

4. You must go, but I will stay. _____

5. She wanted to go swimming, get some sun, and just relax. _____.

29.2 Commas That Separate Basic Elements
(Compound Sentences, Items in a Series, Adjectives)
• Practice 2

▶ **Exercise 1**   **Using Commas With Compound Sentences.**   Add the necessary commas.

EXAMPLE: I have been sending funny Valentine cards to many of my friends every year but I never place my name on them.

I have been sending funny Valentine cards to many of my friends every year, but I never place my name on them.

(1) Valentine's Day is celebrated by most Americans yet few people know the story of how the holiday first began. (2) The holiday originated in ancient Rome but the actual date of its origin is about A.D. 270. (3) According to legend Emperor Claudius II would not allow the troops of the Roman army to marry for he felt that married men made poor soldiers. (4) A priest called Valentinus took pity on two young lovers and he secretly married them against Emperor Claudius's orders. (5) Valentinus was arrested and thrown in jail and Claudius had him beheaded several months later. (6) It was from this Roman jail that the first Valentine card was sent for Valentinus supposedly cured the jailer's daughter of blindness and sent her a note signed "From Your Valentine." (7) You may want to believe this legend or you may feel that this is just a romantic tale that was concocted to explain the origin of Valentine's Day. (8) The first Valentines in America were not covered with sweet verses nor were they elaborate and lacy works of art. (9) Boys and girls of the late 1850's loved to send "Penny Dreadfuls" on Valentine's Day and they looked forward to receiving them from their friends in turn. (10) A typical Penny Dreadful might contain a message such as this one: 'Tis all in vain your fluttering lids, your curly hair, your tinted cheeks, for finding you a Valentine will take at least a HUNDRED weeks!

▶ **Exercise 2**   **Using Commas Between Items in a Series.**   Add commas to each sentence that needs them. If a sentence does not need commas, write *correct*.

EXAMPLE: The speaker was intelligent talented and poised.

The speaker was intelligent, talented, and poised.

1. The student driver nervously pressed down the accelerator turned the key and put the car in gear. _____

2. The flash flood raced through the narrow canyon over the flatlands and into the town's main street. _____

3. Mrs. Robertson offered the children peanut butter and jelly bacon and avocado or cheese and bologna sandwiches. _____

4. The children bowled the parents kept score and the grandparents watched. _____

5. He ate breakfast she read the newspaper and then they both left for work. _____

6. The sheepdog pushed and coaxed and prodded his stubborn charges into their pens. _____

7. Skiing skating and dancing burn up many calories. _____

8. The physician said he wanted to take some X-rays check the results and call us later in the day. _____

9. Did you pack a bathing suit pajamas a sweatshirt and a toothbrush? _____

10. The ball flew over the pitcher's head above the center fielder's glove and into a spectator's waiting hands. _____

29.2 Commas That Set Off Added Elements
(Introductory Material, Parenthetical Expressions)
• Practice 1

Commas After Introductory Material   Use a comma after an introductory word, phrase, or clause.

INTRODUCTORY MATERIAL
Introductory Word: No, I don't think I can go.
Introductory Phrase: Reaching the lake, she searched for her canoe.
Introductory Clause: When she entered the building, she was confused and frightened.

Commas With Parenthetical Expressions   Use commas to set off parenthetical expressions.

PARENTHETICAL EXPRESSIONS
Names of People Being Addressed: I know, *Susan*, that you will do well.
Certain Adverbs: I decided, *therefore*, to wait.
Common Expressions: Mr. Wong agreed, *I believe*, to go.
Contrasting Expressions: The room is narrow, *not wide*.

▶ **Exercise 1**   **Recognizing Introductory Material.**   Write the introductory word, phrase, or clause in each sentence, and add the needed comma.

EXAMPLE: Yes I will attend.   _____Yes,_____

1. No I'm afraid his excuse was not acceptable. _____
2. To grow corn you need fertile soil. _____
3. Determined she stalked into the office. _____
4. If she sings I'm sure she will win. _____
5. Waiting patiently she saw the bear emerge. _____
6. When I try I can write very well. _____
7. Since you wrote the situation has changed entirely. _____
8. Cary why don't you use my typewriter? _____
9. To improve our game we practiced every night. _____
10. Really I'm not sure about this new plan of yours. _____

▶ **Exercise 2**   **Using Commas Correctly.**   Add commas where they are needed in each sentence.

EXAMPLE: His ability not his personality is the issue.
          His ability, not his personality, is the issue.

1. Her room unfortunately is right over the garage.
2. Mrs. Eriksen will you explain that answer again.
3. Our vacation is near the end of July not in August.
4. Although she is excellent at ballet she prefers modern dance.
5. His refusal I am certain can easily be explained.
6. Smiling happily she raced to the front door.
7. You know of course that the President will speak.
8. Yes I certainly would like to visit Walden Pond.
9. To stop the retreat the army landed paratroopers.
10. The decision consequently was reversed by the court.

29.2 Commas That Set Off Added Elements
(Introductory Material, Parenthetical Expressions)
• Practice 2

▶ **Exercise 1**   **Using Commas After Introductory Material.**   Underline the introductory word, phrase, or clause in each sentence, adding any necessary commas.

EXAMPLE: Boys and girls welcome to the Winchester House.
                Boys and girls, welcome to the Winchester House.

(1) After you hear about Sarah Winchester you will probably agree that she was an eccentric woman. (2) Following a short and romantic courtship Sarah Pardee married William Winchester of Winchester rifles. (3) Upon her husband's death Sarah inherited twenty million dollars from his estate. (4) Fearing the ghosts of people killed by Winchester guns she felt she must build continuously to keep them from haunting her. (5) With a great deal of determination she bought an eighteen-room house and hired sixteen workmen to add rooms to it. (6) To keep the ghosts confused she had doors open into brick walls and stairs lead up into the ceiling. (7) Oh the workmen must have thought her strange, but good wages kept them building for thirty-eight years. (8) Testing their loyalty to her Mrs. Winchester occasionally had the gardeners plant her orange trees upside down. (9) When she died it took six moving vans and six weeks to empty the house. (10) Within her 160-room mansion carpenters had installed 2,000 doors and 10,000 windows.

▶ **Exercise 2**   **Using Commas With Parenthetical Expressions.**   Add the necessary commas to set off the parenthetical expressions in each sentence.

EXAMPLE: It is warm enough I think to plant the tomatoes.
                It is warm enough, I think, to plant the tomatoes.

1. The new plants however did not survive the frost.
2. I will vacuum Hazel if you will wash the windows.
3. He went to Harvard Law School I believe.
4. The young rascal furthermore put salt in my sugar bowl.
5. Spread lime in the garden not near the evergreens.
6. Typing your paper you know will make it easier to read.
7. The plane therefore did not arrive on time.
8. Tennis not golf is my favorite sport.
9. May I help you carry that package Mr. Goodman?
10. If it rains the picnic will be postponed until next week I suppose.
11. Did you know Cynthia that tomorrow is Dan's birthday?
12. Aunt Marie similarly enjoys wearing large hats.
13. The twins in any case will be here by noon.
14. Dr. Sanchez not Dr. Monroe is my dentist.
15. Did you have an appointment Ms. Martinez?
16. The backyard on the other hand is well tended.
17. The newspapers and paperbacks however should be recycled.
18. She is friendly enough in my opinion to be a good social coordinator.
19. Dina likes apple not pecan pie.
20. The leaves of course should be raked.

Name _____ Date _____

 29.2 # Commas That Set Off Added Elements
(Nonessential Expressions) • Practice 1

Commas With Nonessential Expressions   A nonessential expression, short or long, gives additional information about someone or something in a sentence. Because it can be left out without changing the basic meaning of the sentence, it is set off with commas.

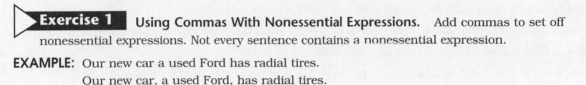

ESSENTIAL AND NONESSENTIAL EXPRESSIONS
Essential: My cousin *the computer expert* is growing rich.
Nonessential: Cathy, *a computer expert*, knows BASIC and COBOL.
Essential: The man *standing in the corridor* is the principal.
Nonessential: Dr. Rogers, *now standing in the corridor*, is the principal.
Essential: The boy *who lives in the next house* plays the French horn.
Nonessential: My cousin Phil, *who lives in the next house*, plays the French horn.

▶ **Exercise 1**   **Using Commas With Nonessential Expressions.**   Add commas to set off nonessential expressions. Not every sentence contains a nonessential expression.

EXAMPLE: Our new car a used Ford has radial tires.
       Our new car, a used Ford, has radial tires.

1. Jackie Robinson a fine hitter was a daring base runner.

2. The girl who leads the chorus speaks three languages.

3. Mendelssohn who was born in 1809 gave his first performance at the age of nine.

4. Alex who works after school makes the Honor Roll each year.

5. The flowers growing in the window box were purchased in a nursery.

6. Ottawa the capital of Canada is a beautiful, clean city.

7. The tape recorder that he wants is very expensive.

8. The story "The Scarlet Ibis" is about the relationship of two brothers.

9. This is Sagamore Hill the home of Theodore Roosevelt.

10. Nashville which is near the center of Tennessee is the home of country music.

▶ **Exercise 2**   **Writing Essential and Nonessential Expressions.**   Complete each sentence. Set off the nonessential expressions with commas.

EXAMPLE: Her shoes _____, *a pair of sandals*, _____ were surprisingly uncomfortable.

1. The woman _____ will tell you where his office is.

2. We visited San Francisco and Los Angeles _____.

3. March _____ was rapidly approaching

4. Stop by and see Mrs. Harding _____.

5. The program _____ was very boring.

6. The car _____ is my brother's.

7. His grandfather _____ tutors students in math.

8. Snacks _____ will be served at intermission.

9. We saw slides of my two favorite cities _____.

10. The dog _____ was barking loudly.

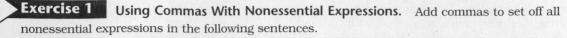

29.2 Commas That Set Off Added Elements
(Nonessential Expressions) • Practice 2

▶ **Exercise 1** **Using Commas With Nonessential Expressions.** Add commas to set off all nonessential expressions in the following sentences.

EXAMPLE: Esmeralda our curious and friendly dog likes to explore the neighborhood.
Esmeralda, our curious and friendly dog, likes to explore the neighborhood.

1. My orthodontist who just came back from a trip to Hawaii tightened my braces.

2. The woman who was hired as a company consultant made some fine suggestions to the management.

3. The President's wife is the one boarding the plane right now.

4. Calligraphy the art of beautiful writing takes practice and skill in order for one to become proficient at it.

5. The suit worn by the model on the left probably costs a fortune.

6. The museum held the saddle of John Wayne one of the most famous Hollywood cowboys.

7. Have you ever visited the Alamo a fascinating building in Texas?

8. Yosemite Falls which drops 2,425 feet to the river below almost dries up after a hot summer.

9. Joanne Lewis who happens to be my cousin writes news articles for local television.

10. Pélé a famous soccer player from Brazil played in the United States several years ago.

11. This strange locust which spends seventeen years developing in the earth lives only six weeks as an adult.

12. Dinosaurs the animals that dominated the earth for over 140 million years became extinct 65 million years ago.

13. The newborn guppy called a fry must swim to the surface and take a gulp of air before it can swim well.

14. Mark Twain the author of *The Adventures of Huckleberry Finn* used a riverboat term as his pen name.

15. Patricia's last vacation a bicycle trip across China did not cost as much as she had anticipated.

▶ **Exercise 2** **Writing Sentences With Nonessential Expressions.** Write a sentence for each nonessential expression. Be sure to set off the nonessential expression with a comma or commas.

EXAMPLE: the capital of our state

_____*Sacramento, the capital of our state, has a diverse population.*_____

1. Alex's best friend

_____

2. my neighbor's cat

_____

3. the first one to taste the soup

_____

4. Tim's favorite program

_____

5. who means a great deal to me

_____

29.2 Commas That Set Off Added Elements
(Places, Dates, Titles, Other Uses) • Practice 1

Commas With Places, Dates, and Titles When a geographical name or a date is made up of two or more parts, use a comma after each item except in the case of a month followed by a day. Use commas to set off a title following a name.

Geographical Name	Houston, Texas, is a rapidly growing city.
Date	On September 19, 1939, German panzers invaded Poland.
Name With Title	Jim Thon, M.D., discussed safe ways to lose weight.

Other Uses of the Comma Use commas in the situations shown in the chart below.

Address	Send the package to J. Brown, 10 Elk Lane, Glen Cove, New York 11542.
Salutation and Closing	Dear Peter, Very truly yours,
Numbers	31,654 envelopes
Elliptical Sentence	Lorraine plays the guitar; her brother Sam, the flute.
Direct Quotation	"In a few minutes," laughed Julio, "you'll know the surprise."
To Prevent Confusion	For Carla, Jonas had designed a unique costume.

▶ **Exercise 1** **Adding Commas to Sentences.** Insert commas where they are needed.

EXAMPLE: Sean Miles D.D.S. lectured on dental hygiene.

Sean Miles, D.D.S., lectured on dental hygiene.

1. Write to Real-Trucks 72 Wall Avenue Norwalk Connecticut 06850.

2. The math assignment took forty-five minutes; the science an hour.

3. The population of the next county is 42375.

4. The band director remarked "We'll have our next rehearsal on January 10."

5. John Briggs Jr. inherited his father's business.

6. After the storm clouds were white and fleecy.

7. On June 20 1793 Eli Whitney applied for a patent for his cotton gin.

8. In 1957 the United States had 1558691 hospital beds in 6818 hospitals.

9. "For the last time" exclaimed Sue "will you be quiet!"

10. In spring planting begins.

▶ **Exercise 2** **Punctuating a Letter.** Add commas wherever necessary in the following letter.

154 Morris Drive
Los Angeles California 90039
October 12 1985

Dear Pam

I am researching the Lindbergh kidnapping case. On March 1 1932 Lindbergh's eighteen-month-old son was taken from the Lindbergh home in Hopewell New Jersey. A ransom note demanding $50000 was found. Bruno Hautpmann was arrested for the crime on September 15 1934. Police found $14000 of the ransom money in his home. Found guilty, Hautpmann was executed on April 3 1936.

Your friend

Gina

29.2 Commas That Set Off Added Elements
(Places, Dates, Titles, Other Uses) • Practice 2

▶ **Exercise 1** **Using Commas With Places, Dates, and Titles.**   Add the necessary commas in the following sentences.

EXAMPLE: On June 9 1987 we moved to Houston Texas.
On June 9, 1987, we moved to Houston, Texas.

1. Microtec Inc. opened on the New York Stock Exchange at $14 per share.

2. The bus stopped in Texarkana on its way to Little Rock Arkansas.

3. The nurse signed her letter of resignation "Allison Evans R.N."

4. On July 4 1884 the Statue of Liberty was officially presented to the United States.

5. Is it true that your ancestors traveled from St. Louis Missouri to San Francisco California by wagon train?

6. Professor John H. Coleman Ph.D. accepted a position at another university.

7. Please cancel delivery of our newspaper from Tuesday August 8 to Sunday August 19.

8. Are Randall Knudtsen Sr. and Randall Knudtsen Jr. working for the same electronics company now?

9. The boy was an exchange student from Stuttgart Germany.

10. The boat will stop in Bridgetown Barbados on January 11.

▶ **Exercise 2** **Using Commas in Other Situations.**   Add the necessary commas in the following sentences.

EXAMPLE: Ann guessed that the jar contained 3864 jelly beans.
Ann guessed that the jar contained 3,864 jelly beans.

1. The last-known address of the Parker family was 1318 View Ridge Drive Missoula Montana.

2. Chicago is 2189 miles from Los Angeles.

3. The parents headed off to work; the children to school.

4. Regina was born on September 15 1972 in Honolulu Hawaii.

5. Outside the house looked as new as the day we bought it.

6. Someone once said "A grandparent is a child's best press agent."

7. The school's address is P.O. Box 900 Cupertino California 95014.

8. When reading the boy hears nothing around him.

9. "It is much easier to be critical than to be correct" Benjamin Disraeli once observed.

10. The first horse shown was an Arabian; the second a quarter horse; the third a thoroughbred.

29.3 # The Semicolon • Practice 1

Semicolons and Independent Clauses Use a semicolon to join independent clauses not already joined by a comma and a coordinating conjunction. A semicolon can also be used to join two independent clauses joined by a conjunctive adverb or a transitional expression.

Two Independent Clauses	Alan reached the mouth of the cave first; he peered inside and decided to wait for his friends.
Independent Clauses With a Conjunctive Adverb	Karen wants a new car; however, she will wait until she has saved $2,000 for a down payment.
Independent Clauses With a Transitional Expression	My sister is an outstanding student; as a result, she won a four-year college scholarship.

Semicolons Used to Avoid Confusion Use a semicolon to avoid confusion when independent clauses or items in a series already contain commas.

EXAMPLE:
My aunt traveled to Lisbon, Madrid, and Seville; and, next year, she hopes to visit England and France.

▶ **Exercise 1** **Using Semicolons Correctly.** In each sentence a comma is used instead of a semicolon. Circle the comma to show that a semicolon is needed.

EXAMPLE: Ben arrived later (,) consequently, he missed the meeting.

1. My sister likes to save money, in fact, she already has saved a thousand dollars.
2. We bought peaches, plums, and nectarines, but the peaches were not ripe.
3. The dog, whose tail wagged continuously, barked, but its owner, a nice man, reassured us.
4. Billy, wait for little Joey, he can't walk that fast.
5. Selling ice cream, Beth earned almost $100, that was the most for any one day.
6. We sang, danced, and went for a moonlit swim, and a good time was had by all.
7. It's time to mow the lawn, also, the garden needs to be weeded.
8. You can't start writing now, first, you must do some research.
9. Paris, Florence, and Venice are all beautiful cities, but my favorite is Florence.
10. I had been there before, as a result, I didn't pay attention to the directions.

▶ **Exercise 2** **Writing Compound Sentences With Semicolons.** Complete the sentences below.

EXAMPLE: _____ *I love exotic food* _____ ; however, _____ *that meal was too much for me.* _____

1. _____ ;
   however, _____
2. _____ ;
   for instance, _____
3. _____ ;
   otherwise, _____
4. _____ ; _____
5. _____ ;
   on the other hand, _____

29.3 The Semicolon • Practice 2

Exercise 1 **Using Semicolons to Join Independent Clauses.** For each sentence write the word that goes before the semicolon, the semicolon, and the word that goes after it.

EXAMPLE: A raccoon has claws its name means "scratcher." _____*claws; its*_____

(1) Raccoons sometimes live in hollow trees they have also been found living in burrows made by other animals. (2) These creatures seem to be quite intelligent they can learn how to open small packages and to turn on appliances. (3) When raccoons are young, their mother provides food when they are older, they must find their own. (4) Some raccoons love fish others prefer bird and turtle eggs. (5) Raccoons can distinguish between different sounds one raccoon appears to like listening to Beethoven. (6) Raccoon litters may include only two babies they sometimes include as many as seven. (7) Some people think baby raccoons make good pets usually, however, they do not. (8) Raccoons are sometimes pests to farmers they get into the garbage cans and the poultry house. (9) Raccoons also raid garbage cans in suburban neighborhoods they sometimes make nuisances of themselves at camp sites and garbage dumps. (10) Raccoon hats were popular during frontier days raccoon coats were popular during the 1920's.

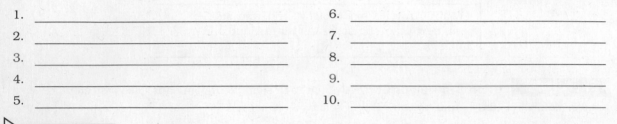

1. _____   6. _____
2. _____   7. _____
3. _____   8. _____
4. _____   9. _____
5. _____   10. _____

Exercise 2 **Using Semicolons and Commas to Join Clauses.** Some of the following sentences are missing semicolons; some are also missing commas. Make the necessary corrections.

EXAMPLE: Stocks were soaring to an all-time high in 1929 consequently people were buying more stocks.
        Stocks were soaring to an all-time high in 1929; consequently, people were buying more stocks.

(1) Stockholders hoped to get rich when their stocks rose in price therefore many borrowed money to buy stocks. (2) On Black Thursday in October 1929, stocks tumbled to forty percent of their original value as a result many people lost almost everything they owned. (3) Pandemonium broke out on the stock exchange floor fist fights for instance were common. (4) Frantic orders to sell came into the exchange many orders to sell however could not be completed because there were no buyers. (5) Some stockholders were forced to sell their homes, businesses, and other possessions to pay back money they had borrowed others could not pay their debts at all. (6) There were several short rallies in stock prices nevertheless prices generally spiraled down. (7) Some tragedies were caused by the stock market crash in fact the president of Union Cigar jumped to his death when his stock dropped over $100 in one day. (8) The President assured the public that business was good many business leaders continued to buy stocks. (9) Some of the richest people did manage to survive the stock market crash most people however had barely enough left to survive. (10) The collapse of the stock market almost destroyed the business world it is a tragic lesson to people today.

29.3 # The Colon • Practice 1

The Colon as an Introductory Device   Use a colon before a list of items following an independent clause, to introduce a quotation that is formal or lengthy or not preceded by a verb that shows speech, to introduce a sentence that summarizes or explains the sentence before it, and to introduce a formal appositive.

List	Grandfather always grew a variety of vegetables: tomatoes, beans, cucumbers, carrots, and squash.
Quotation	The judge nodded slowly: "Case dismissed."
Explanatory Sentence	In conclusion, the speaker emphasized her main point: Leash laws protect dogs as well as people.
Formal Appositive	She showed slides of the most isolated spot on Earth: Antarctica.

Special Uses of the Colon   Use a colon in a number of special writing situations.

Numerals Giving Time	9:10 A.M.	10:15 P.M.
References to Periodicals	*Cornell Law Review* XIV: 76 (volume: page)	
Biblical References	Ecclesiastes 1:5 (chapter: verse)	
Subtitles for Books and Magazines	"Emotion: Learning to Control Feelings"	
Salutations in Business Letters	Dear Ms. Green:	Gentlemen:
Labels Used to Signal Important Ideas	Warning: This product is for external use only.	

▶ **Exercise 1**   **Using the Colon as an Introductory Device.**   Add colons where they are needed.

EXAMPLE: I examined the parts of the book preface, text, and index.
    I examined the parts of the book: preface, text, and index.

1. The salad contains three ingredients lettuce, tomatoes, and mushrooms.

2. She glanced at herself in the mirror "I could certainly use a haircut."

3. We're pleased to have with us tonight Elmwood's most widely traveled citizen Bess Simca.

4. On our trip we took three forms of transportation train, bus, and airplane.

5. There is only one lesson to be learned from this experience Think before you speak.

6. The day brought all sorts of weather sun, showers, haze.

7. The master of ceremonies announced "Please rise for the national anthem."

8. It's been a pleasure to work with a thoroughly professional actress Meryl Streep.

9. She listed her three favorite sports baseball, football, and hockey.

10. I read four magazines every month *National News, Stereo Listening, Popular Collectibles,* and *World Review.*

▶ **Exercise 2**   **Using Colons in Special Writing Situations.**   Add colons where they are needed.

EXAMPLE: My favorite childhood book was *Lad A Dog.*
    My favorite childhood book was *Lad: A Dog.*

1. The text of the sermon was Psalms 23 1.

2. Did she take the 6 05 or the 6 37 from Penn Station?

3. The book was called *Gourmet Cooking Recipes for the Beginner.*

4. The quotation comes from *The Ohio State Quarterly* X 132.

5. Note The cover of this bottle is not childproof.

Name _____ Date _____

29.3 The Colon • Practice 2

Exercise 1 **Using Colons as Introductory Devices.** Read each sentence and decide where colons are required. Write the word that goes before the colon, the colon, and the word that goes after it, adding any necessary capitals. One of the sentences is already correct. For this sentence, write *correct*.

EXAMPLE: The huge metal eagle on the roof of the high school sparked my interest in a new hobby collecting weather vanes.

_____ *hobby: collecting* _____

(1) Weather vanes were first used two thousand years ago in a mighty, noble city Athens. (2) Years later, the Pope sent out an important order a statue, or weather vane, of a rooster was to be placed on top of every Christian church. (3) The rooster-shaped weather vanes had a significant purpose it was to remind church members to attend church regularly. (4) The symbol of the rooster was chosen because of Christ's prediction "I tell you, Peter, the cock will not crow this day, until you three times deny that you know me." (5) As weather vanes began to be made in other shapes, those made in the shape of a banner were given a special name bannerets. (6) Only one group was entitled to use bannerets in medieval times this was the nobility. (7) In later centuries, countries in which weather vanes could be found included England, France, and the United States. (8) In the United States, many different shapes of weather vanes could be seen barnyard animals, carriages, fire engines, ships, and lions, among others. (9) In the nineteenth century, weather vanes often took the shape of the following patriotic symbols flags, liberty bells, and eagles. (10) These weather vanes could be seen on the tops of a variety of buildings barns, houses, churches, schools, and government offices.

1. _____   6. _____
2. _____   7. _____
3. _____   8. _____
4. _____   9. _____
5. _____   10. _____

Exercise 2 **Using Colons in Special Writing Situations.** Add the necessary colons in each of the following items.

EXAMPLE: Warning The contents of this bottle are poisonous.
　　　　　Warning: The contents of this bottle are poisonous.

1. One of my favorite stories in the Bible is Mark 4 3.

2. Dear Mr. Harrison

3. The schedule indicated that the train from Chicago should arrive at 5 38 P.M.

4. Note The following information has not yet been verified by the main office.

5. Our coach suggested that we read *Playing Team Soccer A Study in Offense and Defense Skills.*

6. My teacher suggested I check in *Business News* 61 12 for further information for my report.

7. Dear Mrs. Phillips

8. I took out a reference book called *Rules for Writing A Guide to Better Compositions.*

9. The minister asked the congregation to turn to Exodus 6 2.

10. Are we supposed to leave at 6 15 A.M. or 6 45 A.M.?

29.4 Quotation Marks With Direct Quotations
(Introductory, Concluding, Interrupting Expressions)
• Practice 1

Direct Quotations   Use quotation marks before and after an uninterrupted direct quotation.

One Sentence	"The sea lies all around us."—Rachel Carson
Two Sentences	"Nonviolence is the first article of my faith. It is also the last article of my creed."—Mohandas Gandhi
Phrase	In the words of Theodore Roosevelt, we must have our "eyes on the stars" and our "feet on the ground."

Introductory, Concluding, and Interrupting Expressions   Expressions such as *she said* or *they replied* are often used to identify the speaker in a direct quotation. These expressions can occur at the beginning, at the end, or in the middle of the quote.

Rules for Punctuation	Examples
Use a comma after an introductory expression.	My father confided, "I expect to get a promotion today."
Use a comma, question mark, or exclamation mark after a quote followed by a concluding expression.	"I am very pleased," said Mother. "When will you leave?" I asked. "That's absurd!" she exclaimed.
Use a comma before and after an interrupting expression.	"I know," she smiled, "what you really want for your birthday."

▶ **Exercise 1**   **Punctuating Direct Quotations.**   Place quotation marks, commas, and other punctuation marks where they are required.

EXAMPLE: I agree said the teacher that the grade is low.
　　　　　"I agree," said the teacher, "that the grade is low."

1. This is the first time I've heard of that process he said.

2. In spite of everything I still believe that people are really good at heart—Anne Frank

3. This report Mr Gray said does not contain footnotes.

4. Mother asked me Don't you hear the telephone

5. What wonderful news Ted exclaimed.

6. Which bus asked the visitor should I take

7. What can that letter mean asked Alice

8. Coach Willis said We need this game to make the finals

9. I like basketball she said much more than baseball

10. Anne Morrow Lindbergh called mothers and housewives the great vacationless class.

▶ **Exercise 2**   **Writing Direct Quotations.**   Complete the sentences below.

EXAMPLE: "____*It was in the year 1960*____," she answered.

1. "_____?" he asked.

2. Father explained, "_____."

3. "_____," I said. "_____."

4. "_____!" Pam exclaimed.

5. "_____," she agreed, "_____."

29.4 Quotation Marks With Direct Quotations
(Introductory, Concluding, Interrupting Expressions)
• Practice 2

▶ **Exercise 1** **Recognizing Direct Quotations.**   Decide whether the underlined material in each of the following items is a direct or indirect quotation. Add the necessary quotation marks and capitals to each direct quotation.

EXAMPLE: He often thought, someday I will know enough to become a poet.
        He often thought, "Someday I will know enough to become a poet."

1. Christine said that she would like to play badminton tomorrow afternoon.

2. Each fact that a person learns is, in the words of E.L. Youman, a key to other facts.

3. Eleanor Roosevelt once said, no one can make you feel inferior without your consent.

4. Carlyle once defined endurance in two precise words: patience concentrated.

5. After listening to a weather forecast, our coach announced that there would be no practice today.

6. You must know which song contains the words in the dawn's early light.

7. During the first lap, Andrea decided, I must win today since my parents are watching.

8. Later in the race, she decided that they would have to be satisfied with second place this time.

9. A book with an unhappy ending were the words he used to describe his checkbook.

10. Emerson once wrote, the creation of a thousand forests is in one acorn.

▶ **Exercise 2**   **Writing Direct Quotations With Introductory, Concluding and Interrupting Expressions.**   Rewrite the following quotations, correctly punctuating and capitalizing them.

EXAMPLE: my mother cautioned you better be home on time this evening
        My mother cautioned, "You better be home on time this evening."

1. persuasively, the sales clerk added this particular radio won't be on sale much longer
   _____

2. the park will be closed the ranger said so that we can repair the picnic area
   _____

3. that jacket looks nice on you my father said as he walked in the door
   _____

4. with growing irritation, the taxi driver asked have you decided where we are going yet
   _____

5. Henry Ward Beecher once made this important distinction between work and worry it is not work that kills me; it is worry
   _____

6. he who has imagination without learning warns Joubert has wings but no feet
   _____

7. when you get to the rodeo my cousin warned watch out for wild horses and bulls
   _____

8. don't forget june 15 his wife reminded him that's our anniversary
   _____

9. you've got to keep your eye on the ball every second instructed my coach
   _____

10. when the dance is over my date informed me we are going to go out for some pizza
   _____

29.4 Quotation Marks With Direct Quotations
(With Other Punctuation Marks, Special Situations)
• Practice 1

Quotation Marks With Other Punctuation Marks   Place commas and periods inside the quotation marks. Place semicolons and colons outside. Use the meaning of the whole sentence to determine the placement of question marks and exclamation marks.

PLACING OTHER PUNCTUATION MARKS	
Commas and Periods	"I think," she said, "this will be enough.
Colons and Semicolons	Bob remarked, "We need help"; he was right.
Question Marks and Exclamation Marks	Dolores asked, "Where is the key?" Did Dolores say, "I lost the key"?

Quotation Marks in Special Situations   For dialogue, use a new paragraph for each new speaker. For long quotations, use quotation marks at the beginning of each paragraph and at the end of the final paragraph. For a quotation within a quotation, use single quotation marks.

SPECIAL SITUATIONS	
Dialogue	"Do it now," my friend said. "I'm much too busy," I replied.
Quotation Within a Quotation	The policeman testified, "When we asked her, she said, 'I've never been there before.'"

▷ **Exercise 1**   **Punctuating Direct Quotations.**   In each sentence one or two punctuation marks are missing. Add them correctly to the sentences.

EXAMPLE: Dr. Wang said "You are in perfect health"

Dr. Wang said, "You are in perfect health."

1. "I will meet your train at the station" she replied.
2. "His explanation" I thought "is difficult to accept."
3. Marion stormed "What an outrage!"
4. Bill reported, "Ted said, See you soon, as he departed."
5. "I agree" Jean said "to follow your suggestions."
6. "Let's pay all our bills now" Father said.
7. The teacher smiled and said "I think you need an up-to-date atlas"
8. Judy nodded, "I heard Sid say, Good luck, to the gymnast."
9. How amazing it was when she said, "It's OK"
10. "My efforts" said the captain "were in vain."

▷ **Exercise 2**   **Paragraphing Dialogue.**   Circle the first word in each sentence that requires indentation for a new paragraph.

"I really would like to go shopping with you, Mother," said Joan, "but I want to finish my report." "How much more do you have?" asked Mother. "I have another five pages to write and revise," said Joan, "and I also have to put together a table of contents and an index." Mother asked, "Can't you do that tomorrow? After all, it's only Saturday." "All right," said Joan, "you win."

29.4 Quotation Marks With Direct Quotations
(With Other Punctuation Marks, Special Situations)
• Practice 2

▷ **Exercise 1** **Using Punctuation With Direct Quotations.** One or two punctuation marks are missing in each of the following sentences. Add the punctuation marks to the sentences.

EXAMPLE: "Please hand in your papers" Miss Smithson said.

"Please hand in your papers," Miss Smithson said.

1. The boys shouted, "We won the championship"

2. "When the film comes back" Jim announced, "we will set up a slide show"

3. The teacher said, "You will need to study hard for this test" he also said we should get plenty of rest the night before the test.

4. The salesperson in the shoe department asked, "Do those boots pinch your toes"

5. Carlos shouted frantically, "The man in the gray parka stole my wallet"

6. The clerk asked, "Are you certain you want just a one-way ticket"

7. My mother felt my forehead and said, "You get into bed right this minute"

8. She constantly reminded us of "the keys to success" hard work, a goal, and a little luck.

9. Did the coach say, "Be at the field at eight in the morning or at eight in the evening"

10. The garage attendant said, "Your exhaust pipe has a hole in it" however, he didn't offer to fix it.

▷ **Exercise 2** **More Work With Punctuation.** Follow the instructions given in Exercise 1.

1. I got the lead in this year's one-act play: "Roses and Wine"

2. My friend asked, "Why don't you go jogging with me in the morning before school"

3. "The plane will take off" the flight attendant stated, "as soon as the fog clears a bit more"

4. The new father proudly announced, "We have a beautiful baby girl"

5. Are you certain the doctor specifically said, "Take two pills fifteen minutes before eating"

6. She gave us her list of "absolute travel necessities" makeup, hair dryer, and bathing suit.

7. Did Emerson say, "If a man owns land, the land owns him"

8. Angela confessed, "I should read the newspaper more"

9. "We must try harder" he said, "if we truly want to win this debate"

10. I heard him ask, "Can you tell me where a drinking fountain is"

29.4 Underlining and Other Uses of Quotation Marks • Practice 1

Underlining   Underline the titles of books, plays, long poems, magazines, newspapers, movies, radio and TV series, long musical compositions, albums, and art

WORKS THAT ARE UNDERLINED	
Book: The Wizard of Oz	*Movie:* The Yellow Submarine
Magazine: City Life	*Paper:* The New York Herald Tribune
Musical Composition: Vivaldi's The Four Seasons	

Quotation Marks   Use quotation marks around the titles of short written works and songs.

WORKS WITH QUOTATION MARKS
Short Story: "The Ransom of Red Chief"
Poem: "When I Was Young and Twenty"
Chapter of Book: "Recalled to Life" from A Tale of Two Cities

Titles Without Underlining or Quotation Marks   Do not underline or place in quotation marks mentions of the Bible or other holy scriptures or the titles of government charters, alliances, treaties, acts, statutes, or reports.

EXAMPLES: the Bible, the Koran (religious works) the Constitution, the Magna Carta (government documents)

▶ **Exercise 1**   **Punctuating Different Types of Works.**   Use underlining or quotation marks with the works in each sentence. A few items require no punctuation.

EXAMPLE: I read Robert Frost's A Young Birch to the class.

> *I read Robert Frost's "A Young Birch" to the class.*

1. The Saturday Evening Post was an excellent magazine.
2. Do you still study the Bible regularly?
3. I have just read Anne Tyler's book If Morning Ever Comes.
4. Everyone should read Steinbeck's The Grapes of Wrath.
5. I think Malamud's best short story is The Magic Barrel.
6. I borrowed Anne Roger's album Keep It Real.
7. The Bridge Over the River Kwai won many Academy Awards.
8. Did you buy Pat Stanton's new album Awareness?
9. James Baldwin has a beautiful short story called The Rock Pile.
10. The Constitution of the United States is must reading.

▶ **Exercise 2**   **Choosing the Correct Form.**   Circle the correct form below.

EXAMPLE: DeMaupassant's short story "The Necklace" or The Necklace

1. The Christian Review or "The Christian Review"
2. O. Henry's short story "The Last Leaf" or The Last Leaf
3. George Orwell's essay "Why I Write" or Why I Write
4. Shakespeare's play "Romeo and Juliet" or Romeo and Juliet
5. The Old Testament or the Old Testament

29.4 Underlining and Other Uses of Quotation Marks • Practice 2

▶ Exercise 1 **Underlining Titles, Names, and Words.** Underline each title, name, and word that requires underlining in each of the following sentences. If there are no such items in a sentence, write *correct*.

EXAMPLE: <u>Ben Hur</u>, starring Charlton Heston, is my all-time favorite movie.

1. The book David Copperfield by Charles Dickens is considered a classic.
2. The Concert by Jan Vermeer is one of only thirty-six existing paintings by this Dutch artist.
3. Gemini 5 played an important role in the U.S. space program.
4. I always have trouble spelling the word occasion.
5. The works of Picasso make a valuable addition to any individual's art collection.
6. The first two sections of Lord Byron's Childe Harold, published in 1812, shocked English society and established the young poet's reputation.
7. When I walked into the room, I had a strong sense of déjávu.
8. I like to read the newspaper The New York Mirror and watch the TV series Direct Line on Sunday mornings.
9. Our high school is putting on the operetta The Mikado by Gilbert and Sullivan.
10. The Empire State Building is no longer the tallest building in the world.

▶ Exercise 2 **Using Quotation Marks With Titles.** Either enclose in quotation marks or underline the titles from the following sentences.

EXAMPLE: We listened to Solveig's Song from Grieg's Peer Gynt Suite.

   "Solveig's Song"   <u>Peer Gynt Suite</u>

1. We were studying the chapter called The Character Sketch.
2. Trifles by Susan Glaspell can be found in a collection called Plays.
3. We listened to the Surprise Symphony from The Complete Symphonies of Haydn.
4. Almost everybody in California knows the song California Here I Come.
5. I read an article in Science World entitled Frog Talk: Chirp, Chuckle, and Thump.
6. Edgar Allan Poe wrote a good horror story when he wrote The Masque of the Red Death.
7. Emily Dickinson wrote an interesting poem on death called I Heard a Fly Buzz—When I Died.
8. Public Broadcasting Television showed The Prince and the Pauper on Once Upon a Classic.
9. Once More to the Lake by E. B. White is an essay that looks back to the childhood of the writer.
10. Eleanor Clark's short story Hurry, Hurry begins and ends with the activities of a poodle named de Maupassant.

29.5 # Dashes • Practice 1

Uses of the Dash   Use dashes to indicate an abrupt change of thought, a dramatic interrupting idea, or a summary statement. Dashes are also used to set off certain nonessential modifiers.

FOUR USES OF THE DASH	
To show an abrupt change of thought	I found this information in an old reference book—you know, I found it only by accident.
To set off interrupting ideas dramatically	The musical star—I've never seen a better dancer—gave an interview to student editors.
To set off a summary statement	Good grades, school service, some sports activities, and decent SATs—all of them help in getting into a good college.
To set off certain nonessential appositives and modifiers	Some acronyms—NATO, UNESCO, CARE—are now recognized by most readers. The report—which included a table of contents, footnotes, bibliography, and index—took days to type.

▶ **Exercise 1**   **Using the Dash.**   Add one or two dashes to each sentence.

EXAMPLE: I had three good reasons oh, forget it.

    I had three good reasons—oh, forget it.

1. Basketball, baseball, hockey, football, and tennis all these sports are popular at our school.

2. I went to the library it was a rainy, dismal day and did all the research for my report.

3. Four of Steinbeck's novels *The Pearl, Cannery Row, Tortilla Flat,* and *The Grapes of Wrath* portray the lives of poor, humble people.

4. The house was built you may find this somewhat amazing in fewer than six weeks.

5. I spent most of the period trying to do my homework in class oh, here comes our teacher now.

▶ **Exercise 2**   **More Work With Dashes.**   Follow the instructions for Exercise 1.

1. A clean windshield, good tires, good brakes, and the use of seat belts all of these contribute to safe driving.

2. Some parents unfortunately, my father and mother are included are opposed to long trips by teenagers on their own.

3. Many American presidents I'm thinking of Harry Truman, Richard Nixon, Gerald Ford, and John Kennedy have served in Congress.

4. Shall we open some of the presents now I really can't wait for everyone to arrive.

5. The concert, which was held in of all places the Municipal Stadium, attracted a huge crowd.

29.5 Dashes • Practice 2

Exercise 1   **Using the Dash.**   Add the necessary dashes to the following sentences.

EXAMPLE: Shall we pack a lunch it's such a beautiful day and go on a picnic?

    Shall we pack a lunch—it's such a beautiful day—and go on a picnic?

1. Food, housing, and clothing all of these are getting more expensive.
2. Tobogganing sounds like something oh, here comes Mario.
3. We will play tennis or at least attempt to play tennis at school today.
4. The man underwent an emergency appendectomy the surgical removal of an appendix and is now recovering.
5. Our guest speaker who had a flat tire as he was coming here was a little late.
6. I'd like to introduce you to what did you say your name was?
7. That the plane burned huge amounts of fuel this was the concern voiced by the conservationists.
8. The Crusades there were four major ones, weren't there? were not an overwhelming success.
9. Some of the instruments the drums, guitars, and piano still need to be loaded onto the truck.
10. The parents say that their talented they use this term loosely daughter will perform in a piano recital.
11. Pencils, paper, book covers, and pens these will all be required in this course.
12. That old table which is on its last legs, to say the least was the first item sold at the flea market.
13. Feeding, exercising, and providing the necessary medical care all of these constitute important aspects of pet ownership.
14. I got Danielle a bracelet for her why, Dani, what a surprise to see you!
15. Our club raised fifty dollars more or less for the U.S. Olympic team.
16. Some horror writers for instance, Stephen King have wonderful imaginations.
17. It bothers me when you continually oh, never mind.
18. Eating, watching fireworks, and being with friends there is no better way to celebrate the Fourth of July.
19. They sent me four identical forms why, I'll never understand for the insurance claim I'm submitting.
20. Some bad habits biting your nails, grinding your teeth, and drumming your fingers seem almost impossible to break.

Exercise 2   **Using the Dash in Paragraphs.**   Add necessary dashes to the following paragraph.

EXAMPLE: The mayor's greatest achievement finding shelter for the homeless was not easy to accomplish.

    The mayor's greatest achievement—finding shelter for the homeless—was not easy to accomplish.

Fishing Don's favorite sport is something that he can do any time of the year. His favorite time if he had to choose one is in the winter. During this time I'm sure you already know this many lakes in the eastern and midwestern United States are frozen solid. Don likes to chop a hole in the ice and fish through it a fishing method that was developed long ago by the Native Americans. Ice fishermen like Don build small sheds and put them on sled runners can you just imagine doing this? The shed is pulled out onto the lake and a hole is chopped in the ice with an axe or a heavy iron rod this rod is called a *spud*. The ice is then chipped away what a tedious task! to make an opening about twelve inches square. The shed is then pulled over the hole and the fisherman sits in a comfortable chair if you can believe this to do the fishing. Because it is dark inside the shed, the fisherman can see the fish swimming in the water below it hardly seems fair to the poor little fish. Just give Don a fishing shed, a frozen lake, and fishing gear that's all he needs to be happy.

Parentheses • Practice 1

Uses of Parentheses Parentheses are used to enclose phrases and sentences that offer nonessential explanations. They also enclose letters, numbers, and dates.

Phrases	For a while I slept in the basement (near the door).
Sentences	This is a new school policy. (The old one just seemed to fade away.)
Letters, Numbers, and Dates	Our teacher suggested three types of book reports: (a) oral, (b) written, and (c) a combination of both. Tom Paine wrote *Common Sense* (1776).

Capitalization and Punctuation with Parentheses Follow the examples in the chart below to punctuate and capitalize material in parentheses.

Declarative Sentence in Parentheses	The lead guitar player (it was a woman) was terrific.
Interrogative or Exclamatory Sentence in Parentheses	The party last night (Why did I go?) was horrible.
Parenthetical Sentence Between Two Sentences	He relaxed. (In fact, he almost fell asleep.) Then he perked up.
Punctuation in Main Sentence	When you arrive (I hope it's early), you can help with preparations.

▶ **Exercise 1** **Using Parentheses.** Add parentheses wherever they are appropriate.

EXAMPLE: Three ingredients are needed: 1 bananas, 2 cream, and 3 sugar.

_____*Three ingredients are needed: (1) bananas, (2) cream, and (3) sugar.*_____

1. Joseph C. Brown opened and mapped the Santa Fe Trail 1825–27.

2. We have had this policy for some time. In fact, I can no longer remember the old one.

3. The tree the one across the road was struck by an auto.

4. That dog Can you believe he's ten years old? is always ready for action.

5. We can improve extracurricular activities by a developing new clubs, b getting more advisers, c adding a ninth period to the day, and d getting more student support.

▶ **Exercise 2** **More Work With Parentheses.** Rewrite each item, adding parentheses and capitalization where necessary.

EXAMPLE: She laughed it was a hearty chuckle at her mother's remark.

_____*She laughed (it was a hearty chuckle) at her mother's remark.*_____

1. The most important point we hope you agree is to do this as cheaply as possible.

   _____

2. If I understand you correctly I think I do, the work was satisfying.

   _____

3. Paul did a report on Mozart 1756–1791, who began composing at the age of five.

   _____

4. The high point of the concert what a concert it was! came just before intermission.

   _____

5. Jane Lawson called you do you know her?; however, your line was busy.

   _____

29.5 Parentheses • Practice 2

Exercise 1 **Using Parentheses.** Add the necessary parentheses to the following sentences.

EXAMPLE: We sang the songs of Woody Guthrie 1912–1967.

We sang the songs of Woody Guthrie (1912–1967).

1. The lamp sale held only twice a year at Bueners usually offers some outstanding bargains.
2. The first place winner was Ronald Carmassi Italy with a world-record-breaking time.
3. We will study character development Chapter 6 in the text as it relates to this novel.
4. My grandmother 1900–1980 saw many changes occur during her lifetime.
5. Don't forget the four cans 16-ounce size of canned tomatoes.
6. The kit calls for the following tools: 1 screwdriver, 2 hammer, and 3 wrench.
7. The ice cream machine more often than not, broken took my quarter and dime but didn't give me any ice cream again today.
8. The angler a fisher who uses a hook and line pulled in a 25-pound northern pike to win the competition.
9. We listened to the last song "The Night They Drove Old Dixie Down" and then left.
10. The Dachshund Races a favorite event on Picnic Day were fun to watch.
11. The bill said she owed sixty-four dollars and ten cents $64.10.
12. Steve stifled a yawn having been up thirty-six hours straight and tried to look interested.
13. I must get some items at the store: a cleansing powder, b paper towels, and c window cleaner.
14. My paper route brings in a steady income though getting up so early is a strain.
15. She made a lot of mistakes seventeen, to be exact during rehearsal today.

Exercise 2 **Capitalizing and Punctuating With Parentheses.** In the following sentences, add any necessary punctuation and underline any word that should be capitalized.

EXAMPLE: The flight we are taking (how I love to fly) leaves at noon.

The flight we are taking (How I love to fly!) leaves at noon.

1. I have an appointment today (right after the game)
2. Will you meet me at 716 Elm Street (the building right across from the library)
3. The dress (it was the most beautiful shade of blue) fit perfectly.
4. When we go to Seacliff Beach (a resort just south of Santa Cruz) we will have a picnic on the beach or possibly a clambake.
5. Something in the refrigerator smelled (some meat had gone bad) so I cleaned it out.
6. I watched the ants. (there was an ant hole within three feet of me) They were busy gathering crumbs from the sandwich I was trying to eat for lunch.
7. She has honey-blonde hair (do you think it is natural) and blue eyes.
8. Using the flowers (dahlias, I think) I created a lovely centerpiece.
9. The road appears to be lined with oaks. (do you think that is the right type of tree)
10. I slowly savored the pistachio ice cream (my favorite flavor) until it was gone.

29.5 # Hyphens • Practice 1

When to Use the Hyphen   A hyphen is used to form numbers from twenty-one to ninety-nine and with fractions that are used as modifiers. Hyphens are also used with certain prefixes and suffixes, with compound words, and for clarity.

USES OF THE HYPHEN	
With Numbers	thirty-two colors, four-fifths majority
With Prefixes and Suffixes	ex-president, anti-American, self-contained, commissioner-elect
With Compound Nouns	carry-all, secretary-treasurer, sister-in-law
With Compound Modifiers	never-to-be-forgotten concert, well-attended lecture
For Clarity	doll-like, three quart-bottles

Rules for Dividing Words at the End of a Line   Divide words only between syllables. Do not leave a single letter or *-ed* alone on a line. Do not divide proper nouns and adjectives. Divide a hyphenated word only after the hyphen.

Correct	Incorrect
cen-ter	a-part
hea-then	walk-ed
dis-tance	Mar-y
self-sufficiency	self-suf-ficiency

▶**Exercise 1**   **Using Hyphens.**   Place hyphens where they are needed.

EXAMPLE: My brother is an ex lieutenant.
　　　　　My brother is an ex-lieutenant.

1. My father owns a three fourths share of this business.

2. I was able to reach my sister in law and my father in law.

3. The sergeant said, "Round up all able bodied men."

4. There were anti French demonstrations in the capital.

5. I wrote immediately to the governor elect.

6. The old man of war sat in the harbor.

7. What a beautiful bright eyed young lady!

8. My grandmother was a well educated woman even then.

9. My father loves old fashioned dresses.

10. She bought twenty two greeting cards and thirty five small gifts for children.

▶**Exercise 2**   **Hyphenating Words.**   Draw vertical lines between syllables that can be divided at the end of a line. Circle words that should not be divided at the end of a line.

EXAMPLE: below   be | low   jumped   ⟨jumped⟩

1. athlete   6. mountain

2. drudge   7. compound

3. custom   8. tennis

4. study   9. incite

5. partridge   10. remark

29.5 Hyphens • Practice 2

Exercise 1 **Using Hyphens With Compound Numbers, Word Parts, and Words.** Add necessary hyphens to the following paragraph.

EXAMPLE: Chocolate is my all time favorite kind of candy.

_____Chocolate is my all-time favorite kind of candy._____

(1) The able bodied explorer Columbus introduced the well loved treat chocolate to Western Europe. (2) When Columbus returned from the Central American terrain with some chocolate beans, the Spanish king did not recognize their potential. (3) Hernando Cortes, however, did see the potential of the dark, bitter drink he was served by Montezuma, and he dreamed up a far fetched plan to cultivate chocolate beans in Spain. (4) This quick witted explorer had his sailors learn to cultivate the bean. (5) For over ninety nine years, Spain was the sole European producer of a thickly sweet drink they had made from the beans. (6) But other Western European nations were not left out for long. (7) They discovered the sought after secret and were soon enjoying chocolate. (8) During the post Renaissance period, chocolate was expensive, and less than one fourth of the population could afford it. (9) However, mass produced chocolate was soon available to the general public. (10) Today, chocolate is greatly loved in the United States and around the world.

Exercise 2 **Dividing Words.** If a word has been divided correctly, write _correct_. If not, rewrite the word, dividing it correctly or writing it as one word if it cannot be divided.

EXAMPLE: The teacher told me that my essay was too word-

y._____wordy_____

1. When I read the directions, I saw they were self-expla-natory. _____

2. Yesterday, we drove past countless fields of grazing ca-ttle. _____

3. With Marion helping, it didn't take long to clean the ta-ble. _____

4. The high altitude in the mountains gave me a very head-y feeling. _____

5. After crossing the rickety bridge, we slowly walked do-wn to the water's edge. _____

6. The three of us had an early morning meeting with Super-intendent Glaros. _____

7. As we watched from afar, the horse and her colt gallop-ed across the pasture. _____

8. Do you suppose that your invitation to Maryann Ellins-worth will arrive in time? _____

9. The building was so badly burnt that it was unrecogniza-ble. _____

10. The man ahead of me bought a first-class ticket to New Zea-land. _____

© Prentice-Hall, Inc.

Name _____ Date _____

 29.6 # The Apostrophe (With Possessive Nouns, Joint and Individual Ownership) • Practice 1

Apostrophes With Possessive Nouns   Use the following rules to form the possessives of nouns.

FORMING POSSESSIVE NOUNS	
Add an apostrophe and -s to show the possessive of most singular nouns.	a girl's notebook the inventor's sketch
Add an apostrophe to show the possessive case of plural nouns ending in -s or -es.	three girls' notebooks the nurses' passes
Add an apostrophe and -s to show the possessive case of plural nouns that do not end in -s or -es.	the children's toys three men's watches
Make the last word in a compound noun possessive.	Red Cross's volunteers station wagons' drivers
Treat time and amount like other possessives.	a month's vacation two months' vacation

Joint and Individual Ownership   To show joint ownership, add an apostrophe and -s to the last noun of a series. To show individual ownership, add an apostrophe and -s at the end of each noun in a series.

Joint Ownership	Keller and Schmidt's two-family house
Individual Ownership	Karen's, Sue's, and Pam's reports

▶ **Exercise 1**   **Writing Possessive Forms.**   Write the possessive form in the space provided.

EXAMPLE: the radio of my cousin ___*my cousin's radio*___

1. the books of the women _____
2. a vacation for a week _____
3. the campus of City College _____
4. the career of an actress _____
5. the children of Ken and Pam _____
6. the worth of two dollars _____
7. the coats of Jim and Susan _____
8. the absences of pupils _____
9. the textbook of my sister _____
10. the pizza of my father-in-law _____

▶ **Exercise 2**   **Using Possessives.**   Add an appropriate possessive noun to each sentence.

EXAMPLE: ___*Mrs. Johnson's*___ car wouldn't start Monday morning.

1. The next meeting of the photography club will be at _____ house.
2. _____ speech was by far the best we heard today.
3. His _____ response was not what he had hoped for.
4. Three _____ names were mentioned in the article.
5. She put the saddle on the _____ back.

29.6 The Apostrophe (With Possessive Nouns, Joint and Individual Ownership) • Practice 2

▶ Exercise 1 **Using Apostrophes to Make Singular Nouns Possessive.** Write the underlined nouns, putting them in the possessive form.

EXAMPLE: The door of the bird cage was open. _____bird's_____

1. The student paper discussed the book in great detail. _____
2. Phyllis hair looked good styled that way. _____
3. The dog water bowl needs to be refilled. _____
4. Andrew pet turtle wandered from his bowl sometime last night. _____
5. The new representative performance on the floor of the House of Representatives was quite impressive. _____
6. New courses were listed in the college fall catalog. _____
7. Jim coat shrank in the wash. _____
8. The cat claws need to be trimmed. _____
9. We read three of Robert Graves books. _____
10. A part of each month wages was added to our small but growing savings account. _____

▶ Exercise 2 **Using Apostrophes to Make Plural Nouns Possessive.** Write the underlined nouns, putting them into the possessive form.

EXAMPLE: The members dues should be paid this week. _____members'_____

1. The ladies desserts came with their coffee. _____
2. The children toys were scattered all over the floor. _____
3. The twins presents were to be kept hidden until their birthday. _____
4. Many important issues were discussed at the governors conference. _____
5. The critics reviews helped boost the confidence of the actors. _____
6. The presidential candidate promised to uphold the people interests. _____
7. The relatives invitations must be mailed immediately. _____
8. Neat and well-written was the best way to describe the women tests. _____
9. The visitors suitcases had not yet been unpacked. _____
10. The report said that the cities problems continue to grow worse each year. _____

▶ Exercise 3 **Using Apostrophes with Compound Nouns.** In each blank, write the possessive form of the compound noun in each sentence.

EXAMPLE: The Red Cross lifesaving class starts next week. _____Red Cross's_____

1. The Secretary of State home was the scene of a recent reception for foreign dignitaries. _____
2. Colbert and Nelson store is having a three-day sale on sandals. _____
3. My father-in-law hair has a streak of gray in it. _____
4. The police chief wife is a police officer, too. _____
5. The Camp Fire Girls summer program teaches children a great deal about nature. _____

Name _____ Date _____

 29.6 # The Apostrophe (With Pronouns) • Practice 1

Apostrophes With Pronouns   Use an apostrophe and an -s with indefinite pronouns to show possession. Do not use an apostrophe with possessive forms of personal pronouns. Personal pronouns are already possessive.

POSSESSIVE FORMS OF PRONOUNS		
Indefinite		**Personal**
someone's	one another's	my, mine, our, ours
everybody's	one's	your, yours
anyone's	each other's	his, her, hers, its, their, theirs

▶ **Exercise 1**   **Using Apostrophes Correctly With Pronouns.**   Write the correct pronoun from parentheses to complete each sentence.

EXAMPLE: The tree has lost two of ____*its*____ lower branches. (it's, its)

1. I lost my camera, but I borrowed _____. (theirs, their's)

2. Our teacher was pleased with _____ success. (everyones', everyone's)

3. Did you try to get _____ opinion? (somebody elses', somebody else's)

4. I don't know too much about _____ new schedule. (their, they're)

5. It is important to respect _____ country. (one's, ones')

6. _____ record collection was taken, not mine. (Someone else's, Someone elses')

7. This set of notes probably belongs to _____. (her, her's)

8. The grizzly bear carefully protected _____ lair. (its, it's)

9. You received Steve's birthday card, but did you get _____? (ours, our's)

10. We looked at _____ photograph albums. (one another's, one anothers')

▶ **Exercise 2**   **Writing Sentences With Pronouns.**   Use each set of words to write an original sentence showing possession with pronouns.

EXAMPLE: Someone-game ____*Someone's game was found yesterday.*____

1. everybody-favorite _____

2. its-kittens _____

3. anyone-CD player _____

4. his-answer _____

5. someone else-house _____

6. theirs-jackets _____

7. one-success _____

8. our-request _____

9. another-jewelry _____

10. hers-skates _____

29.6 The Apostrophe (With Pronouns) • Practice 2

▶ **Exercise 1** **Using Apostrophes with Pronouns.** If a sentence uses apostrophes correctly, write *correct*. If not, rewrite the sentence correcting all of the errors.

EXAMPLE: Someone's else's package was delivered to them.
_____*Someone else's package was delivered to them.*_____

1. Robin gave his' coconut cake to her.
_____

2. When the coat didn't fit, he decided he had picked up another's by mistake.
_____

3. It's my duty to fight crime whenever and wherever I find it.
_____

4. Her's was the first car to be pulled over for routine inspection.
_____

5. Someone's car keys have been left behind on the kitchen table.
_____

6. Everybodys' presents were so thoughtful and generous.
_____

7. When he was cooking the steaks, he cooked their's a little longer since they liked them well-done.
_____

8. According to the job description, emptying trash cans is nobodys' responsibility.
_____

9. Is that your umbrella that is making that huge puddle on the floor?
_____

10. Anybody elses' actions would have been suspect, but nobody doubts his word.
_____

▶ **Exercise 2** **Using Possessive Forms of Pronouns.** Complete each sentence by writing in the blank the possessive form of the type of pronoun indicated in parentheses.

EXAMPLE: Did you find ____*your*____ keys? (personal)

1. That afternoon, the peach sherbet was _____ favorite dessert. (indefinite)
2. Where did you get _____ new bicycle? (personal)
3. _____ keys were found under the couch. (indefinite)
4. This definitely falls under the heading of _____ problem, not mine. (personal)
5. The two cats ate from _____ plate. (indefinite)

29.6 The Apostrophe (With Contractions, Special Uses)
• Practice 1

Apostrophes With Contractions   Use an apostrophe in a contraction to indicate the position of the missing letter or letters. The most common contractions are those formed with verbs.

CONTRACTIONS WITH VERBS		
Verbs + not	aren't (are not) don't (do not)	isn't (is not) wasn't (was not)
Pronouns + the verb _will_	I'll (I will) she'll (she will)	we'll (we will) who'll (who will)
Pronouns and nouns + the verb _be_	I'm (I am) it's (it is)	we're (we are) Bob's (Bob is)
Pronouns + the verb _would_	I'd (I would) he'd (he would)	we'd (we would) who'd (who would)

Special Uses of the Apostrophe   Use an apostrophe and -s to write the plurals of numbers, symbols, letters, and words used to name themselves.

EXAMPLES: two _7_'s   too many _!_ 's   his _p_'s and _q_'s
Why do you keep using so many _like_'s?

▶ **Exercise 1**   **Using Contractions Correctly.**   Make contractions from the words in the parentheses and fill them in where they belong.

EXAMPLE: going to the beach later. (We are)

_____We're_____ going to the beach later.

1. _____ Mary's turn to walk the dog. (It is)
2. I wonder whether _____ coming tonight. (they are)
3. _____ willing to build the sets for the play. (George is)
4. You use far too many _____ in your writing papers. (_and_)
5. Do you think _____ like the bracelet I bought? (she will)
6. _____ bring the ice cream and soda? (Who will)
7. I _____ want to hear your excuses again. (do not)
8. You write your _____ very much like your _____. (_m, w_)
9. _____ you ready yet? (Are not)
10. _____ lend you her stereo if you pick it up. (Sue will)

▶ **Exercise 2**   **Supplying Contractions.**   Add an appropriate contraction in each sentence.

EXAMPLE: _____They'd_____ be much happier if they had quieter neighbors.

1. Do you expect _____ arrive in time for the concert?
2. _____ be right with you.
3. _____ they at the depot when you arrived?
4. _____ baby-sit for you if she had the time.
5. I know that _____ qualified for this job.

Name _____ Date _____

29.6 The Apostrophe (With Contractions, Special Uses)
• Practice 2

▷ **Exercise 1** **Using Apostrophes With Contractions.** If a contraction is underlined in the following sentences, write the two words that make it up. If two words are underlined, write the contraction they would form.

EXAMPLE: I've always been an Alfred Hitchcock fan.

_____I have_____

Alfred Hitchcock was a filmmaker of whom many people said, "This (1) man's a legend in his own time." The legend of Alfred Hitchcock began in England, when he produced his first film, *Pleasure Garden.* However, we (2) don't see the now-famous Hitchcock style until his third film, *The Lodger.* Hitchcock moved to the United States early in his career, but he (3) did not plan to remain here. However, he and his wife (4) could not return to England, considering his growing popularity here. Instead, they decided (5) they'd become residents of California. (6) It has been the movies of Alfred Hitchcock that have brought a new dimension to the horror film. His films (7) aren't just shock; (8) they're stories that explore artistically the irrational aspects of life. In these films, (9) we've got the quality (10) we'd like to find in all films. Among the films (11) he has made in the most creative periods in his life—the (12) '30's, '40's, and '50's — (13) you'll find such thrillers as *Notorious* and *Psycho.* You (14) should not ignore these films; (15) they're classics (16) that will entertain movie fans for years to come. We (17) shouldn't forget the contributions this man has made. One (18) thing's certain: (19) We'll never forget the thrills his (20) work's brought us.

1. _____   11. _____
2. _____   12. _____
3. _____   13. _____
4. _____   14. _____
5. _____   15. _____
6. _____   16. _____
7. _____   17. _____
8. _____   18. _____
9. _____   19. _____
10. _____   20. _____

▷ **Exercise 2** **Recognizing Special Uses of the Apostrophe.** Write each sentence, adding an apostrophe and an -s wherever necessary. Underline any items that appear in italics.

EXAMPLE: Please dot all your *i* carefully.

Please dot all your i's carefully.

1. I cut out six *8* for my bulletin board.

_____

2. Do you spell this word with one *c* and two *s* or two *c* and one *s* ?

_____

3. Should I put two *?* in this sentence, Miss Mellgren?

_____

4. I had to write twenty *f* in my calligraphy class before I was able to master that letter.

_____

5. Now that we have a new house number, we will need to buy two more *4.*

_____

Diagraming Basic Sentence Parts (Subjects, Verbs, and Modifiers: Adding Conjunctions) • Practice 1

Subjects, Verbs, and Modifiers

In diagrams of sentences, words that make up the basic sentence pattern are written on a horizontal line. A vertical line separates the subject from the predicate. Articles, adjectives, and adverbs are written on slanted lines below the words they modify.

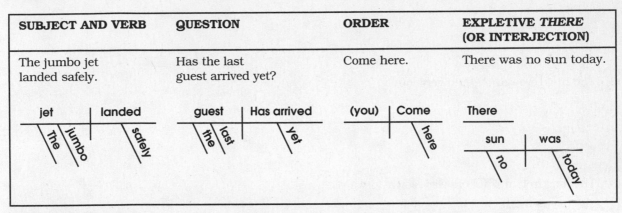

SUBJECT AND VERB	QUESTION	ORDER	EXPLETIVE *THERE* (OR INTERJECTION)
The jumbo jet landed safely.	Has the last guest arrived yet?	Come here.	There was no sun today.

Adding Conjunctions

In diagrams, conjunctions are written on dotted lines between the words they connect.

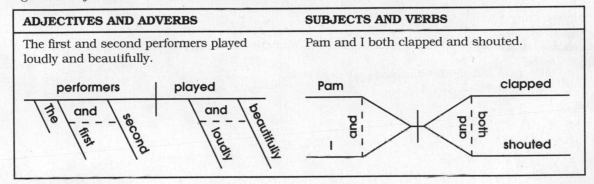

ADJECTIVES AND ADVERBS	SUBJECTS AND VERBS
The first and second performers played loudly and beautifully.	Pam and I both clapped and shouted.

▶ **Exercise 1** **Diagraming Subjects, Verbs, and Modifiers.** Correctly diagram each sentence. Refer to the examples above if necessary.

1. Several colorful floats passed by.

2. A graceful seagull soared overhead.

▶ **Exercise 2** **Diagraming Sentences with Conjunctions.** Diagram this sentence correctly. Refer to the examples above if necessary.

The excited and eager fans whistled and shouted loudly.

Diagraming Subjects, Verbs, and Modifiers
• Practice 2

▶ **Exercise 1**   **Diagraming Subjects, Verbs, and Modifiers.**   Correctly diagram each sentence

1. Come here.

2. The huge crowed cheered very loudly.

3. The long freight train crawled slowly forward.

▶ **Exercise 2**   **Diagraming Sentences with Conjunctions.**   Correctly diagram each sentence.

1. The marigolds and zinnias bloomed profusely.

2. Bob walks fast but runs slowly.

3. The sparrow and the finch flew upward and quickly disappeared.

Diagraming Basic Sentence Parts (Complements)

• Practice 1

Complements

In diagrams, most kinds of complements are placed on the base line after the verb. A straight line that meets the base line separates a direct object from the verb. A slanted line that meets the base line comes before an objective complement or a subject complement. An indirect object is joined to the rest of the sentence below the verb. Compound complements are joined as other compound parts.

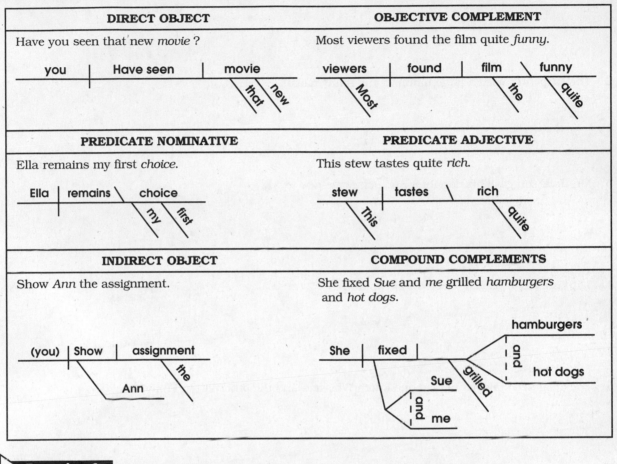

DIRECT OBJECT	**OBJECTIVE COMPLEMENT**
Have you seen that new *movie* ?	Most viewers found the film quite *funny*.
PREDICATE NOMINATIVE	**PREDICATE ADJECTIVE**
Ella remains my first *choice*.	This stew tastes quite *rich*.
INDIRECT OBJECT	**COMPOUND COMPLEMENTS**
Show *Ann* the assignment.	She fixed *Sue* and *me* grilled *hamburgers* and *hot dogs*.

▶ **Exercise 1**   **Diagraming Complements.**   Correctly diagram this sentence.

1. The prospective buyer found the old house attractive and sound.

▶ **Exercise 2**   **More Work with Complements.**   Correctly diagram this sentence.

1. The music sounded harsh and too loud.

Diagraming Basic Sentence Parts (Complements)
• Practice 2

▶ **Exercise 1** **Diagraming Complements.** Correctly diagram each sentence.

1. Many pesky mosquitoes annoyed the campers.

2. The carpenter used a large hammer and shiny nails.

3. Mr. Johnson gave his daughter and son some new toys.

4. The basketball players elected Bill captain.

5. The delighted children named one kitten Whiskers and the other kitten Fluffy.

6. This is the one.

Diagraming Phrases (Prepositional Phrases, Appositives and Appositive Phrases) • Practice 1

Prepositional Phrases

A prepositional phrase is diagramed to show how it relates the object of the preposition to another word in the sentence. The preposition is written on a slanted line joined to the word the phrase modifies. The object is written on a horizontal line. Modifiers are diagramed in the usual way. The model on the right below shows prepositional phrases that do not modify words on the base line.

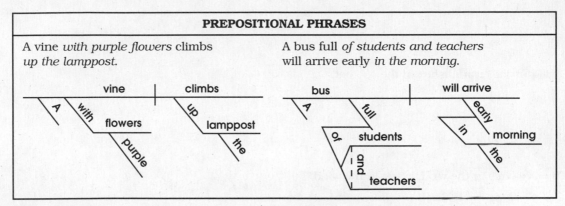

PREPOSITIONAL PHRASES

A vine *with purple flowers* climbs *up the lamppost.*

A bus full *of students and teachers* will arrive early *in the morning.*

Appositives and Appositive Phrases An appositive is diagramed in parentheses next to the noun or pronoun it renames. Any modifiers in an appositive phrase are diagramed as usual.

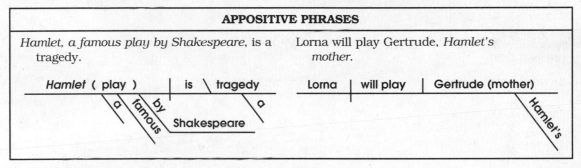

APPOSITIVE PHRASES

Hamlet, a famous play by Shakespeare, is a tragedy.

Lorna will play Gertrude, *Hamlet's mother.*

▶ **Exercise 1** **Diagraming Prepositional Phrases.** Correctly diagram this sentence.

1. A row of rose bushes twines around the fence in the yard.

▶ **Exercise 2** **Diagraming Appositives and Appositive Phrases.** Correctly diagram each sentence.

1. My brother Tony has taken a job in Minneapolis.

2. Our speaker, the director of the science museum, talked about dinosaurs.

Diagraming Prepositional Phrases (Prepositional Phrases, Appositives and Appositive Phrases) • Practice 2

▶ **Exercise 1** Diagraming Prepositional Phrases. Correctly diagram each sentence.

1. The corporation is moving to another city.

2. I will put the clean dishes in the cabinet.

3. The large tree in the yard sways in the wind.

▶ **Exercise 2** Diagraming Appositives and Appositive Phrases. Correctly diagram each sentence.

1. The newscaster, a radio announcer for forty years, will retire soon.

2. This is our new mayor, Ms. Peterson.

3. The giant vehicle, an oversized dump truck, has a flat tire.

Diagraming Phrases (Participles and Participial Phrases, Gerunds and Gerund Phrases) • Practice 1

Participles and Participial Phrases

The diagram for a participle or a participial phrase looks much like the diagram for a prepositional phrase, below the noun or pronoun it modifies. Notice, though, that the participle is written beginning on the slanted line and continuing onto the horizontal line.

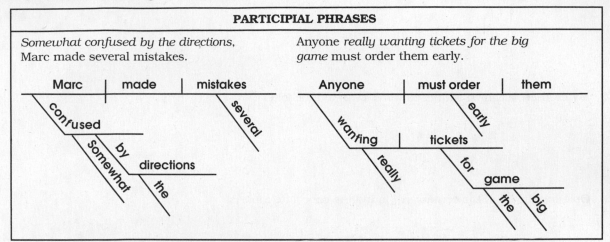

PARTICIPIAL PHRASES

Somewhat confused by the directions, Marc made several mistakes.

Anyone *really wanting tickets for the big game* must order them early.

Gerunds and Gerund Phrases   When a gerund is used as a basic sentence part, its pedestal is placed on the base line where that sentence part would normally be. The gerund itself is written on the stepped line, and modifiers and complements, if any, are written in their usual positions. A gerund or gerund phrase used as an indirect object or object of a preposition is written on a stepped line attached to the slanted line down from the base line.

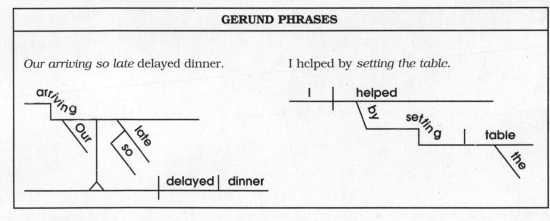

GERUND PHRASES

Our arriving so late delayed dinner.

I helped by *setting the table.*

▶ **Exercise 1**   **Diagraming Participles and Participial Phrases.**   Correctly diagram the sentence.

1. The cat sitting in the tree looked at the barking dog.

▶ **Exercise 2**   **Diagraming Gerunds and Gerund Phrases.**   Correctly diagram the sentence.

1. Ms. Nelson appreciated our helping with the decorations.

Diagraming Phrases (Participles and Participial Phrases Gerunds and Gerund Phrases) • Practice 2

▶ **Exercise 1** **Diagraming Participles and Participial Phrases.** Correctly diagram each sentence.

1. Frowning at me, Ned shook the broken radio.

2. My brother, laughing with each word, repeated the joke.

3. Opening the lid of the container, I found the chocolate cookies.

▶ **Exercise 2** **Diagraming Gerunds and Gerund Phrases.** Correctly diagram each sentence.

1. Swimming is a form of exercise.

2. Eating a good breakfast can provide energy for a long day.

3. Traveling to new places can be an enjoyable experience.

Diagraming Phrases (Infinitives and Infinitive Phrases)
• Practice 1

Infinitives and Infinitive Phrases

An infinitive or infinitive phrase used as a noun is diagramed on a pedestal in any of the positions a noun or pronoun would occupy. Subjects, complements, or modifiers of the infinitive—if any—occupy normal positions. Notice how an omitted *to* is handled. An infinitive or infinitive phrase used as an adjective or an adverb is diagramed in much the same way as a prepositional phrase.

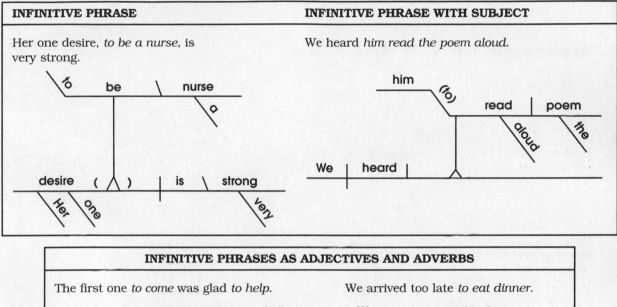

INFINITIVE PHRASE	INFINITIVE PHRASE WITH SUBJECT
Her one desire, *to be a nurse*, is very strong.	We heard *him read the poem aloud*.

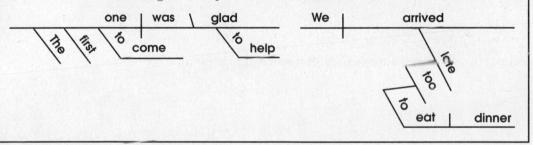

INFINITIVE PHRASES AS ADJECTIVES AND ADVERBS

The first one *to come* was glad *to help*.

We arrived too late *to eat dinner*.

▶ **Exercise 1** Diagraming Infinitives and Infinitive Phrases Used as Nouns. Correctly diagram the sentence.

1. We offered to prepare a very special meal.

▶ **Exercise 2** Diagraming Infinitives and Infinitive Phrases Used as Adjectives and Adverbs. Correctly diagram the sentence.

1. The man to see about that job will call you tomorrow.

Diagraming Phrases (Infinitives and Infinitive Phrases)
• Practice 2

 Exercise 1 Correctly diagram each sentence.

1. This is the brand to buy.

2. His greatest wish is to grow more crops in the future.

3. To clean your room is your next chore.

4. His sister told him to read the front page of the newspaper.

5. I watched the ambulance approach the highway entrance ramp.

6. She wants to pass her driving test.

Diagraming Clauses (Compound Sentences) • Practice 1

Compound Sentences. Diagram each independent clause of a compound sentence separately. Then join the verbs with a dotted, stepped line, writing the conjunction or semicolon on the dotted line.

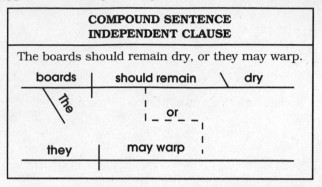

▶ **Exercise 1** **Diagraming Compound Sentences.** Diagram each sentence correctly.

1. Reporters wanted an interview, but the ex-champ refused.

2. Bowser was an ugly mutt, but the family loved him.

▶ **Exercise 2** **More Work with Compound Sentences.** Correctly diagram each sentence.

1. King Midas had plenty of gold, but he wanted still more.

2. The liquid must be added slowly, or the sauce will curdle.

3. Cans belong in this bin; bottles go in that one.

Diagraming Clauses (Compound Sentences) • Practice 2

Exercise 1 Correctly diagram each sentence..

1. He finished his history project, and he studied the math problems.

2. We can go to the movies today, or we can wait for a better picture.

3. Spring begins soon, but we are still shoveling snow.

4. Television can be fun, but reading is more enjoyable.

5. I found the video, and I returned it to Adam.

6. The baby shook her rattle, and then she dropped it on the floor.

Diagraming Clauses (Complex Sentences) • Practice 1

Complex Sentences   Both adjective and adverb clauses are diagramed on a line beneath the independent clause and connected to the independent clause by a dotted line. With an adjective clause, the dotted line extends from the noun or pronoun the clause modifies to the relative pronoun or relative adverb in the clause. With an adverb clause, the dotted line extends from the word modified to the verb in the adverb clause. The subordinating conjunction is written along the dotted line.

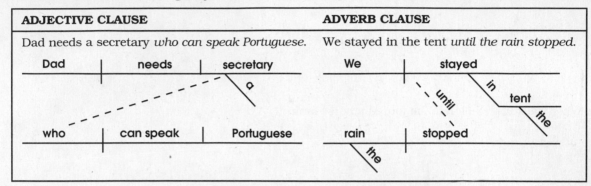

ADJECTIVE CLAUSE	ADVERB CLAUSE
Dad needs a secretary *who can speak Portuguese.*	We stayed in the tent *until the rain stopped.*

A noun clause is placed on a pedestal extending upward from the position it fills in the independent clause. If the introductory word has no function in the noun clause, it is written along the pedestal.

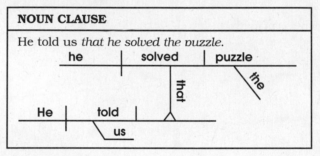

NOUN CLAUSE

He told us *that he solved the puzzle.*

▶ **Exercise 1**   **Diagraming Adjective and Adverb Clauses.**   Correctly diagram the sentence.

1. Since it was a pleasant day, Natalie went to the beach.

▶ **Exercise 2**   **Diagraming Noun Clauses.**   Correctly diagram the sentence.

1. The boy soon forgot what he had been told.

Diagraming Clauses (Complex Sentences) • Practice 2

1. The shirt that I chose is blue with a white collar.

2. When Jack visited Florida, he toured a horse farm.

3. The book that you ordered has arrived.

4. The actor was excited because he received good reviews.

5. The lake that we will visit has a beautiful beach.

6. We visited the laboratory where Thomas Edison worked.

Diagraming Phrases (Compound-Complex Sentences)

• Practice 1

Compound-Complex Sentences   When diagraming a compound-complex sentence, begin by diagraming each of the independent clauses. Then diagram the subordinate clause(s).

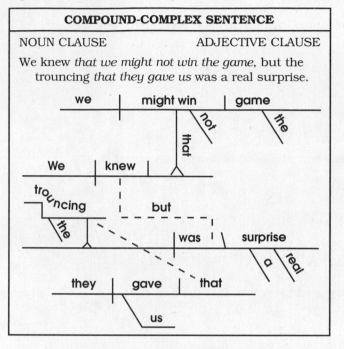

COMPOUND-COMPLEX SENTENCE

NOUN CLAUSE   ADJECTIVE CLAUSE

We knew *that we might not win the game*, but the trouncing *that they gave us* was a real surprise.

▶ **Exercise 1**   **Diagraming Compound-Complex Sentences.**   Correctly diagram each sentence.

1. Joan said that she would never forget me, and I believe her.

2. While Beth cleaned the fish, Paula collected firewood, and Nancy unpacked the supplies.

▶ **Exercise 2**   **Diagraming Sentences of Varying Structures.**   Identify the structure of each sentence and diagram it correctly. The sentences may be compound, complex, or compound-complex.

1. We visited the house where Washington had his headquarters.

2. My sister, who lives in Houston, is planning a visit; but we do not know when she will come.

Diagraming Phrases (Compound-Complex Sentences)
• Practice 2

▶ **Exercise 1**   Correctly diagram each sentence.

1. When Jeremy left, Mike hid the presents and Susan phoned the guests.

2. The news that he read was good, but he wore a serious expression.

3. They wished that they could stay, but they could not.

4. When the rescuers reached the trapped miners, some rescuers held flashlights, and others carefully dug.

5. The students looked with disbelief as they approached the library, for the building was closed.

6. Before the game began, the fans were excited and the players were nervous.

Answers

16.1 Nouns (Names, Compound Nouns) (Page 1)
Practice 1
Exercise 1 Recognizing Nouns
1. February, snowstorm
2. daisies, garden
3. children, merry-go-round
4. animals, zoo
5. Uncle Pete, pilot
6. party, plates
7. Poverty, problem
8. dream, Far East
9. silverware, drawer
10. sign, Dennis

Exercise 2 Adding Nouns to Sentences
Sample nouns are given.
1. animal, coyote
2. city, movie
3. dark, child
4. Green, color
5. noon, Detroit
6. days, wait
7. people, change
8. pictures, coffee table
9. Alice, nurse
10. park, well

16.1 Nouns (Names, Compound Nouns) (Page 2)
Practice 2
Exercise 1 Identifying Nouns as People, Places, or Things
1. baby, musician / people
2. rabbit, chair / things
3. prison, mountainside / places
4. misery, success / things
5. forest, swamp / places
6. sailor, explorer / people
7. table, dog / things
8. dentist, mayor / people
9. rock, pie / things
10. beach, pasture / places
11. courage, freedom / things
12. lion, kite / things
13. conductor, woman / people
14. king, president / people
15. bedroom, school / places
16. desk, thought / things
17. construction, pain / things
18. hunter, nurse / people
19. pelican, honor / things
20. plaza, library / places

Exercise 2 Recognizing Compound Nouns
1. airport
2. ticket agent, boarding pass, seatbelt
3. takeoff, flight attendant, soft drink
4. meatloaf, string beans, fruit salad
5. landing gear, tray table
6. touchdown
7. runway, grandmother, grandfather
8. mix-up, suitcases
9. station wagon
10. freeway

16.1 Nouns (Common and Proper Nouns) (Page 3)
Practice 1
Exercise 1 Recognizing Proper Nouns
1. Mark Twain
2. Texas
3. Mars
4. Maple Avenue
5. German
6. Buckingham Palace
7. Emerson High School
8. Seville
9. Donna
10. Vermont

Exercise 2 Adding Proper Nouns to Sentences
Sample nouns are given.
1. Marie
2. Ernest Hemingway
3. Rocky Mountains
4. Hill Street
5. Buick
6. May
7. England
8. Central High School
9. Johnny Carson
10. Rio Grande

16.1 Nouns (Common and Proper Nouns) (Page 4)
Practice 2
Exercise 1 Distinguishing Between Common and Proper Nouns
1. Smithville
2. Black Beauty
3. Texas
4. Nile
5. Washington Monument
6. Whitman
7. French
8. Lassie
9. Paris
10. Italy
11. Thanksgiving
12. Mediterranean
13. September
14. Maple Lane
15. Sophie

Writing Application
Writing Sentences with Nouns
Sample sentences are given.
1. Over the years, the New York Yankees have been one of the best teams in baseball.
2. Finches and hamsters make excellent pets.
3. Yellowstone National Park has geysers and hot springs.
4. Linda is on the Lincoln High School tennis team.
5. Louis Armstrong played the trumpet in a band.

16.2 Pronouns (Antecedents, Personal Pronouns) (Page 5)
Practice 1
Exercise 1   Recognizing Pronouns and Antecedents
Antecedents follow the slashes.
1. you / Lisa
2. his / Paul
3. she / Phyllis
4. its / house
5. I / child
6. their / Joneses
7. you / Joel
8. her / woman
9. he / Mozart
10. you / Tom

Exercise 2   Using Personal Pronouns
1. her
2. you
3. their
4. its
5. his
6. her
7. their
8. they
9. his
10. her

16.2 Pronouns (Antecedents, Personal Pronouns) (Page 6)
Practice 2
Exercise 1   Recognizing Antecedents
1. children
2. Andrea
3. CD
4. horse
5. Frank
6. explorers
7. Joneses
8. Joe
9. boat
10. twins
11. fans
12. time
13. Marcia
14. umpire
15. mayor

Exercise 2   Identifying Personal Pronouns

Personal Pronoun	Antecedent
1. he, his	Henry
2. his	Paul
their	parents
3. their, them	twins
4. her, she	Jody
5. their	Grants
it	piano
6. their, they	fans
7. its, it	movie
8. her	Tracy
it	trip
9. he	Ned
it	cake
10. her	Ellen
his	brother
11. his	Todd
it	bag
12. her	Diane
their	roses

13. his, he	O. Henry
14. he	Jamie
them	poems
15. her	Annie
it	dress

16.2 Pronouns (Reflexive and Intensive Pronouns) (Page 7)
Practice 1
Exercise 1   Distinguishing Between Reflexive and Intensive Pronouns
1. reflexive
2. reflexive
3. intensive
4. reflexive
5. intensive
6. intensive
7. reflexive
8. intensive
9. reflexive
10. reflexive

Exercise 2   Adding Reflexive and Intensive Pronouns to Sentences
1. themselves
2. herself
3. himself
4. himself
5. itself
6. yourself
7. themselves
8. ourselves
9. myself
10. yourself

16.2 Pronouns (Reflexive and Intensive Pronouns) (Page 8)
Practice 2
Exercise 1   Distinguishing Between Reflexive and Intensive Pronouns
1. myself (intensive)
2. ourselves (reflexive)
3. herself (intensive)
4. herself (intensive)
5. himself (intensive)
6. himself (reflexive)
7. themselves (reflexive)
8. themselves (reflexive)
9. himself (reflexive)
10. herself (reflexive)
11. yourself (reflexive)
12. yourselves (intensive)
13. myself (reflexive)
14. himself (intensive)
15. herself (reflexive)

Exercise 2   Writing Sentences with Pronouns
Sample sentences are given.
1. Maryanne herself made an appearance at the party.
2. Flo bought herself a new pair of shoes.
3. I myself do not care for parties.
4. Speaking for myself, I do not care for parties.
5. We ourselves had nothing to do with it.
6. We should get ourselves some new equipment.
7. You yourself are responsible for your own actions.
8. Do yourself a favor and get some rest.
9. Kareem himself has signed this card.
10. The program itself cannot help you.

11. The dishwasher will not start itself.
12. You yourselves must figure this out.
13. Why don't you buy yourselves some tickets?
14. The boys themselves prepared the dinner.
15. The boys prepared the dinner for themselves.

16.2 Pronouns (Demonstrative, Relative, and Interrogative Pronouns) (Page 9)
Practice 1
Exercise 1 Identifying Demonstrative, Relative, and Interrogative Pronouns
1. demonstrative
2. relative
3. interrogative
4. relative
5. interrogative
6. demonstrative
7. interrogative
8. relative
9. demonstrative
10. relative

Exercise 2 Adding Demonstrative, Relative, and Interrogative Pronouns to Sentences
Sample pronouns are given.
1. What
2. these
3. who
4. that
5. Who
6. That
7. Who
8. who
9. which
10. whom

16.2 Pronouns (Demonstrative, Relative, and Interrogative Pronouns) (Page 10)
Practice 2
Exercise 1 Recognizing Demonstrative, Relative, and Interrogative Pronouns
1. Which (interrogative)
2. who (relative)
3. What (interrogative)
4. This (demonstrative)
5. Who (interrogative)
6. who (relative)
7. that (demonstrative)
8. What (interrogative)
9. who (relative)
10. These (demonstrative)
11. whom (interrogative)
12. those (demonstrative)
13. Whose (interrogative)
14. whom (relative)
15. Which (interrogative)

Exercise 2 Using Pronouns in Sentences
1. That
2. whom
3. What
4. that
5. Which
6. which
7. Those
8. whom
9. that
10. who

16.2 Indefinite Pronouns (Page 11)
Practice 1
Exercise 1 Recognizing Indefinite Pronouns
1. Each
2. Everyone, some
3. Many, some
4. Few, anything
5. No one, all
6. Some, another
7. Most, something
8. little
9. Neither
10. most

Exercise 2 Adding Indefinite Pronouns to Sentences
Sample pronouns are given. Antecedents follow the slashes.
1. None / players
2. all / contestants
3. something
4. much
5. All / questions
6. everyone
7. few / tickets
8. Each / candidates
9. everything
10. Some / fans

16.2 Indefinite Pronouns (Page 12)
Practice 2
Exercise 1 Identifying Indefinite Pronouns
1. none
2. Everyone, some
3. others
4. Few
5. more
6. No one, many
7. Some
8. All
9. One, another
10. anything

Writing Application
Writing Sentences with Pronouns
Sample sentences are given.
1. He is the person whom she knows.
2. You yourself have a chance to win.
3. That is an unusual rock formation.
4. We are the ones who planned the party.
5. Which of the photographs were taken during World War II?
6. He thought that little could be done to help her.
7. She herself saw to that.
8. I would like to get myself a dog that would bring in the newspaper.
9. Who wrote this and that?
10. She herself invited several of the troublemakers, which was a big mistake.

17.1 Action Verbs (Page 13)
Practice 1
Exercise 1 Recognizing Visible and Mental Actions
1. wandered

2. considered

3. gives

4. wrote

5. glided

6. (wanted)

7. built

8. talked

9. (wished)

10. planted

Exercise 2   Distinguishing Between Transitive and Intransitive Verbs
1. transitive
2. intransitive
3. transitive
4. transitive
5. transitive
6. intransitive
7. intransitive
8. transitive
9. intransitive
10. intransitive

17.1   Action Verbs (Page 14)
Practice 2
Exercise 1   Recognizing Action Verbs
1. drove (visible)
2. learned (mental)
3. worry (mental)
4. held (visible)
5. jogs (visible)
6. filed (visible)
7. sleeps (visible)
8. chased (visible)
9. appreciated (mental)
10. wondered (mental)

Exercise 2   Distinguishing Between Transitive and Intransitive Verbs
1. called (intransitive)
2. ate (transitive)
3. reads (transitive)
4. hung (intransitive)
5. reads (intransitive)
6. saw (transitive)
7. searched (intransitive)
8. feared (transitive)
9. directed (transitive)
10. shouted (transitive)
11. shouted (intransitive)
12. crawled (intransitive)
13. danced (intransitive)
14. followed (transitive)
15. pitched (transitive)
16. pitched (intransitive)
17. walks (transitive)
18. walked (intransitive)
19. waited (intransitive)
20. offered (transitive)

17.2   Linking Verbs (*Be*, Other Linking Verbs) (Page 15)
Practice 1
Exercise 1   Recognizing Forms of *Be* Used as Linking Verbs
1. fans (were) eager
2. purpose (was) clear
3. Some (were) angry
4. I (am) lover
5. candidates (were) optimistic
6. One (was) empty
7. Reviews (were) unfavorable
8. people (are) anxious
9. poster (is) suitable
10. T-shirts (are) dress

Exercise 2   Recognizing Other Linking Verbs
1. patient (looks) better
2. lemonade (tastes) sour
3. crowd (became) angry
4. barn (smelled) musty
5. music (sounds) loud

17.2   Linking Verbs (*Be*, Other Linking Verbs) (Page 16)
Practice 2
Exercise 1   Recognizing Forms of *Be* Used as Linking Verbs

	Linking Verb	Words Linked
1.	is	Helena, president
2.	were	candidates, certain
3.	was	patient, man
4.	am	I, nervous
5.	was	play, success
6.	are	Homans, neighbors
7.	is	governor, considerate
8.	was	press, critical
9.	am	I, person
10.	was	score, lopsided
11.	should have been	campers, afraid
12.	could be	Darlene, sister
13.	must have been	You, thrilled
14.	were being	children, rude
15.	must have been	error, serious

Exercise 2   Identifying Other Linking Verbs

	Linking Verb	Words Linked
1.	became	book, classic
2.	sounded	Erica, happy
3.	stayed	Peter Pan, child
4.	feels	Everyone, lonely
5.	became	bill, law
6.	remained	boys, friends

7. looks   style, good
8. turned   weather, colder
9. seemed   car, attractive
10. grew   child, sleepy

17.2 Linking Verbs (Linking Verb or Action Verb?) (Page 17)
Practice 1
Exercise 1   Distinguishing Between Linking Verbs and Action Verbs
1. action
2. action
3. action
4. action
5. linking
6. action
7. linking
8. action
9. action
10. linking

Exercise 2   Adding Verbs to Sentences
Answers will vary; samples are given.
1. tastes, linking
2. tasted, action
3. grows, linking
4. turns, linking
5. turned, action
6. grows, action
7. became, linking
8. sounds, linking
9. looked, action
10. looked, action

17.2 Linking Verbs (Linking Verb or Action Verb?) (Page 18)
Practice 2
Exercise 1   Distinguishing Between Linking Verbs and Action Verbs
1. turned (action)
2. tasted (linking)
3. tasted (action)
4. smelled (action)
5. grows (linking)
6. looked (linking)
7. became (linking)
8. turned (linking)
9. smells (linking)
10. stayed (action)
11. sounded (action)
12. appeared (action)
13. looked (action)
14. remained (linking)
15. appeared (linking)
16. remained (action)
17. felt (linking)
18. grows (action)
19. stayed (linking)
20. sounds (linking)

Writing Application
Writing Sentences with Linking and Action Verbs
Sample sentences are given.
1. The day turned cloudy in the afternoon.
   I turned the volume down on the TV.
2. The senator looks good for his age.
   The students looked intently at the equation on the chalkboard.
3. The train whistle sounds loud.
   He sounded the alarm.

4. This corn tastes delicious.
   We tasted all of the salads.
5. Aunt Judy feels fine after her bout with the flu.
   Jerry felt the coarse fabric of the sweater.

17.3 Helping Verbs (Page 19)
Practice 1
Exercise 1   Adding Helping Verbs to Sentences
Sample helping verbs are given.
1. have been
2. is
3. could have
4. will
5. Will be
6. was
7. should have
8. may be
9. did
10. should have

Exercise 2   Identifying Helping Verbs
1. should have (repeated)
2. does (announce)
3. Will be (starting)
4. could have (been)
5. Did (make)
6. do (need)
7. must have (left)
8. may (call)
9. is (crying)
10. have (put)

17.3 Helping Verbs (Page 20)
Practice 2
Exercise 1   Supplying Helping Verbs
Sample helping verbs are given.
1. has
2. Have
3. have
4. will be
5. may have
6. Has
7. may be
8. will be
9. will be
10. may have been

Exercise 2   Locating Helping Verbs
1. have been faced
2. may spend
3. can be crossed
4. must travel
5. have presented
6. must search
7. have been killed
8. can be
9. can be
10. Would explore

Writing Application
Writing Sentences with Helping Verbs
Sample sentences are given.
1. This lawn mower can not be fixed until Monday.
2. How does this sewing machine work?
3. We should never really have started on such a long hike without the proper clothing.
4. The water must have definitely been running all night.
5. Do you think that the mayor will succeed in her campaign for reelection?

18.1 Adjectives (Modification, Articles) (Page 21)
Practice 1
Exercise 1   Identifying Adjectives
1. apple, eager
2. proud, new
3. calm, turbulent
4. giant, ten
5. fresher, greener
6. correct, last
7. old, heavy
8. first, interesting
9. last, stronger
10. new, eager

Exercise 2   Using Articles in Sentences
1. an
2. the
3. a
4. a
5. an
6. the
7. a
8. the
9. the
10. an

18.1 Adjectives (Modification, Articles) (Page 22)
Practice 2
Exercise 1   Recognizing Words Modified by Adjectives
1. creature, water
2. diet, food, nutrients
3. winner, grin
4. game, day
5. drive, oaks, mansion
6. people, record
7. You, piece
8. wish, thought
9. time, she
10. sun, warmth
11. distances, animals
12. fur, spots
13. birds, claws
14. eagles, deer
15. ducks and geese, feathers

Exercise 2   Using Definite and Indefinite Articles
1. the
2. a
3. an
4. the
5. the
6. an
7. an
8. The
9. a
10. an
11. the
12. a
13. an
14. The
15. a

18.1 Adjectives (Nouns Used as Adjectives, Proper and Compound Adjectives) (Page 23)
Practice 1
Exercise 1   Recognizing Nouns Used as Adjectives, Proper Adjectives, and Compound Adjectives
1. compound adjective
2. noun
3. proper adjective
4. proper adjective
5. compound adjective
6. noun
7. noun
8. compound adjective
9. noun
10. proper adjective

Exercise 2   Using Proper and Compound Adjectives to Modify Nouns
1. sidewalk cafe
2. cowboy hat
3. Mexican serape
4. inner-city streets
5. Hawaiian island

18.1 Adjectives (Nouns Used as Adjectives, Proper and Compound Adjectives) (Page 24)
Practice 2
Exercise 1   Identifying Nouns Used as Adjectives
1. grocery, breakfast, fruit, soap
2. household
3. Name
4. name
5. package, shelf

Exercise 2   Recognizing Proper and Compound Adjectives
1. Egyptian, Mesopotamian
2. fugitive-hunting
3. high-pitched
4. nearsighted, colorblind
5. far-off
6. Mesopotamian, greyhound-like
7. Labrador, Irish, Russian
8. long-lived
9. German, English, Siberian, hard-working
10. Yorkshire, Mexican, French

Writing Application
Writing Sentences with Adjectives
Sample adjectives are given.
1. picnic table
2. last house / picket fence
3. Chinese food
4. three-year-old child
5. nearsighted driver

18.1 Pronouns Used as Adjectives (Page 25)
Practice 1
Exercise 1   Recognizing Possessive Adjectives

1. your   typewriter

2. its   paws

3. their (seats)

4. her (office)

5. my (tennis racquet)

6. our (vacation)

7. their (records)

8. my (notes)

9. its (moorings)

10. his (surprise)

Exercise 2   Adding Other Pronouns Used as Adjectives
Sample pronouns are given.
1. These
2. Many
3. Each
4. What
5. Which

18.1   Pronouns Used as Adjectives (Page 26)
Practice 2
Exercise 1   Recognizing Personal Pronouns That Act as Adjectives

1. your (parents)

2. his (help)

3. their (helmets)

4. her (friends)

5. Our (grandparents)

6. my (homework)

7. its (tail)

8. their (bicycles)

9. its (nest)

10. their (shelves)

Exercise 2   Recognizing Other Pronouns Used as Adjectives
1. Some (indefinite)
2. Which (interrogative)
3. All (indefinite)
4. What (interrogative)
5. these (demonstrative)
6. several (indefinite)
7. Each (indefinite)
8. That (demonstrative)
9. Whose (interrogative)
10. those (demonstrative)

Writing Application
Writing Sentences with Pronouns Used as Adjectives
Sample sentences are given. Modified words are underlined.
1. Each contestant had to answer four questions.
2. The bird flew into its nest.
3. This week seems especially long.
4. That car is beginning to rust.
5. Which color goes best with blue?

18.2   Adverbs (Modifying Verbs) (Page 27)
Practice 1
Exercise 1   Recognizing Adverbs That Modify Verbs
1. completely, to what extent
2. promptly, when
3. nearby, where
4. here, where
5. cautiously, in what manner
6. up, where
7. away, where
8. hard, in what manner
9. incorrectly, in what manner
10. immediately, when

Exercise 2   Adding Adverbs to Modify Verbs
Sample adverbs are given.
1. upward
2. eagerly
3. carefully
4. tonight
5. late
6. easily
7. usually
8. mournfully
9. thoroughly
10. here

18.2   Adverbs (Modifying Verbs) (Page 28)
Practice 2
Exercise 1   Recognizing Adverbs That Modify Verbs

	Where?	When?	In What Manner?	To What Extent?
1.		now		
2.			badly	
3.		late		
4.			briskly	
5.				completely
6.	inside			
7.	away			
8.			bravely	
9.				fully
10.		early		
11.			brilliantly	
12.	there			
13.			confidently	
14.		Yesterday		
15.			softly	

18.2   Adverbs (Modifying Adjectives and Other Adverbs) (Page 29)
Practice 1
Exercise 1   Recognizing the Words Adverbs Modify
1. adjective
2. adverb
3. adjective
4. adverb
5. adjective
6. adverb

adjective
adjective
9. adverb
10. adjective

Exercise 2   Adding Adverbs to Sentences

Sample adverbs are given.
1. quite beautiful
2. almost completely
3. very unhappy
4. nearly hopeless
5. only partially
6. Very early
7. somewhat tired
8. nearly always
9. quite thoroughly
10. totally sincere

18.2   Adverbs (Modifying Adjectives and Other Adverbs) (Page 30)

Practice 2

Exercise 1   Recognizing Adverbs That Modify Adjectives

1. That child seems unusually (bright).

2. Are you nearly (ready) for the party?

3. The road was barely (visible) through the dense fog.

4. Your answer is partially (correct).

5. The candidate was thoroughly (upset) by the question.

6. Lisa looked extremely (pale).

7. The auditorium was almost (full) on opening night.

8. The doctors remained somewhat (hopeful).

9. A very (sharp) noise woke us at three a.m.

10. I was especially (happy) to see Gladys.

11. As a basketball coach, Pat is quite (talented).

12. The rock concert was surprisingly (brief).

13. Cynthia was an exceptionally (beautiful) baby.

14. The skier was particularly (careful) near the trees.

15. The conductor was visibly (moved) by the music.

Exercise 2   Recognizing Adverbs That Modify Other Adverbs

1. The flood waters spread very (rapidly).

2. The train arrived unusually (late).

3. The horse ran surprisingly (fast).

4. The dog moved somewhat (closer) to the squirrel.

5. The turtle moved more (quickly) than we had expected.

6. Arnold just (barely) finished in time.

7. Clare speaks more (clearly) than her brother.

8. The cookies are almost (completely) gone.

9. The jury reached its verdict unexpectedly (soon).

10. Please move the couch farther (forward).

11. Stan takes himself too (seriously).

12. The speaker pronounced every word very (carefully).

13. Joseph speaks annoyingly (slowly).

14. The car was moving frighteningly (fast).

15. The driver applied the brakes quite (suddenly).

18.2   Adverbs (Adverb or Adjective?) (Page 31)

Practice 1

Exercise 1   Distinguishing Between Adjectives and Adverbs

1. adverb
2. adjective
3. adjective
4. adverb
5. adjective
6. adverb
7. adjective
8. adverb
9. adverb
10. adverb

Exercise 2   Adding Adverbs and Adjectives to Sentences

1. eager
2. quick
3. fondly
4. nervously
5. fond
6. bad
7. eagerly
8. nervous
9. promptly
10. badly

18.2   Adverbs (Adverb or Adjective?) (Page 32)
Practice 2
Exercise 1   Distinguishing Between Adverbs and Adjectives
1. adverb
2. adjective
3. adjective
4. adverb
5. adjective
6. adverb
7. adjective
8. adjective
9. adverb
10. adjective
11. adjective
12. adverb
13. adverb
14. adverb
15. adjective
16. adjective
17. adverb
18. adverb
19. adjective
20. adverb

Exercise 2   Using Adverbs in Sentences
Sample adverbs are given.
1. totally
2. over, loudly
3. eventually
4. Slowly
5. carefully
6. finally
7. soon, very
8. later, quite, fluently
9. successfully
10. extremely, hard

19.1   Prepositions (Page 33)
Practice 1
Exercise 1   Identifying Prepositions
1. before
2. to, without
3. in, to
4. through, on
5. According to, in
6. along, until
7. in
8. in
9. since
10. but, of

Exercise 2   Identifying Prepositional Phrases
1. Among (five) , of (us) , for (pizza)
2. throughout (town)
3. with (briefcase)
4. of (figure) , on (horseback)
5. Despite (shower) , in (park)
6. of (flowers) , in front of (fireplace)
7. because of (traffic)

8. During (summer) , at (playground)
9. among (rocks) , beneath (surface)
10. in spite of (myself)

19.1   Prepositions (Page 34)
Practice 2
Exercise 1   Recognizing Prepositions
Sample prepositions are given.
1. on
2. beside
3. without
4. behind
5. before
6. from
7. down
8. after
9. beside
10. to
11. despite
12. for
13. between
14. through
15. Instead

Exercise 2   Identifying Prepositional Phrases
1. Very little could be seen through the fog. (1)
2. In spite of his low test scores, he was admitted to the program. (2)
3. The children dropped their mittens into the muddy creek. (1)
4. The squirrels chased each other around the park. (1)
5. The huge dog dragged his master along the path. (1)
6. Cars and trucks streamed across the bridge during the rush hour. (2)
7. You will find the beach house next to the pier and in back of the parking lot. (2)
8. For three years she traveled the same road. (1)
9. They hiked in the Rocky Mountains for two weeks. (2)
10. Every morning, he passes by on roller skates. (1)
11. The path winds through the hills and into a valley. (2)
12. The person standing near the kitchen seems angry. (1)
13. Life on a raft on the Mississippi gave Huck a chance for adventure. (3)
14. After an hour I finally arrived at the home of my new friend. (3)
15. The book opens with a mystery concerning a lost bracelet. (2)

19.1   Preposition or Adverb? (Page 35)
Practice 1
Exercise 1   Distinguishing Between Prepositions and Adverbs
1. adverb
2. preposition
3. preposition
4. adverb
5. preposition
6. adverb
7. adverb
8. preposition

Adverb
preposition

Exercise 2   Adding Prepositions and Adverbs to Sentences
Sample prepositions and adverbs are given.
1. a. inside house
   b. inside
2. a. below water
   b. below
3. a. within
   b. within family
4. a. before
   b. before play
5. a. by
   b. by author

19.1   Preposition or Adverb? (Page 36)
Practice 2
Exercise 1   Distinguishing Between Prepositions and Adverbs
1. preposition
2. adverb
3. adverb
4. preposition
5. preposition
6. adverb
7. adverb
8. preposition
9. adverb
10. preposition

Writing Application
Writing Sentences with Prepositions
Sample sentences are given.
1. We dove into the water.
2. The jetliner flew above the clouds.
3. Except for one student, everyone was present at the assembly.
4. The neighbor's dog ran toward my house.
5. There won't be another concert until next Saturday.
6. He plays two sports in addition to soccer.
7. The dogwood tree outside the window is in bloom.
8. The climber scaled the steep cliff without any fear.
9. The mailbox in front of the post office was completely filled with letters.
10. We enjoyed our weekend in spite of the rain.

19.2   Conjunctions and Interjections (Different Kinds of Conjunctions) (Page 37)
Practice 1
Exercise 1   Identifying Conjunctions
1. while, subordinating
2. yet, coordinating
3. but, coordinating
4. both/and, correlative
5. while, subordinating
6. than, subordinating
7. Neither/nor, correlative
8. as soon as, subordinating
9. so that, subordinating
10. wherever, subordinating

Exercise 2   Adding Conjunctions in Sentences
Sample conjunctions are given.
1. If
2. both/and
3. and

4. neither/nor
5. Although
6. so
7. Whenever
8. or
9. both/and
10. After

19.2   Conjunctions and Interjections (Different Kinds of Conjunctions) (Page 38)
Practice 2
Exercise 1   Identifying Conjunctions
1. Either, or (correlative)
2. nor (coordinating)
3. When (subordinating)
4. until (subordinating)
5. either, or (correlative)
6. Wherever (subordinating)
7. but (coordinating)
8. not only, but also (correlative)
9. yet (coordinating)
10. because (subordinating)
11. Both, and (correlative)
12. As soon as (subordinating)
13. or (coordinating)
14. Neither, nor (correlative)
15. If (subordinating)
16. while (subordinating)
17. because (subordinating)
18. so (coordinating)
19. after (subordinating)
20. and (coordinating)

Exercise 2   Using Conjunctions in Sentences
Sample conjunctions are given.

Jason had always wanted to visit the Capitol, (1) so (coordinating) he signed up for the 1:00 tour. At the appointed time, the tourists (2) and (coordinating) their guide set out on the tour of the famous building. The guide pointed out interesting items (3) as (subordinating) the group got close to them.

It was (4) neither hot nor (correlative) extremely humid, (5) but (coordinating) Jason could barely concentrate. (6) Even though (subordinating) he had looked forward to the tour, he was now eager for it to end.

Jason looked at his watch, (7) for (coordinating) he was wondering how much longer the tour would continue. It was three o'clock, (8) and (coordinating) the tour was supposed to be over. It seemed (9) as if (subordinating) the tour guide would never stop talking. (10) "Either this guide ends the tour immediately or (correlative) I will have to be rude and leave," thought Jason.

19.2   Conjunctions and Interjections (Page 39)
Practice 1
Exercise 1   Recognizing Conjunctive Adverbs
1. besides
2. therefore
3. none
4. indeed
5. nevertheless
6. none
7. again
8. then
9. none
10. consequently

Exercise 2   Adding Interjections to Sentences

Sample interjections are given.
1. Ouch!
2. Alas,
3. Gosh!
4. Super!
5. Wow!
6. Oh!
7. Drat!
8. Darn!
9. Wow!
10. Whew!

19.2   Conjunctions and Interjections (Page 40)
Practice 2
Exercise 1   Recognizing Conjunctive Adverbs

Sample conjunctive adverbs (the ones not underlined) are given.
1. nevertheless
2. however
3. therefore,
4. thus,
5. consequently
6. otherwise,
7. moreover
8. finally
9. however,
10. then,

Exercise 2   Supplying Interjections

Sample interjections are given.
1. Darn!
2. Wow!
3. Ouch!
4. Goodness!
5. Oh!

Writing Application
Using Conjunctions and Conjunctive Adverbs to Combine Sentences

Sample conjunctions and conjunctive adverbs are given in the sentences.
1. The team practiced hard all week, but they did not win the match.
2. We yanked the door open and Jody stumbled out.
3. Either I will go or I will stay.
4. He insisted on driving although he had never driven a truck before.
5. It rained; therefore, the game was canceled.

20.1   The Sentence (Complete Subjects and Predicates) (Page 41)
Practice 1
Exercise 1   Recognizing Complete Subjects and Predicates

1. S
2. S
3. P
4. P
5. P
6. S
7. P
8. S
9. S
10. P

Exercise 2   Identifying Complete Subjects and Predicates

1. Several members of that family have served in the armed forces.

2. Louise borrowed my sweater last week.
3. A pane in one of the bedroom windows cracked.
4. Lemmings follow their leader to their death.
5. A portrait of my grandmother hangs above the mantel.
6. The first pianist on the program seemed nervous.
7. All the children in the neighborhood enjoyed the new playground.
8. Searchlights from the rescue ships flashed across the water.
9. The fans of the losing team groaned.
10. Philip or his brother will surely help you.

20.1   The Sentence (Complete Subjects and Predicates) (Page 42)
Practice 2
Exercise 1   Recognizing Complete Subjects and Predicates

1. The car swerved away from the child.
2. My favorite radio station plays all of the hit songs.
3. Grandfather Kim owns an art gallery in Chicago.
4. Mexico City was built on a lake.
5. The evening news summarizes the day's events.
6. Shakespeare's father was a glove maker.
7. Computers process information very quickly.
8. My older brother has a telephone shaped like Mickey Mouse.
9. The bags of coins were placed in an armored truck.
10. Damascus, the capital of Syria, has been continuously inhabited for over four thousand years.
11. Mr. Axelrod worked for years as a traveling salesman.
12. The magma in a volcano is called lava when it reaches the air.
13. The ancient Greeks were the first people to have free public museums.
14. People in ancient times used the abacus to compute numbers.
15. Some museums are devoted entirely to computers.
16. Some species of bats are very beneficial to the environment.
17. More than five hundred volcanoes have erupted over the centuries.
18. Our sun is a typical, medium-sized star.
19. The gravity of the sun is almost twenty-eight times the gravity of Earth.
20. Some planets have one or more moons.

Exercise 2   Recognizing Complete Subjects and Predicates

(1) The giant panda lives in the remote mountains of southern China. (2) This animal is a frustrating mystery to zoologists. (3) The Chinese name for the panda is xiong-mao, or "bear-cat." (4) However,

mal is not a cat. (5) Zoologists do not agree

_at its identity. (6) Some call it a bear. (7) Others

place it in the same family as the raccoon. (8) Sadly,

the panda is becoming rare. (9) The reason for this is

the scarcity of bamboo, their main food. (10) The panda

populations can be saved only through worldwide

efforts.

20.1 The Sentence (Sentence or Fragment?) (Page 43)
Practice 1
Exercise 1 Distinguishing Between Sentences and Fragments
1. F
2. F
3. S
4. F
5. S
6. F
7. F
8. F
9. S
10. S

Exercise 2 Adding Words to Make Sentences from Fragments
Sample sentences are numbered according to the numbers of the fragments from which they are made.
1. We did the job without any trouble at all.
2. The children played quietly after dinner.
4. We succeeded beyond our wildest expectations.
6. People from all parts of the world visit Washington, D.C.
7. The contestant with the most unusual costume will win a prize.
8. My uncle has traveled widely throughout the United States.

20.1 The Sentence (Sentence or Fragment?) (Page 44)
Practice 2
Exercise 1 Distinguishing Between Sentences and Fragments
1. fragment
2. fragment
3. sentence
4. fragment
5. fragment
6. sentence
7. fragment
8. sentence
9. fragment
10. sentence
11. fragment
12. sentence
13. fragment
14. sentence
15. fragment

Writing Application
Using Fragments to Make Sentences
Sample pairings are given.
1. His Roman costume / was tangled in the stage scenery.
2. The children / scored a goal for the opposing team.

3. The girl with butterflies in her stomach / spoke to the flag instead of to the class.
4. The curious horse / wandered into the tack room.
5. The boy with the confused expression / took the wrong bus.
6. Lemon jello inside empty eggshells / can fool people.
7. Their cousins coming for dinner / thought the raccoon was a ghost.
8. The man standing on the corner/ was wearing his shirt inside out.
9. Her long, pointed putty nose / stuck to the stage.
10. Her friends at the slumber party / put sugar at the bottom of her sleeping bag.

20.1 Subjects and Verbs (Simple Subjects and Predicates) (Page 45)
Practice 1
Exercise 1 Recognizing Complete and Simple Subjects and Predicates
1. The (album) with the original cast / (is) now available in most stores.
2. (Senator Billings) / (will propose) the new law.
3. The fourth (Thursday) in November / (is celebrated) as Thanksgiving Day.
4. The (skydiver) / (landed) safely.
5. (Youngsters) / sometimes (jump) from those high rocks.
6. (Dignitaries) from all over the world / (attended) the reception.
7. The children's elaborate (skyscraper) / (collapsed) .
8. (Ghosts) / (are) popular Halloween characters.
9. Several (students) from Europe / (are staying) with local families.
10. The mysterious (figure) in black / (vanished) .

Exercise 2 Adding Sentence Parts
Sample sentences are given.
1. From among the many entries, only (one) (will win) .
2. Every (visitor) to our school (must check) in at the office.

3. (Ed) gradually (overcame) the fear of heights.

4. My younger (brother) (has) just (learned) to ride a two-wheeler.

5. (One) of my classmates (has misplaced) a library book.

20.1 Subjects and Verbs (Simple Subjects and Predicates) (Page 46)
Practice 2
Exercise 1 Recognizing Simple Subjects and Predicates

1. A sixteen-year-old girl from California / gave the best dramatic interpretation.
2. A muddy dog of unknown breed / ran away with Bernard's lunch.
3. Her friends at school / helped her get a job.
4. The weary commuters / were angry about the delay.
5. The freshman with the most unusual hat / won the contest.
6. The boxes under the sink / are empty.
7. The frightened witnesses / wrote reports for the police.
8. The speaker / caught his fishing pole on the light fixture.
9. Students going on the trip / left early this morning.
10. The forward with the knee brace / made ten baskets.

Exercise 2 Finding Subjects and Verbs

Subject	Verb
1. tourist	gets
2. visitors	can take
3. Hikers	may want
4. walls	make
5. trip	is
6. Trips	enable
7. Tourists	can take
8. passengers	can see
9. aircraft	can fly
10. tourists	can see

Writing Application
Using Subjects and Verbs to Write Sentences
Sample sentences are given.
1. The truck is stopping near the store.
2. The girl jumped from the couch to the floor.
3. The steak shriveled as it cooked.
4. During the hurricane, the wind was shrieking.
5. The radio blared rock music.
6. The lawnmower sputtered as it started.
7. The antique automobile is wobbling down the road.
8. The warm water in the pool feels good.
9. The waiter dropped a tray filled with desserts.
10. The newscaster hiccupped during the evening newscast.

20.1 Compound Subjects and Verbs (Page 47)
Practice 1
Exercise 1 Recognizing Compound Subjects
1. carrots, tomatoes
2. Cheese, crackers
3. Nancy, Darryl, I
4. Time, tide
5. ferns, wildflowers
6. brother, I
7. table, food
8. Jason, Ulysses
9. Pueblos, hogans, tepees
10. stocks, pillories

Exercise 2 Recognizing Compound Verbs
1. eats, sleeps
2. checked, posed, snapped
3. did hesitate, acted
4. hoisted, pulled
5. ate, drank
6. baked, cooked
7. organized, began
8. pruned, fertilized
9. waved, looked
10. study, do

20.1 Compound Subjects and Verbs (Page 48)
Practice 2
Exercise 1 Recognizing Compound Subjects

1. flowers, perfume
2. David, Marie
3. pets, pianos
4. Lettuce, tomatoes, peppers, cucumbers
5. Hurricanes, tornadoes

Exercise 2 Recognizing Compound Verbs
1. skidded, hit
2. howled, died
3. lifted, crushed
4. is, offers
5. waddled, splashed, paddled
6. built, used
7. washed, put
8. survived, died
9. erected, faced
10. rehearsed, had, gave

Writing Application
Writing Sentences with Compound Subjects and Verbs

Students' sentences should demonstrate proficiency in forming compound subjects and compound verbs.

20.2 Hard-to-Find Subjects (in Orders and Directions, in Questions) (Page 49)
Practice 1
Exercise 1 Finding the Subject in Orders or Directions
The subject of every sentence is [you].
1. Bank, ^ turn
2. difficulties, ^ do
3. ^ Please
4. Alison, ^ don't
5. ^ Blacken
6. Derek, ^ please
7. ^ Meet
8. Mandy, ^ please

...t, ^ buckle
    /Help

1. you
2. parents
3. casserole
4. you
5. anyone
6. Claytons
7. Shakespeare
8. Who
9. Sue
10. we

20.2   Hard-to-Find Subjects (in Orders and Directions, in Questions) (Page 50)
Practice 2
Exercise 1   Finding Subjects in Orders or Directions
1. After school, [you] come straight home.
2. Joanne, [you] give me a quarter.
3. Now [you] tell me what happened.
4. When using that machine, [you] always wear safety goggles.
5. Sue, [you] order me a milkshake, please.
6. After class, [you] meet me at the library.
7. Pete, during takeoff, [you] keep your seatbelt fastened.
8. Before leaving, [you] pack a good lunch.
9. Dad, [you] turn left at the end of the exit ramp.
10. When filling out that form, [you] use ink.

Exercise 2   Finding Subjects in Questions
1. Have you seen the new horror movie?
2. When will Sally be home?
3. Who baked this cake?
4. About what will Andy write?
5. Are the final reports complete?
6. Is the story ready for publication?
7. Why hasn't Judy answered my note?
8. What did Jack wear to the game?
9. Has Joyce finished her term paper yet?
10. Which team won the championship?

20.2   Hard-to-Find Subjects (in Sentences Beginning with *There* or *Here*, in Sentences Inverted for Emphasis) (Page 51)
Practice 1
Exercise 1   Finding the Subject in Sentences Beginning with There or Here
1. mayor
2. proofs
3. sunset
4. land
5. custodian
6. restaurant
7. book
8. doubt
9. chance
10. helicopter

Exercise 2   Finding the Subject in Inverted Sentences
1. rabbit
2. meadow
3. rumors
4. bush
5. story
6. throng
7. generations
8. Statue of Liberty
9. tons
10. houses

20.2   Hard-to-Find Subjects (in Sentences Beginning with *There* or *Here*, in Sentences Inverted for Emphasis) (Page 52)
Practice 2
Exercise 1   Finding Subjects in Sentences Beginning with *There* or *Here*
1. keys
2. bus
3. excuse
4. kite
5. pizza
6. rest
7. papers
8. rolls
9. sister
10. seeds

Exercise 2   Finding Subjects in Inverted Sentences
1. rainbow
2. bells
3. peaks
4. children
5. leaves
6. feeling
7. neighbors
8. man
9. possessions
10. sound

Writing Application
Writing Sentences with Hard-to-Find Subjects
Sample sentences are given.
1. Take this letter to the post office.
2. Are you going to the park?
3. There goes the last bus of the day.
4. Out of the tunnel roared the freight train.

20.3   Direct Objects (The Direct Object, Compound Direct Objects) (Page 53)
Practice 1
Exercise 1   Recognizing Direct Objects
1. tapes
2. performance
3. classes
4. reward
5. decay
6. call
7. basketball
8. turn
9. pencils
10. her

Exercise 2   Recognizing Compound Direct Objects
1. basketball, soccer
2. fame, fortune
3. soup, salad
4. car, jackpot
5. chess, checkers
6. roller, brush
7. pancakes, omelets
8. boots, purse
9. sandwich, milk
10. biology, chemistry

20.3 Direct Objects (The Direct Object, Compound Direct Objects) (Page 54)

Practice 2

Exercise 1 Recognizing Direct Objects

1. history
2. them
3. power
4. king
5. symbol
6. it
7. shape
8. sunshade
9. hat
10. parasols

Exercise 2 Recognizing Compound Direct Objects

1. hammer, nails
2. jacket, shirt, trousers
3. house, barn
4. Joan, Jack
5. cars, trucks
6. fruit, cereal
7. shrubs, bushes
8. cinnamon, sugar
9. you, me
10. cabbage, tomatoes, lettuce, peppers
11. bulletin board, pamphlets
12. salad, soup
13. woodchucks, rabbits
14. roses, carnations
15. filing, word processing
16. Montana, Idaho
17. sonnets, plays
18. points, plugs
19. sprouts, radishes
20. history, literature

20.3 Direct Objects (Direct Object or Object of a Preposition) (Page 55)

Practice 1

Exercise 1 Distinguishing Between Direct Objects and Objects of Prepositions

Direct objects are given.

1. fruit
2. (none)
3. novel
4. (none)
5. planes
6. fruit
7. blanket
8. sunset
9. fear
10. (none)

Exercise 2 Writing Sentences with Direct Objects

Sample sentence endings are given.

1. her ankle
2. a prize
3. the movie
4. the band
5. *The Last of the Mohicans*
6. a poem about a bird
7. everything in the house
8. a nest in the pine tree
9. the championship game
10. your books away

20.3 Direct Objects (Direct Object or Object of a Preposition) (Page 56)

Practice 2

Exercise 1 Distinguishing Between Direct Objects and Objects of Prepositions

1. none
2. none
3. umbrellas
4. them
5. umbrellas
6. uproar
7. view
8. dispute
9. none
10. games

Writing Application

Writing Sentences with Direct Objects

Sample sentences are given.

1. The police will escort the prisoner.
2. The truck dented the trunk of the car.
3. Mr. Lopez described the school in great detail.
4. The elephant trampled the bushes.
5. The water ruined the carpet.
6. Eileen organized the charity luncheon.
7. Craig should have won the race, but he couldn't after his shoe fell off.
8. Grasshoppers can destroy crops.
9. The detectives found clues to the murder case.
10. A loud noise shook the whole house.

20.3 Indirect Objects (Indirect Objects, Compound Indirect Objects) (Page 57)

Practice 1

Exercise 1 Recognizing Indirect Objects

1. us
2. children
3. teacher
4. school
5. warden
6. guests
7. you
8. him
9. player
10. dog

Exercise 2 Recognizing Compound Indirect Objects

1. Mom, Dad
2. teachers, aides
3. painter, helper
4. me, others
5. Doug, Karen
6. Mom, Grandma
7. cousins, me
8. players, families
9. chain, sprocket, axles
10. Santa, reindeer

20.3 Indirect Objects (Indirect Objects, Compound Indirect Objects) (Page 58)

Practice 2

Exercise 1 Recognizing Indirect Objects

1. He told his parents the news.
2. Greg ordered us seconds.
3. The receptionist gave the messenger an envelope.
4. The sitter read Paul two stories at bedtime.
5. I lent Amanda my pink sweater.
6. Ms. Hall showed us slides of Venice.
7. Who sent you these flowers?

andy hasn't written <u>me</u> a letter for weeks.
....om left the <u>painters</u> a note.
....Mr. Poirot teaches his <u>students</u> French.
11. You owe <u>me</u> a more complete explanation than that.
12. Please do <u>Sylvia</u> this favor.
13. Give <u>James</u> a call about your plans for the trip.
14. The <u>federal</u> government sent the flooded <u>city</u> aid.
15. Henry gave the <u>school</u> a memorial bench.
16. The coach handed the team <u>members</u> their new jerseys.
17. Mr. Costanza bought his <u>daughter</u> a new bicycle for her birthday.
18. Emma knitted her <u>granddaughter</u> a lavender blanket.
19. The store owner sold the young <u>child</u> a defective toy.
20. The politician told the <u>people</u> his plans for the future.

Exercise 2 Recognizing Compound Indirect Objects
1. us
2. (Joyce), (me)
3. us
4. group
5. (Helen), (Max)
6. us
7. (Helen), (Joyce), (Max)
8. ourselves
9. (raccoons), (animals)
10. us

20.3 Indirect Objects and Objective Complements (Page 59)
Practice 1
Exercise 1 Distinguishing Between Indirect Objects and Objects of Prepositions
1. indirect object
2. object of preposition
3. indirect object
4. indirect object
5. object of preposition
6. object of preposition
7. indirect object
8. object of preposition
9. indirect object
10. indirect object

Exercise 2 Recognizing Objective Complements
1. proud, adjective
2. treasurer, noun
3. guilty, adjective
4. quiet, adjective
5. Jem, noun

20.3 Indirect Objects and Objective Complements (Page 60)
Practice 2
Exercise 1 Distinguishing Between Indirect Objects and Objects of Prepositions
1. prepared us a
2. handed the rattle to
3. showed four apartments to
4. sold the county his
5. bring the children some

Exercise 2 Recognizing Objective Complements
1. treasurer

2. depressed
3. wizard
4. red
5. angry

Writing Application
Using Indirect Objects to Combine Sentences
1. The sitter prepared Paul a snack.
2. The waiter served Ann my order.
3. I made my mother a macramé belt.
4. The realtor rented us the apartment.
5. The principal gave our class an award.

20.3 Subject Complements (Predicate Nominative, Predicate Adjective) (Page 61)
Practice 1
Exercise 1 Recognizing Predicate Nominatives
1. team
2. subjects
3. lawyer
4. figure
5. fondue
6. one
7. success
8. choice
9. officer
10. detective

Exercise 2 Recognizing Predicate Adjectives
1. unworkable
2. unbecoming
3. disappointed
4. cheerful
5. restless
6. beautiful
7. nervous
8. better
9. stronger
10. sunny

20.3 Subject Complements (Predicate Nominative, Predicate Adjective) (Page 62)
Practice 2
Exercise 1 Recognizing Predicate Nominatives
1. player
2. children
3. I
4. classic
5. thing
6. ones
7. governor
8. swordfish
9. friends
10. candidate
11. sister
12. chaos
13. salmon
14. cinnamon
15. friend

Exercise 2 Recognizing Predicate Adjectives
1. heavenly
2. awful
3. moldy
4. delicious
5. better
6. cloudy
7. angry
8. hot
9. unhappy

10. tan
11. treacherous
12. hot
13. full
14. unhappy
15. high

20.3 Subject Complements (Compound Subject Complements) (Page 63)
Practice 1
Exercise 1   Recognizing Compound Subject Complements
1. Kim, Karen; PN
2. steak, shrimp, chicken; PN
3. attractive, affordable; PA
4. lawyer, politician; PN
5. mean, vicious; PA
6. hard, dusty; PA
7. pancakes, sausage; PN
8. ready, waiting; PA
9. owner, chef; PN
10. bent, discolored; PA

Exercise 2   Writing Sentences with Compound Subject Complements
Sample subject complements are given.
1. and unkind
2. and spicy
3. and welcome
4. or Becky
5. and Jay
6. and excited
7. and cheese
8. and talented
9. nor angry
10. and February

20.3 Subject Complements (Compound Subject Complements) (Page 64)
Practice 2
Exercise 1   Recognizing Compound Subject Complements

1. visitors, out-of-towners (predicate nominative)
2. furniture, paintings (predicate nominative)
3. larger, better (predicate adjective)
4. old, valuable (predicate adjective)
5. pastels, watercolors, oils (predicate nominative)
6. Dutch, Italian (predicate adjective)
7. graceful, elegant (predicate adjective)
8. table, clock, lamp (predicate nominative)
9. rugs, gardens (predicate nominative)
10. free, open (predicate adjective)

Writing Application
Writing Sentences with Subject Complements
Sample sentences are given.
1. Our best friends are Jason and Todd.
2. The dogs became restless.
3. The baby grew tired and grouchy.
4. Eric became president of the class.
5. The singer was Diana Ross.
6. The leaves turned red and orange in the fall.
7. My favorite vegetables are carrots and peas.
8. The guests looked amazed.
9. The announcer's voice sounded hoarse.
10. Through the years, Agnes remained a fine lawyer.

21.1   Prepositional Phrases (Page 65)
Practice 1
Exercise 1   Identifying Adjective Phrases
1. (one) of us
2. (houses) on our street
3. (report) about a different capital
4. (party) for Mary
5. (teacups) from different countries
6. (bike) in the shop window
7. (difference) between Gerri and her twin sister
8. (lot) down the street
9. (statue) of a bird
10. (top) of the wall

Exercise 2   Identifying Adverb Phrases
1. (good) for another month
2. (moved) to Mexico
3. After all your hard work, (deserve)
4. With your help, (finished)
5. After high school, (became)
6. (arrived) at the theater
7. With only slight hesitation, (approached)
8. (slipped) under the gate
9. Outside the theater (watched)
10. (far) into the country

21.1   Prepositional Phrases (Page 66)
Practice 1
Exercise 1   Identifying Adjective Phrases

	Adjective Phrase	Word Modified
1.	of the car	price
2.	of books	box
3.	in the yellow sweater	one
4.	on the corner	house
	of our street	corner
5.	of the wounded animal	cry
6.	by the same author	book
7.	of the two objects	shapes
8.	in the corner	something
	of the room	corner
9.	behind the couch	window
10.	about Mr. Hill	article

Adverb Phrase	Word Modified
over low heat	simmer
2. on newcomers	tougher
3. to the wrong house	delivered
4. during the storm	hit
5. across the roof	ran
into the tree	jumped
6. from us	away
7. around the world	sailed
8. before dark	returned
9. over the breakwater	rose
onto the roadway	rose
10. into the backyard	run
out of the rain	take

21.1 Appositives and Appositive Phrases (Page 67)

Practice 1

Exercise 1 Identifying Appositives

1. (play) *Cats*

2. (president) George Washington

3. (magazine) *Time*

4. (award) Oscar

5. (park) Hammer Field

6. (friend) Dora

7. (principal) Mrs. Spiegel

8. (April 19) Patriots' Day

9. (brother) Mike

10. (capital) St. Paul

Exercise 2 Identifying Appositive Phrases

1. (Norma Ellis), a local TV reporter

2. (Talmadge), the candidate with the best record

3. (unicorn), a creature with one horn

4. (Natick), a Native American language

5. (wok), a large pan with a rounded bottom

6. (movie), another in the popular science-fiction series

7. (flowers), members of the same family

8. (road), a link between the two largest cities in the state

9. (Judy), the girl in the last row

10. (cousin), a senior at Eastern High

21.1 Appositives and Appositive Phrases (Page 68)

Practice 2

Exercise 1 Identifying Appositives

1. lawyer, (Mr. Smith)

2. Alice, (sister)

3. saltbox, (house)

4. Ms. Hughes, (reporter)

5. "Snowbound," (poem)

6. Ms. Jenkins, (teacher)

7. Mary Cassatt, (artist)

8. cheesecake, (dessert)

9. Shelley, (poet)

10. pizza, (dinner)

11. Dorothy, (cousin)

12. Sharon, (candidate)

13. *The Thinker*, (work)

14. Thames, (river)

15. Bill Carlton, (suspect)

Exercise 2 Identifying Appositive Phrases

1. a trip for two to Hawaii, (prize)

2. an old station wagon, (car)

3. a track star at UCLA, (sister)

4. a comedy about army life, (movie)

5. friend of ours, (boys)

6. a pitcher on the second team, (player)

7. our noisy neighbor, (Mrs. Hunt)

8. a federal court judge, (father)

9. her favorite game, (Chess)

10. a genius with a paint brush, (artist)

11. an ancient city in Greece, (Thebes)

12. a talented skateboarder, (Stevie)

13. a restored Victorian, (house)

14. a novel by Herman Melville, (Moby-Dick)

15. the longest river in South America, (Amazon)

21.1 Appositives and Appositive Phrases (Compound Appositives) (Page 69)
Practice 1
Exercise 1 Identifying Compound Appositives

1. (desserts) , cheesecake and brownies

2. (tragedy) , *Hamlet* or *Macbeth*

3. (states) , Alaska and Hawaii

4. (awards) , a Tony, an Oscar, and an Emmy

5. (explorers) , Lewis and Clark

6. (houses) , a small Cape Cod or a rambling ranch-style

7. (battery) , pitcher and catcher

8. (couple) , a man and woman from Utah

9. (Marx Brothers) , Harpo, Groucho, Chico, Zeppo, and Gummo

10. (dignitaries) , the King and Queen of Spain

Exercise 2 Writing Sentences with Appositives, Appositive Phrases, and Compound Appositives
Sample sentences are given.

1. Ed Jenkins, a local disc jockey, went to college with my father.
2. Ebenezer Scrooge, the main character in Dickens' *A Christmas Carol*, is a symbol of miserliness.
3. Mom had several choices, stuffed chicken, lasagna, or baked fish, for the main course.
4. Both home teams, the Bears and the Cubs, were high in the standings.
5. Their new apartment, once a loft with fourteen-foot ceilings, is quite spacious.

21.1 Appositives and Appositive Phrases (Compound Appositives) (Page 70)
Practice 2
Exercise 1 Identifying Compound Appositives

	Compound Appositive	Words Renamed
1.	fish, plants	food
2.	pearls, sponges, shells	riches
3.	skin diving, breath-hold diving	method
4.	a very simple type of diving, a popular form of recreation today	Skin diving
5.	fins, masks, snorkels	equipment
6.	hollow reeds for snorkels, tortoise shells for goggles	equipment
7.	glass, plastic	materials
8.	Cousteau, Gagnan	Frenchmen
9.	more mobility, increased time under water	advantages
10.	compressed-air tanks, wet suits	gear

Writing Application
Using Appositives and Appositive Phrases to Combine Sentences

1. The book, an autobiography, was published in many languages.
2. A neighbor's tree became the graveyard for their colorful kite, a large dragon with a silver tail.
3. Candice completed the race in spite of her injury, a twisted ankle.
4. The memorial, a simple, symbolic structure made of white stone, honors the people who died while in service during World War II.
5. Mount Shasta, a volcano, towers thousands of feet above the surrounding valleys and plateaus.

21.1 Participles and Participial Phrases (Participles; Verb or Participle?) (Page 71)
Practice 1
Exercise 1 Identifying Participles

1. falling (star) , present

2. leading (hitter) , present

3. puzzled (expression) , past

4. broken (vase) , past

5. baked (apples) , past

6. casting (director) , present

7. pressing (appointment) , present

8. frightened (child) , past

9. flying (carpet) , present

10. borrowed (book) , past

Exercise 2 Distinguishing Between Verbs and Participles
1. verb
2. participle
3. participle
4. verb
5. participle
6. verb
7. verb
8. participle
9. participle
10. verb

21.1 Participles and Participial Phrases (Participles; Verb or Participle?) (Page 72)
Practice 1
Exercise 1 Identifying Participles
1. howling, present
2. injured, past
3. crumbling, present
4. Stumbling, present
5. falling, present
6. frozen, past
7. disappointed, past
8. Hurt, past
9. blaring, present
10. torn, past
11. freezing, present

hausted, past
ndling, present
cornered, past
5. broken, past

Exercise 2 Distinguishing Between Verbs and Participles
1. verb
2. participle, delegation
3. participle, yogurt
4. verb
5. verb
6. participle, company
7. verb
8. participle, truck
9. participle, jewels
10. verb
11. verb
12. participle, poodle
13. verb
14. participle, sonnets
15. participle, soldiers

21.1 Participles and Participial Phrases (Participial Phrases) (Page 73)
Practice 1
Exercise 1 Recognizing Participial Phrases

1. (train) arriving on track 10

2. (book) signed by the author

3. Looking hot and tired, (players)

4. (seafood) cooked in that restaurant

5. Found in an abandoned barn, (painting)

6. (girl) passing out the programs

7. (Anyone) wishing an application

8. Frightened by the horror movie, (child)

9. (bush) growing beside the front steps

10. (dog), chained to a stake

Exercise 2 Writing Sentences with Participial Phrases
1. The small boy sitting at the end of the pier has caught nothing all day.
2. The sun setting behind the mountains is a beautiful sight.
3. Many books written by that author have been bestsellers.
4. Appearing somewhat nervous, the speaker approached the microphone.
5. The players sitting on the bench cheered for their teammates.

21.1 Participles and Participial Phrases (Participial Phrases) (Page 74)
Practice 1
Exercise 1 Recognizing Participial Phrases

Participial Phrase	Word Modified
1. shaded by trees	house
2. Kicking stones	children
3. packed with people	subway

4. Frightened by the smoke they
5. steaming from the oven pie

Writing Application
Using Participial Phrases to Combine Sentences
Sample sentences are given.
1. Not accepting the coins, the tollbooth buzzed. Word Modified: tollbooth
2. The soft music, flowing out of the restaurant, invites passersby to enter. Word Modified: music
3. Spraying water onto the faces of the crew, the outrigger canoe raced along the tops of the waves. Word Modified: canoe
4. Snapped by the hurricane, the telephone poles hung dangerously over the road. Word Modified: poles
5. Placing her shot carefully, Dolores hit the ball to her opponent's backhand. Word Modified: Dolores

Writing Application
Writing Sentences with Participial Phrases
Sample sentences are given.
1. Writing a letter to his wife, the soldier took advantage of some free time.
2. Laughing at the comedian's jokes, the audience enjoyed the show.
3. Cooked to a golden brown, the steak was delicious.
4. Her passport stamped, Marie continued on her journey.
5. Amusing the researcher, the nineteenth-century photographs provided a glimpse into a time long past.

21.1 Gerunds and Gerund Phrases (Gerunds; Verb, Participle, or Gerund?) (Page 75)
Practice 1
Exercise 1 Recognizing Gerunds
1. Winning, S
2. learning, OP
3. dieting, OP
4. knitting, S
5. swimming, OP
6. Jogging, S
7. reading, DO
8. painting, Appos.
9. drilling, OP
10. fishing, PN

Exercise 2 Distinguishing Between Verbs, Participles, and Gerunds
1. V
2. P
3. G
4. G
5. V
6. P
7. P
8. G
9. V
10. G

21.1 Gerunds and Gerund Phrases (Gerunds; Verb, Participle, or Gerund?) (Page 76)
Practice 2
Exercise 1 Identifying Gerunds
1. reading, OP
2. acting, DO
3. Dribbling, S
4. picnicking, DO

© Prentice-Hall, Inc.

5. sewing, PN
6. chirping, Appos.
7. Loving, S; trusting, PN
8. dancing, DO
9. Weeding, S
10. batting, OP; running, OP
11. Swimming, S
12. studying, S
13. climbing, DO
14. skating, IO
15. dreaming, OP

Exercise 2 Distinguishing Between Verbs, Participles, and Gerunds

1. participle
2. gerund
3. verb
4. verb
5. gerund
6. participle
7. gerund
8. participle
9. verb
10. verb
11. gerund
12. participle
13. participle
14. verb
15. gerund

21.1 Gerunds and Gerund Phrases (Gerund Phrases) (Page 77)

Practice 1

Exercise 1 Recognizing Gerund Phrases

1. working in the garden, DO
2. collecting old coins, PN
3. Practicing for several hours a day, S
4. changing the menu, DO
5. Driving along the mountain road, S
6. the swelling around the injury, DO
7. thanking all her campaign workers, OP
8. writing a rough draft, PN
9. cooking gourmet meals, Appos.
10. becoming a rock star, OP
11. disturbing anyone, OP
12. running for office, IO
13. Recognizing shapes and colors, S
14. the singing of the national anthem, OP
15. setting the table before each meal, DO
16. his exquisite cooking, OP
17. taking far too much time on the project, OP
18. Decorating the gym, S
19. working crossword puzzles, DO
20. her yawning so openly, OP

Exercise 2 Writing Nouns and Pronouns Before Gerunds

1. our
2. His
3. Tom's
4. Her
5. My

21.1 Gerunds and Gerund Phrases (Gerund Phrases) (Page 78)

Practice 1

Exercise 1 Identifying Gerund Phrases

1. running down a hill (object of a preposition)
2. climbing mountains in state parks (predicate nominative)

3. following the pro golfers around the course (object of a preposition)
4. camping by the river (direct object)
5. panning gold (object of a preposition)
6. Flying an airplane in bad weather (subject), extensive training (direct object)
7. Running out of gas (subject)
8. riding the waves (object of a preposition)
9. Going to bed late (subject), getting up early (subject)
10. hearing a story (object of a preposition), playing a game (object of a preposition), hearing a story (direct object)
11. Visiting the art museum (subject)
12. flying kites (object of a preposition)
13. conducting the choir (direct object)
14. jumping from airplanes (predicate nominative)
15. Watching television all day (subject)

Writing Application

Writing Sentences with Gerund Phrases

Sample sentences are given.
1. His staring at me made me uncomfortable.
2. A good antidote to sadness is joking as much as possible.
3. The TV program was about driving in heavy traffic.
4. They continued whispering about the teacher.
5. We tried sliding the huge box.

21.1 Infinitives and Infinitive Phrases (Infinitives; Prepositional Phrase or Infinitive?) (Page 79)

Practice 1

Exercise 1 Identifying Infinitives

1. to beat, adj.
2. to refuse, adv.
3. to win, noun
4. to take, adj.
5. to make, adv.
6. to lead, adj.
7. to win, adv.
8. to keep, adj.
9. to learn, adv.
10. to sit, adj.

Exercise 2 Distinguishing Between Prepositional Phrases and Infinitives

1. Inf.
2. PP
3. PP
4. Inf.
5. PP
6. Inf.
7. Inf.
8. PP
9. Inf.
10. PP

21.1 Infinitives and Infinitive Phrases (Infinitives; Prepositional Phrase or Infinitive?) (Page 80)

Practice 1

Exercise 1 Identifying Infinitives

1. to protest (noun)
2. to win (noun)
3. to drive (noun)
4. to succeed (adverb)
5. to visit (adjective)
6. to swim (noun)

read (adjective)

_write (noun)

_o buy (adjective)

_. to take (adjective)

11. to open (noun)
12. to invite (noun)
13. to reach (adjective)
14. to cook (adjective)
15. to continue (adverb)

Exercise 2   Distinguishing Between Prepositional Phrases and Infinitives

1. to study (infinitive)
2. To win (infinitive)
3. to Seattle (prepositional phrase)
4. to ski (infinitive)
5. to school (prepositional phrase)
6. to visit (infinitive)
7. to headquarters (prepositional phrase)
8. to Alaska (prepositional phrase)
9. to go (infinitive)
10. to Europe (prepositional phrase)
11. to say (infinitive)
12. to the audience (prepositional phrase)
13. to lend (infinitive)
14. to Pam (prepositional phrase)
15. to teach (infinitive)

21.1   Infinitives and Infinitive Phrases (Infinitive Phrases) (Page 81)
Practice 1
Exercise 1   Recognizing Infinitive Phrases

1. to ask for directions, adj.
2. to call home, adj.
3. infants to ride in special seats, noun
4. to see the new car, adv.
5. to invite her to the party, noun
6. to finish the job in time, adv.
7. to defend against the enemy, adv.
8. to help with refreshments, adj.
9. to vote for, adj.
10. Phil to rake the yard, noun

Exercise 2   More Work with Infinitive Phrases

1. the Olympic torch bearer *(to) pass* by
2. *to give* me extra help
3. him *(to) sing* in person
4. the sun *(to) rise* over the ocean
5. visitors *to tour* the house
6. *(to) ask* for another piece of pie
7. Linda *(to) change* her mind
8. *to read* the directions carefully
9. Clare *to visit* for the weekend
10. us *(to) find* a good place for dinner.

21.1   Infinitives and Infinitive Phrases (Infinitive Phrases) (Page 82)
Practice 1
Exercise 1   Identifying Infinitive Phrases

1. To carry out their missions (adv.)
2. to become astronauts (adv.)
3. to have a degree in engineering, physical science, or mathematics (dir. obj.)
4. to perform scientific experiments (adv.)
5. to complete flight training (dir. obj.)
6. To prepare for missions (adv.)
7. to train for missions (adv.)
8. to work hard (obj. of prep.)
9. to succeed at difficult tasks (adj.)
10. us feel proud of their accomplishments (dir. obj.)

Writing Application
Writing Sentences with Infinitive Phrases
Sample sentences are given.

1. His main ability is to change his way of working when adapting to new situations.
2. Exercises ____ to build muscle ____ also make bones stronger.
3. To paint the interior of the house was a big job.
4. She had the option to refuse help.
5. The dancer decided to leap across the stage.
6. Helen's objective is to know William well.
7. This package to send to your sister weighs six pounds.
8. To spoil the story by telling the ending is not very nice.
9. I have always wanted to meet you.
10. To advise others about their behavior requires great tact.

21.2   Adjective Clauses (Page 83)
Practice 1
Exercise 1   Recognizing Adjective Clauses

1. who led in the polls
2. that are on sale
3. who lives in this state
4. that was elected four times
5. that can say several sentences
6. whom the police arrested
7. that once stood here
8. which was crumpled and torn
9. who was favored to win the race
10. who can speak Portuguese

Exercise 2   Identifying Adjective Clauses and the Words They Modify

1. (people) who have experience with lions and tigers
2. (carton) that contained the dishes
3. (trapper) who knew the woods well
4. (dollar) that he ever earned
5. (uncle) who had been kind to him
6. (beggar) whom the poor farmer helped
7. (treasurer) who can add and subtract
8. (girl) who made the dragon kite
9. (page) that has the brownie recipe on it
10. (woman) whom she had admired for so long

21.2   Adjective Clauses (Page 84)
Practice 1
Exercise 1   Identifying Adjective Clauses

1. I met a woman (who) works with your mother.
2. Have you thought of a place (where) we can meet?

3. Is this the person (whom) you saw in the library?

4. I found the book (that) I needed.

5. She remembers the days (when) there were trolley cars.

6. Did Harriet tell you the reason (why) she left?

7. I lost the sweater (that) Aunt Sue made me.

8. Have they found the girl (who) was lost?

9. Most people (who) visit the museum are impressed.

10. The pictures (that) I took are not ready yet.

11. James Fenimore Cooper, (who) wrote *The Last of the Mohicans*, died in 1851.

12. The baseball cards (that) Peter bought last year have increased in value.

13. My aunt, (whom) you met last week, is on vacation now.

14. The restaurant, (which) is near the river, has an outdoor patio.

15. Carol grows vegetables in the backyard, (where) she also grows flowers.

Exercise 2 Identifying Adjective Clauses and the Words They Modify
1. Crocuses are usually the first flowers that bloom. flowers
2. She works in the town where the movie was filmed. town
3. The boys who play handball with me go to Central. boys
4. Is this the weekend that you are leaving? weekend
5. The scene that reveals the hero's secret is the best. scene
6. The dessert that I ordered never came. dessert
7. Did you find all of the tools that you needed? tools
8. They can subpoena anyone who refuses to testify. anyone
9. The books that you ordered will be in next week. books
10. Is he the one who told you about the meeting? one
11. The advice that my dad gave me could apply to you as well. advice
12. The poem, which is written in iambic pentameter, is quite lovely. poem
13. The three girls who tried out for the team all made it. girls

14. The space under the porch, where the dog rests during the day, is very cool. space
15. The yarn that the cat is playing with is made of fine wool. yarn

21.2 Adjective Clauses (Relative Pronouns and Relative Adverbs) (Page 85)
Practice 1
Exercise 1 Recognizing the Use of Relative Pronouns
1. (that) I wanted to read, DO (of infinitive)
2. (who) returned her lost dog, S
3. in (which) those lines appear, OP
4. (who) has the fewest points, S
5. (whose) name everyone knows, Adj.
6. (that) should follow this one, S
7. in (which) the President flies, OP
8. (whose) opinions are usually sound, Adj.
9. (that) I am reading now, DO
10. with (whom) I usually play doubles, OP

Exercise 2 Recognizing Adjective Clauses with Relative Adverbs
1. (where) flooding was severe
2. (why) Laura was so late
3. (where) the treasure is buried
4. (before) the telegraph was invented
5. (when) the fire occurred

21.2 Adjective Clauses (Relative Pronouns and Relative Adverbs) (Page 86)
Practice 1
Exercise 1
1. (whose) paintings are among the most famous in the world (adjective)
2. with (whom) he worked for several years (object of a preposition)
3. (who) needed the services of an artist (subject)
4. (that) were usually the jobs of an engineer (subject)
5. on (which) plays were performed (object of a preposition)

Exercise 2 Recognizing the Use of Relative Adverbs
1. Anna wouldn't tell us the reason (why) she quit.

2. In the week (since) the report was filed, many of the facts have been changed.

3. It was a day (when) we all enjoyed every minute.

4. The stands (where) the dignitaries would sit were draped with bunting.

5. In the twelve years (since) I visited Greece, I have learned to speak German.

Writing Application
Using Adjective Clauses to Combine Sentences

1. Give this package to the person who is at the door.

2. Tomorrow is the day when school starts.

3. The player who is everyone's favorite struck out.

4. The book that I got from the library is about Africa.

5. For a reason that no one knows, the candidate has withdrawn.

21.2 Adverb Clauses (Page 87)
Practice 1
Exercise 1 Identifying Adverb Clauses

1. (unless) both doors are closed

2. (where) the other reference books are shelved

3. (whenever) she gets the chance

4. (After) you have beaten the eggs

5. (if) the door is opened

6. (until) the shortage ends

7. (because) the lighting was poor

8. (even though) it rained off and on

9. (while) the red light is on

10. (as) the jet taxied to the runway

Exercise 2 Completing Elliptical Clauses
1. When he was younger
2. than they valued the prize money
3. as if they were dazed
4. than the Seals are
5. if it is possible
6. as an adverb does (or *acts*)
7. than theirs is
8. as Glenda does
9. If they are ready
10. than Van Winkle is

21.2 Adverb Clauses (Page 88)
Practice 1
Exercise 1 Identifying Adverb Clauses

1. (when) you have time

2. (Because) the music was so loud

3. (since) I forgot to mail the invitations

4. (when) you were in Bloomington

5. (before) I had finished breakfast

6. (Even though) it was raining

7. (wherever) she goes

8. (since) I saw you last

9. (until) the report was finished

10. (Before) you leave

Exercise 2 Identifying Adverb Clauses and the Words They Modify

1. I (called) you before I fell asleep.

2. I will not be able (to finish) while you are here.

3. (Will) you (wait) until I get a sweater ?

4. Mom likes (skating) when the ice is thick.

5. (Put) those books where the others are.

6. The old house was (quiet) after the guests had left.

7. Though it was still early, many of the picnickers (were leaving) .

8. I feel (better) than I did yesterday.

9. Jay (stood) in the wings while he waited for his cue.

10. Daisy plans (to work) as soon as we leave.

Exercise 3 Recognizing Elliptical Adverb Clauses

1. than I (was) .

2. where we had left them.

3. as if no one knew their whereabouts.

4. than our team (is) .

5. than (they wanted) a videotape machine.

21.2 Noun Clauses (Page 89)

Practice 1

Exercise 1 Identifying Noun Clauses

1. When the next meeting will be held, S
2. what we have, OP
3. that he had driven in the winning run, DO
4. what she said, DO
5. that she could have a horse of her own, PN
6. how tall the robber had been, OP
7. What happened next, S
8. that the cost of living would keep rising, DO
9. how the movie ends, PN
10. if the Penguins won this afternoon, DO

Exercise 2 Recognizing the Use of Introductory Words

1. (Whose) woods these are, adj.

2. (where) the treasure is buried, adv.

3. (who) will be playing tennis next week, S

4. (Whoever) leaves last, S

5. (what) she said next, DO

21.2 Noun Clauses (Page 90)

Practice 1

Exercise 1 Identifying Noun Clauses

1. No one understands why Tim is afraid of the dark. (direct object)
2. Jean chose to write about how bees communicate. (object of a preposition)
3. Where the treasure is buried remains a mystery. (subject)
4. He wrote to whoever promised to write back. (object of a preposition)
5. Our biggest worry was where we would end up. (predicate nominative)
6. My sister has not decided what she wants to study. (direct object)
7. That he didn't ask his neighbors to the party suggests his dislike of them. (subject)
8. The most difficult question was whether the land should be re-zoned. (predicate nominative)
9. He gave whoever flattered him his friendship. (indirect object)
10. They consulted about who would do the job. (object of a preposition)
11. We wondered which route was shorter. (direct object)
12. Her excuse was that she had lost the assignment. (predicate nominative)
13. Why he dropped the class isn't clear. (subject)
14. Whoever you hire must speak French. (subject)
15. They worried about how they would cross Death Valley. (object of a preposition)

Exercise 2 Recognizing the Uses of Introductory Words

1. Do you know (whether) Ms. Hall will be in today ? (no function)

2. (What) she wanted to speak about was Judy's decision. (object of a preposition)

3. Just leave a message with (whoever) answers the phone. (subject)

4. Pete feared (that) he would forget his lines. (no function)

5. The university catalog lists (which) professor gives each course. (adjective)

6. (Whether) you go or stay makes no difference. (no function)

7. Do you know (whose) keys these are? (adjective)

8. The governor said (that) she would not run again. (no function)

9. The real issue is (who) would do a better job. (subject)

10. We began without knowing (where) we were headed. (adverb)

11. (Whoever) draws the short straw must do the dishes. (subject)

12. No one told us (what) we were looking for. (object of a preposition)

13. The rumor is (that) the house is haunted. (no function)

14. Someone should have told us (how) he would react. (adverb)

15. No one could remember (where) the keys were. (adverb)

21.2 Sentences Classified by Structure (Page 91)

Practice 1

Exercise 1 Distinguishing Between Simple and Compound Sentences

1. compound
2. simple
3. simple
4. compound
5. compound

Exercise 2 Identifying the Structure of Sentences

1. 3
2. 1
3. 2
4. 2
5. 1
6. 4
7. 1
8. 3
9. 3
10. 4

21.2 Sentences Classified by Structure (Page 92)

Practice 1

Exercise 1 Identifying the Structure of Sentences

1. compound
2. simple
3. complex

4. simple
5. compound
6. simple
7. complex
8. compound-complex
9. compound
10. complex

Writing Application
Writing Sentences with Different Structures
Sample sentences are given.
1. The story opens with a plane crash.
2. I like to dance, but Jerome does not.
3. The snow, which fell during the night, completely covered the little cottage.
4. This photograph, which was taken by my mother, is not very good, but she had it enlarged anyway.
5. Computers have changed the way we live.
6. Sparky is only a small dog, but he has a very loud bark.
7. This Siamese cat, which has beautiful blue eyes, is very curious.
8. Wendy traveled to Venice, where she rode in a gondola, and she also traveled to Egypt.
9. Sally's entire family sat at the same table on Thanksgiving.
10. San Francisco, which is a favorite tourist destination, can get quite cold in the summer, and tourists can often be seen shivering on the cable cars.

22.1 Sentences Classified by Function (Page 93)
Practice 1
Exercise 1 Identifying the Function of Sentences
1. imperative
2. interrogative
3. interrogative
4. declarative
5. imperative
6. exclamatory
7. imperative
8. declarative
9. declarative
10. interrogative

Exercise 2 Choosing the Correct End Mark by Function
1. (!)
2. (?)
3. (!)
4. (!)
5. (.)
6. (?)
7. (!)
8. (.)
9. (.)
10. (.)

22.1 Sentences Classified by Function (Page 94)
Practice 2
Exercise 1 Identifying the Function of Sentences
1. (.) declarative
2. (.) imperative
3. (.) declarative
4. (.) declarative
5. (?) interrogative
6. (.) declarative
7. (!) exclamatory
8. (.) declarative
9. (.) imperative
10. (.) declarative

Writing Application
Writing Sentences with Different Structures and Functions
Sample sentences are given.
1. I enjoy all kinds of food.
2. I like classical music and I like jazz.
3. Julia enjoys her chemistry class even though the class requires much homework.
4. Even though the candidates agree on many issues, one candidate believes in cutting taxes, and the other wishes to hold the tax level where it is.
5. Are you going away for the weekend?
6. Would my friend enjoy bicycle riding or would she like hiking better?
7. If I asked my friend to go to the party with me, would she say "yes"?
8. Because I have that day off, should I go to the basketball game or should I stay home and relax?
9. Clean out that closet right now.
10. I can't believe how roomy the closet is!

22.2 Sentence Combining (Page 95)
Practice 1
Exercise 1 Combining Sentences
Sample sentences are given.
1. Arthur asked a question that the teacher couldn't answer.
2. We visited the house where Abraham Lincoln had lived.
3. Did you see the exam schedule on the bulletin board?
4. Several students who are good writers requested a class newspaper, but no advisor was available.
5. The cake is easy to make if you follow the recipe.

Exercise 2 More Work with Combining Sentences
Sample sentences are given.
1. We tried to make a gingerbread house that we had seen in a magazine, but the walls collapsed.
2. Alvin entered the competition even though his coach advised against it.
3. Because he is a very popular musician, thousands of people showed up to buy tickets for one of his concerts.
4. Marc Chagall, a famous painter, created those stained-glass windows in a chapel in the South of France.
5. I need that book for my report, but the librarian, who ordered it for me, said it has not come in yet.

22.2 Sentence Combining (Page 96)
Practice 1
Exercise 1 Combining Sentences
Sample sentences are given.
1. As the dazed guests stumbled out of the house, the host called the police to report the fire.
2. Last year, farmers turned the soil in the north field and planted soybeans and corn.
3. The moon rose over the hills and cast long shadows across the valley.
4. A hand, a unit of measure used to specify the height of a horse, equals four inches.
5. At the picnic we had some special games: an egg toss, a pie-eating contest, a bake-off, and a three-legged race.

Writing Application
Further Practice in Combining Sentences
Sample sentences are given.
1. Though the eruption of a volcano can be destructive, volcanic eruptions also enrich the soil and bring water up to the surface.
2. Mount Pelée in Martinique and Kilhauea in Hawaii are both active volcanoes.
3. Snow began to fall in the morning and had accumulated to six inches by evening.
4. Though a reporter for a newspaper is very busy, the city desk editor is even busier.
5. A reporter tracks down the details of a story and then writes an article, but the editor must be familiar with all of the developing stories to choose which ones to print.

22.3 Varying Your Sentences (Expanding Short Sentences, Shortening Long Sentences) (Page 97)
Practice 1
Exercise 1 Adding Details to Short Sentences
Sample sentences are given.
1. That plant has magnificent flowers growing on tall spikes.
2. The same menu, a seven-course feast, is served every New Year's Eve.
3. The athletes prepared well to compete in the biggest event of their lives.
4. The story aroused her curiosity because it dealt with a topic that was of great interest to her.
5. They learned more about chess by talking with the expert.

Exercise 2 Shortening Sentences
Sample sentences are given.
1. A group of us had arranged to work together on a huge banner for the pep rally. However, we soon began to disagree about how to design it.
2. Having rehearsed several weeks both in the classroom and on the stage, we felt quite confident when the day of the dress rehearsal finally came. We were firmly convinced that all would go well.

22.3 Varying Your Sentences (Expanding Short Sentences, Shortening Long Sentences) (Page 98)
Practice 2
Exercise 1 Adding Details to Short Sentences
Sample sentences are given.
1. We must develop new sources of energy to provide for the future as well as the present.
2. The teller slowly and tediously counted one-dollar bills.
3. The bicycle rider crossed the finish line, followed closely by an enthusiastically cheering crowd.
4. The noise of the scuba divers salvaging the downed submarine came from beneath the water.
5. The hikers returned eager to tell about their adventure.

Exercise 2 Shortening Long Sentences
Sample sentences are given.
1. Ants are warlike creatures and natural empire builders. They attack weaker insects to increase the numbers of their slaves and the size of their territory.
2. The boat's crew located the sound and used radar to track its course through the harbor but could not identify the sound. Whatever lurked beneath the surface circled the area for almost thirty minutes.

3. Gale-force winds buffeted the tiny seacoast village, including Judd Beere's old, single-masted sloop. Tied to the rotting town dock, the sloop's lines strained against rusty cleats until first one and then another gave way.
4. Helen was determined to compete in the marathon and had been training for the race for several months. She exercised and ran one mile each morning and five miles each afternoon.

22.3 Varying Your Sentences (Using Different Sentence Openers, Using Different Sentence Structures) (Page 99)
Practice 1
Exercise 1 Using Different Sentence Openers
Sample sentences are given.
1. Occasionally, the train makes whistle stops to discharge passengers.
2. To be sure of seeing the kick-off, we allowed plenty of time.
3. When they entertain, my parents ask us to serve and clean up.
4. Usually I have no problem with math.
5. At night, we watched fireflies in the backyard.

Exercise 2 Using Different Sentence Structures
A sample revised paragraph is given.

Not only was Thomas Jefferson a great public leader, but he was also an architect and an inventor. Jefferson bought land on a small mountain and named it Monticello, meaning "little mountain." When Jefferson built a home there, he was his own architect and builder. In addition, Jefferson invented the dumbwaiter that was used in Monticello as well as revolving bookshelves for his library.

22.3 Varying Your Sentences (Using Different Sentence Openers, Using Different Sentence Structures) (Page 100)
Practice 2
Exercise 1 Identifying Sentence Openers
1. When the storm ended (clause)
2. Proudly (one-word modifier)
3. The mayor (subject)
4. To do somersaults on a trampoline (phrase)
5. Hissing loudly (phrase)
6. Lost (one-word modifier)
7. Pedro (subject)
8. In the street eight floors below (phrase)
9. While Angie entertained the guests (clause)
10. Usually (one-word modifier)

Exercise 2 Using Different Sentence Openers
Sample sentences are given.
1. Before you assemble a model, you should read the instructions carefully.
2. Insulted, Carol turned on her heel and stalked out.
3. Because of a jackknifed tractor-trailer, the cars on the highway were backed up for miles.
4. At the end of the graduation ceremony, the auditorium was filled with the sound of cheering.
5. At 1300 hours, the spacecraft encountered the other ship.
6. Happily, the governess waved to Meg on the Ferris wheel.
7. To check for cavities and other problems, see the dentist at least twice a year.
8. Predictably, a mid-afternoon solar eclipse drew hundreds of onlookers into the street.

9. When the great fire erupted, Chicago was a thriving young city.
10. Enthusiastically, the actor campaigned for the senator.

22.4 Fragments (Recognizing Fragments) (Page 101)
Practice 1
Exercise 1   Identifying Sentence Fragments
1. sentence
2. fragment
3. sentence
4. fragment
5. fragment
6. sentence
7. fragment
8. fragment
9. fragment
10. sentence
11. sentence
12. fragment
13. fragment
14. fragment
15. sentence
16. sentence
17. fragment
18. fragment
19. sentence
20. sentence

Exercise 2   Identifying Fragments in a Paragraph
2. Which we would carry ourselves.
4. As some Indians had dragged their tepees.
5. The day before the expedition
8. Including rice, nuts and dried fruits, and beans.
9. After one last check of our list.

22.2 Fragments (Recognizing Fragments) (Page 102)
Practice 2
Exercise 1   Identifying Sentence Fragments
1. F
2. F
3. F
4. F
5. S
6. F
7. S
8. F
9. S
10. F
11. F
12. S
13. F
14. F
15. S
16. F
17. S
18. S
19. F
20. F

Exercise 2   Identifying Fragments in a Paragraph
(1) Basketball is the only major sport that originated in the United States. (2) Invented by a Canadian, James Naismith, who was teaching at the Y.M.C.A. in Springfield, Massachusetts, at the time. (3) The students there were studying to become secretaries and physical education instructors. (4) Bored with the marching, calisthenics, and gymnastics that made up their gym classes. (5) The head of the department had a talk with Naismith. (6) In the fall of 1891. (7) Asking the Canadian teacher to develop a game that could be played in a gym. (8) Had no physical contact. (9) Lightweight ball. (10) To make it safe for the students and also for the school's gym. (11) Each player was to have an equal chance to handle the ball. (12) And to make plays. (13) By December, Naismith had developed what he called "the game." (14) Intended to nail up some boxes to serve as targets. (15) No boxes being available, they nailed up some half-bushel peach baskets instead. (16) The game was soon called *basket ball*. (17) By 1902 the word was often hyphenated. (18) Becoming *basket-ball*. (19) It wasn't until about 1912 that the name of the game was written as one word. (20) It's interesting to note that if the school had had some boxes, we might be playing boxball today.

22.4 Fragments (Correcting Fragments) (Page 103)
Practice 1
Exercise 1   Identifying Kinds of Sentence Fragments
1. phrase
2. series
3. sentence
4. clause
5. sentence
6. phrase
7. clause
8. phrase
9. sentence
10. phrase

Exercise 2   Correcting Fragments
Sample sentences are given.
1. Some people find it hard to make friends in a new place.
2. A wide meadow, a babbling brook, and bright sunshine made a perfect setting for a picnic.
4. Is she someone that you invited to the party?
6. Kelly agreed without a second thought.
7. We can leave whenever you are ready.
8. The reward offered by the dog's owner was generous.
10. The action during the first scene was dull.

22.4 Fragments (Correcting Fragments) (Page 104)
Practice 2
Exercise 1   Using Phrase Fragments to Write Sentences
Sample sentences are given.
1. My aunt was surprised to see my picture on the front page of our local newspaper.
2. To sing folk songs professionally, one must have a beautiful voice.
3. Many beautiful birds visit our bird feeder.
4. I sat on the back porch drinking from a green glass a refreshing ice tea.
5. A dark, menacing cloud loomed just to the west.

Exercise 2   Using Clause Fragments to Write Sentences

Sample sentences are given.
1. When I awoke this morning, I knew this would be my lucky day.
2. This is the poem that my class likes best.
3. You'll never get any better at tennis unless you practice each day.
4. If it is cold tomorrow, I'll wear my warm coat.
5. Who waited in line all day for tickets?

Exercise 3   Using Series Fragments to Write Sentences

Sample sentences are given.
1. The pet shop featured calico kittens, green parakeets, and dachshund puppies.
2. The happy child ran, skipped, and jumped around the yard.
3. The cleanser is either in the drawer, on the top shelf of the closet, or under the sink.
4. I love sunsets that are deep orange, yellow, or red.
5. She skated slowly, methodically, and quite gracefully.

22.4   Run-ons (Recognizing Run-ons) (Page 105)
Practice 1
Exercise 1   Identifying Run-ons

1. sentence
2. run-on
3. run-on
4. run-on
5. sentence
6. sentence
7. run-on
8. run-on
9. run-on
10. sentence
11. sentence
12. run-on
13. run-on
14. sentence
15. run-on
16. sentence
17. run-on
18. sentence
19. sentence
20. run-on

Exercise 2   Identifying Run-ons in a Paragraph

1. Some rooms still need painting not all the light fixtures are in.
4. We have ordered new trees and shrubs, they will be delivered this weekend.
6. Rick and I have picked out a perfect spot for a vegetable garden, Dad has other ideas.
7. Mom plans a flower bed in front there is a perfect sunny spot for it.
8. We have already put in grass seed, it needs to be watered every day.
10. It is hard work every bit is worth it.

22.4   Run-ons (Recognizing Run-ons) (Page 106)
Practice 2
Exercise 1   Identifying Run-ons

1. RO
2. S
3. RO
4. RO
5. S
6. RO
7. RO
8. S
9. S
10. RO
11. RO
12. RO
13. RO
14. S
15. S
16. S
17. RO
18. RO
19. RO
20. RO

22.4   Run-ons (Correcting Run-ons) (Page 107)
Practice 1
Exercise 1   Preparing to Correct Run-ons

1. speaker ^ he
2. C
3. tax, ^ they
4. plants ^ they
5. reward ^ no
6. defense ^ they
7. C
8. life ^ they
9. bend, ^ the castle
10. once ^ it

Exercise 2   Correcting Run-ons

Sample sentences are given.
1. Senator Hill, the graduation speaker, talked about responsibility.
3. Several council members who opposed the tax voted against it
4. Many cactuses are odd-looking plants, but they have beautiful blossoms.
5. Although the owner offered a handsome reward, no trace of the show dog was found.
6. The troops had no defense; they were completely surrounded.
8. Lighthouse keepers have a lonely life, but they do important work.
9. As we rounded the bend, the castle came into view.
10. Judy recognized the bike at once as the one she had sold last week.

22.4   Run-ons (Correcting Run-ons) (Page 108)
Practice 2
Exercise 1   Using Punctuation and Conjunctions to Correct Run-ons

Sample corrections are given.
1. I could hardly wait to jump in; the water looked so inviting.
2. They seemed to expect me to babysit again. I wouldn't do it for any price.
3. When a stray dog wandered onto the field, the outfielder tried to catch it.
4. We spent hours searching for the car keys, but we never found them.
5. Would you care for French dressing on your salad, or would you prefer it unseasoned?

Exercise 2   Forming Simple and Complex Sentences to Correct Run-ons

Sample sentences are given.
1. Because Mr. Adams was a candidate for mayor, he spoke to many community organizations.

2. The iguana, a family pet, raced across the yard.
3. The snow was piled around the parked cars, making it impossible for us to leave.
4. Delighted with the gift, the child began to play with it right away.
5. I couldn't handle the luggage alone because I had three suitcases and a small trunk.

Writing Application
Correcting Run-ons
A sample corrected passage is given.

(1) After flying through a dense, seemingly endless cloud bank, the shuttle plane with its pilot, co-pilot, and three nervous passengers was lost. (2) Neither the pilot nor the co-pilot could recognize any landmarks. (3) One of the passengers a young girl, entered the pilot's cabin and asked if she could help. (4) Although worried, the pilot, who was very good-natured, smiled.

(5) The girl explained that she recognized the terrain. Her father had taken her camping in these hills just last summer. (6) "If you turn slightly and fly over that far ridge," explained the girl, "you will see a highway. (7) Follow it west, and it will lead toward Pescadora."

(8) The pilot and co-pilot thanked the girl and complimented her on her keen sense of direction. (9) Their praises pleased the girl and also gave her an idea. (10) As soon as she finished school, she would take flying lessons.

22.4 Misplaced Modifiers (Page 109)
Practice 1
Exercise 1 Recognizing Misplaced Modifiers
1. with minor flaws
3. with her new baby
4. with a cry of delight
5. that his uncle left him
6. without success
7. in his lunchbox
9. many times that day
10. with whalebone ribs

Exercise 2 Correcting Misplaced Modifiers
Sample sentences are given. Modified words are circled.

1. The sale at Bower's features (shirts) with minor flaws for men.

3. While I was scrubbing the floor, my (sister) dropped in with her new baby.

4. With a cry of delight, Clare (opened) the package brought by the letter carrier.

5. Charlie squandered all the (money) that his uncle left him on new records.

6. Without success, Dad has been (looking) for a mechanic who can repair our car.

7. In his lunchbox, Paul (had) a tomato that he had grown himself.

9. Many times that day, Ms. Dove (threatened) to keep the class after school.

10. In 1700, the first practical (umbrella), with whalebone ribs, was invented by an anonymous Englishman.

22.4 Misplaced Modifiers (Page 110)
Practice 2
Exercise 1 Recognizing Misplaced Modifiers
1. who delivered the package
2. wearing green golf shoes
3. to win the prize
4. correct
5. correct
6. that was hungry
7. happily surprised
8. Sailing into port
9. Soaring gracefully over the treetops
10. Correct

Exercise 2 Correcting Misplaced Modifiers
Sample sentences are given. Modified words are circled.

1. A (sundae), dripping with chocolate sauce, was served to each guest.

2. After a few minutes, Wilkins (realized) the mistake he had made.

3. The dean spoke to the (boys) in the principal's office about loitering.

4. We gave the scraps of (meat) that had been left on our plates to the dog.

5. After shopping carefully, Michelle (bought) an umbrella with red and yellow stripes.

6. The ballad singer (heard), while wandering through the hill country, most of the songs he later sang.

7. Waiting for a bear to come along, the (hunter) with a bow and arrow crouched behind a tree.

8. Sniffing in the bushes, the (bloodhound) picked up the fugitive's scent.

9. Driving through the South, (we) saw many beautiful homes.

10. Wilma put the (trophies) that she had won in golf tournaments into a glass cabinet.

22.4 Dangling Modifiers (Page 111)
Practice 1
Exercise 1 Recognizing Dangling Modifiers
1. Born into a poor family
2. no dangling modifier
3. Taking the stairs two at a time
4. After stepping into the shower

5. Descending by a different trail
6. After walking across the hot sand
7. Practicing for weeks
8. no dangling modifier
9. Sympathizing with the flood victims.
10. Arriving a day late

Exercise 2   Correcting Dangling Modifiers
Sample sentences are given. Modified words are circled.

1. Born into a poor family, (he) thought college was an impossible dream.

3. Taking the stairs two at a time, (he) still could not get to class before the bell rang.

4. After stepping into the shower, (Sarah) could only listen as the telephone rang.

5. Descending by a different trail, (we) avoided the hazardous slope.

6. After walking across the hot sand, (we) were relieved to find a clump of trees.

7. After practicing for weeks, (she) finally mastered the difficult sonata.

9. Sympathizing with the flood victims, (people) from all over the world sent in donations.

10. Arriving a day late, (we) found that our tickets were worthless.

22.4   Dangling Modifiers (Page 112)
Practice 2
Exercise 1   Recognizing Dangling Modifiers
1. Skating across the pond, the ice was very slick.
2. Studying for weeks, the test was easy.
3. Considering my small allowance, the tickets were expensive.
4. Writing letters at camp all afternoon, home seemed far away.
5. Correct

Exercise 2   Correcting Dangling Modifiers
Sample sentences are given. Modified words are circled.

1. Trying to get to town quickly, (we) decided to take the highway.

2. While jogging one morning, (I) discovered the obvious solution to the problem.

3. When Paula was five, her mother (graduated) from the university.

4. Wandering aimlessly in the woods, (we) welcomed the first sight of camp.

5. Hearing of the refugees' plight, the (government) made available emergency funds.

6. Getting up much earlier than usual, (I) found the house strangely quiet.

7. When Dan developed measles, his father (called) the school.

8. Absorbed in the crossword puzzle, (I) found the time passed quickly.

9. Waiting for a ride, (I) watched the rain pounding down all around.

10. Sailing far from shore, (we) saw a squall suddenly arise.

Writing Application
Correcting Misplaced and Dangling Modifiers
A sample corrected paragraph is given.

(1) Washington Irving's stories often contain elements of fantasy. (2) In one story that Irving wrote, Rip van Winkle slept through the whole American Revolution. (3) When Rip awoke, his rusted musket should have told him that something unusual had happened. (4) While strolling into town, Rip was greeted by other puzzling things. (5) The faces of the people he met were all strange. (6) Rip noticed George Washington's portrait hanging over the door of the inn. (7) King George's portrait had always hung there before. (8) Rip then looked for his old friend, the innkeeper. (9) Trying to find the innkeeper, Rip questioned an old man. (10) The old man replied, "He is dead these eighteen years."

23.1   Verb Tenses (Six Tenses of Verbs, Four Principal Parts of Verbs) (Page 113)
Practice 1
Exercise 1   Recognizing Tenses and Forms of Verbs
1. arranged, past
2. was working, past progressive
3. have ordered, present perfect
4. will have been working, future perfect progressive
5. stay, present
6. will visit, future
7. has been snooping, present perfect progressive
8. had hoped, past perfect
9. had been experimenting, past perfect progressive
10. will have left, future perfect

Exercise 2   Identifying Principal Parts
1. arranged, past
2. working, present participle
3. ordered, past participle
4. working, present participle
5. stay, present
6. visit, present
7. snooping, present participle
8. hoped, past participle
9. experimenting, present participle
10. left, past participle

23.1 Verb Tenses (Six Tenses of Verbs, Four Principal Parts of Verbs) (Page 114)

Practice 2

Exercise 1   Recognizing Basic and Progressive Forms

1. progressive
2. progressive
3. basic
4. basic
5. progressive
6. progressive
7. basic
8. basic
9. progressive
10. basic

Exercise 2   Recognizing the Six Tenses

1. present progressive
2. past progressive
3. present perfect
4. past perfect
5. present perfect progressive
6. future perfect progressive
7. past
8. future
9. past perfect progressive
10. future perfect

Exercise 3   Recognizing Principal Parts

1. present participle
2. present participle
3. past participle
4. past participle
5. present participle
6. present participle
7. past
8. present
9. present participle
10. past participle

23.1 Verb Tenses (Regular and Irregular Verbs) (Page 115)

Practice 1

Exercise 1   Writing the Principal Parts of Irregular Verbs

1. write, wrote, (have) written
2. fly, flying, (have) flown
3. seeing, saw, (have) seen
4. spin, spinning, spun
5. hurt, hurting, (have) hurt
6. fight, fought, (have) fought
7. drive, driving, drove
8. spending, spent, (have) spent
9. wind, winding, (have) wound
10. eat, ate, (have) eaten

Exercise 2   Recognizing Principal Parts of Verbs

1. burst
2. shrank
3. drew
4. said
5. climbed

23.1 Verb Tenses (Regular and Irregular Verbs) (Page 116)

Practice 2

Exercise 1   Learning the Principal Parts of Irregular Verbs

1. building, built, built
2. finding, found, found
3. getting, got, gotten

4. holding, held, held
5. drinking, drank, drunk
6. doing, did, done
7. bringing, brought, brought
8. bursting, burst, burst
9. flying, flew, flown
10. teaching, taught, taught

Exercise 2   Recognizing Principal Parts in Sentences

1. swung
2. drove
3. built
4. paid
5. bursting
6. cost
7. slept
8. laid
9. led
10. bound

Exercise 3   Correcting Principal Parts

1. no error
2. cross out *seen*, insert *saw*
3. cross out *knew*, insert *known*
4. no error
5. cross out *took*, insert *taken*
6. cross out *begun*, insert *began*
7. no error
8. no error
9. cross out *fighted*, insert *fought*
10. no error

23.1 Verb Tenses (Conjugating the Tenses) (Page 117)

Practice 1

Exercise 1   Conjugating Basic and Progressive Forms

1. I use, I used, I will use, I have used, I had used, I will have used, I am using, I was using, I will be using, I have been using, I had been using, I will have been using
2. he takes, he took, he will take, he has taken, he had taken, he will have taken, he is taking, he was taking, he will be taking, he has been taking, he had been taking, he will have been taking
3. we go, we went, we will go, we have gone, we had gone, we will have gone, we are going, we were going, we will be going, we have been going, we had been going, we will have been going
4. they see, they saw, they will see, they have seen, they had seen, they will have seen, they are seeing, they were seeing, they will be seeing, they have been seeing, they had been seeing, they will have been seeing

Exercise 2   Supplying the Correct Verbs

1. have been living
2. had lost
3. has found
4. will be visiting
5. is offering

23.1 Verb Tenses (Conjugating the Tenses) (Page 118)

Practice 2

Exercise 1   Conjugating the Basic Forms of Verbs

1. I open, I opened, I will open, I have opened, I had opened, I will have opened
2. you move, you moved, you will move, you have moved, you had moved, you will have moved
3. he knows, he knew, he will know, he has known, he had known, he will have known

Exercise 2   Conjugating the Progressive Forms of Verbs

1. you are walking, you were walking, you will be walking, you have been walking, you had been walking, you will have been walking
2. she is jumping, she was jumping, she will be jumping, she has been jumping, she had been jumping, she will have been jumping
3. they are saying, they were saying, they will be saying, they have been saying, they had been saying, they will have been saying

23.1   Expressing Time Through Tense (Uses of Tense in Present Time) (Page 119)
Practice 1

Exercise 1   Identifying the Use of Tense in Present Time

1. reoccurring action
2. constant action
3. reoccurring action
4. present condition
5. present action
6. continuing action
7. constant action
8. continuing action
9. reoccurring action
10. present action

Exercise 2   Using Present Tense Forms in Sentences
Sample verbs are given.

1. sleeps
2. grow
3. is giving
4. is
5. like
6. rent
7. borrows
8. is knocking
9. smells
10. is shining

23.1   Expressing Time Through Tense (Uses of Tense in Present Time) (Page 120)
Practice 2

Exercise 1   Identifying the Uses of Tense in Present Time

1. regularly occurring action
2. constant condition
3. regularly occurring action
4. present condition
5. present action
6. continuing action
7. constant action
8. continuing action
9. regularly occurring action
10. regularly occurring action
11. regularly occurring action
12. present condition
13. regularly occurring action
14. regularly occurring action
15. continuing action
16. constant condition
17. continuing condition
18. constant condition
19. continuing action
20. regularly occurring action

23.1   Expressing Time Through Tense (Uses of Tense in Past Time) (Page 121)
Practice 1

Exercise 1   Identifying the Use of Tense in Past Time

1. completed before another past event
2. continuous past event
3. indefinite past time
4. indefinite past time continuing to present
5. indefinite past time
6. event continuing to present
7. indefinite past time continuing to present
8. continuous past event before another
9. definite past time
10. continuous past event

Exercise 2   Using Tenses in Past Time

1. raised
2. has been
3. interfered
4. had escaped
5. has grown
6. was lying
7. has been acting
8. phoned
9. was writing
10. has been waiting

23.1   Expressing Time Through Tense (Uses of Tense in Past Time) (Page 122)
Practice 2

Exercise 1   Using Past, Present Perfect, and Past Perfect

1. grew
2. called
3. had waited
4. postponed
5. has ridden
6. visited
7. have been
8. had arrived
9. finished
10. had swum

Exercise 2   Identifying the Uses of the Progressive Forms in the Past

1. action continuing to present
2. continuing action interrupted by another
3. continuous completed action
4. action continuing to present
5. continuous completed action
6. continuous completed condition
7. continuous completed action
8. continuing action interrupted by another
9. action continuing to present
10. continuous completed action

23.1   Expressing Time Through Tense (Uses of Tense in Future Time) (Page 123)
Practice 2

Exercise 1   Identifying the Uses of Tense in Future Time

1. continuing future event
2. future event before another future event
3. continuing future event
4. continuing future event before another
5. future event

Exercise 2   Using Tenses in Future Time

1. will be studying
2. will be giving

3. will have been working
4. will be coming
5. will meet

23.2 Expressing Time Through Tense (Uses of Tense in Future Time) (Page 124)
Practice 2
Exercise 1 Identifying the Uses of Tense in Future Time
1. future action
2. continuing future action
3. future action
4. continuing future action
5. continuing future action completed before another

Exercise 2 Using Tenses in Future Time
1. will be traveling
2. will open
3. will have received
4. will leave
5. will have been speaking

23.1 Expressing Time Through Tense (Shifts in Tense) (Page 125)
Practice 1
Exercise 1 Recognizing Unnecessary Shifts in Tense
1. P
2. P
3. P
4. P
5. P
6. P
7. C
8. P
9. P
10. P

Exercise 2 Correcting Errors in Tense
Sample sentences are given.
1. We never have dinner before Dad gets home from work.
2. My sister will miss the twins when they are away.
3. Marcia began writing her paper before she read any sources.
4. The owner offers a reward to anyone who finds the dog.
5. Most likely we will be happier after we start our trip.
6. If Jason wins the election, he will revise the dress code.
8. Whenever you are ready, we will leave.
9. Hugo barks loudly if he hears anything unusual.
10. When we got to the pier, the boat was already leaving.

23.1 Expressing Time Through Tense (Shifts in Tense) (Page 126)
Practice 1
Exercise 1 Avoiding Unnecessary Shifts in Tense
1. replace *answered* with *answer*
2. replace *reads* with *read*
3. replace *do* with *did*
4. replace *greets* with *greeted*
5. replace *help* with *will help*
6. replace *have gone* with *had gone*
7. replace *get* with *got*
8. replace *got* with *gets*
9. replace *will be* with *are*
10. replace *has mailed* with *had mailed*

11. replace *have seen* with *saw*
12. replace *cleans* with *cleaned*
13. replace *barked* with *barks*
14. replace *has arrived* with *arrived*
15. replace *joined* with *will join*
16. replace *leave* with *left*
17. replace *did* with *does*
18. replace *will have done* with *will do*
19. replace *says* with *said*
20. replace *asks* with *asked*

Exercise 2 Correcting Errors in Tense
Correct answers are underlined.
2. cross out *gives*, insert *gave*
3. cross out *burns*, insert *burned*
5. cross out *is*, insert *had been*
7. cross out *is*, insert *was*
9. cross out *is*, insert *was*
10. cross out *has contained*, insert *contains*

23.2 Active and Passive Voice (Difference Between Active and Passive Voice, Forms of Passive Verbs) (Page 127)
Practice 1
Exercise 1 Distinguishing Between the Active and Passive Voice
1. passive
2. passive
3. active
4. passive
5. passive
6. active
7. passive
8. active
9. active
10. passive

Exercise 2 Forming the Tenses of Passive Verbs
1. it is said, it was said, it will be said, it has been said, it had been said, it will have been said
2. they are driven, they were driven, they will be driven, they have been driven, they had been driven, they will have been driven
3. you are told, you were told, you will be told, you have been told, you had been told, you will have been told
4. we are praised, we were praised, we will be praised, we have been praised, we had been praised, we will have been praised

23.2 Active and Passive Voice (Difference Between Active and Passive Voice, Forms of Passive Verbs) (Page 128)
Practice 2
Exercise 1 Distinguishing Between the Active and Passive Voice
1. passive
2. passive
3. active
4. active
5. passive
6. active
7. passive
8. active
9. active
10. passive
11. passive
12. passive
13. active

14. passive
15. active

Exercise 2 Forming the Tenses of Passive Verbs
1. it is typed, it was typed, it will be typed, it has been typed, it had been typed, it will have been typed, it is being typed, it was being typed
2. we are forgiven, we were forgiven, we will be forgiven, we have been forgiven, we had been forgiven, we will have been forgiven, we are being forgiven, we were being forgiven
3. it is sold, it was sold, it will be sold, it has been sold, it had been sold, it will have been sold, it is being sold, it was being sold
4. they are alerted they were alerted, they will be alerted, they have been alerted, they had been alerted, they will have been alerted, they are being alerted, they were being alerted

23.2 Active and Passive Voice (Using Voice Correctly) (Page 129)
Practice 1
Exercise 1 Distinguishing Between Appropriate and Inappropriate Uses of Passive Voice
1. U
2. A
3. U
4. U
5. A
6. U
7. A
8. U
9. U
10. U

Exercise 2 Using the Active Voice
1. The catcher hit a grand slam home run.
3. My favorite aunt knitted this sweater for me.
4. In 1983, Australia won the America's Cup races.
6. Paul made that model airplane.
8. The voters will judge the candidates on their merits, not on their speeches.
9. That dog has been following me for three blocks.
10. Mom is fixing dinner right now.

23.3 Active and Passive Voice (Using Voice Correctly) (Page 130)
Practice 2
Exercise 1 Correcting Unnecessary Use of the Passive Voice
A sample paragraph is given.

(1) For years, visitors to Loch Ness in Scotland have spotted a so-called monster. (2) Many witnesses have reported the large creature. (3) Do lake monsters really exist? (4) Scientists have questioned these reports. (5) According to some Canadian scientists, temperature inversions may explain the sightings. (6) A temperature inversion occurs when the temperature of a body of water is much lower than the temperature of the air above it. (7) Scientists conducted experiments on Lake Winnipeg, Canada, during a temperature inversion. (8) They took two photos, only three minutes apart, of an ordinary stick floating on the lake. (9) The bending, or refraction, of light caused by the inversion made the stick appear to be a strangely shaped "monster." (10) Some scientists accepted these photos as proof that the lake monsters are really ordinary objects that appear distorted because of a temperature inversion.

Writing Application
Using the Active and Passive Voice in Writing
Students' sentences should demonstrate the appropriate use of the active and the passive voices.

24.1 The Cases of Pronouns (The Three Cases) (Page 131)
Practice 1
Exercise 1 Identifying Case
1. obj.
2. poss.
3. poss.
4. obj.
5. poss.
6. nom.
7. poss.
8. obj.
9. poss.
10. obj.

Exercise 2 Identifying Pronoun Case and Use
1. obj., 4
2. nom., 1
3. obj., 5
4. poss., 6
5. nom., 1
6. obj., 3
7. poss., 6
8. nom., 2
9. poss., 6
10. obj., 5

24.1 The Cases of Pronouns (The Three Cases) (Page 132)
Practice 2
Exercise 1 Identifying Pronoun Case
1. The antique doll with the lace dress belonged to her. objective
2. The two brothers took their responsibilities seriously. possessive
3. Our doubts about getting there on time began to grow. possessive
4. Until the age of thirteen, she was afraid of dogs. nominative
5. His relationship with Elizabeth kept him going. possessive
6. Oscar handed me the tastefully wrapped package. objective
7. We had a garage sale last weekend. nominative
8. You never know what might happen. nominative
9. Do not pay any attention to them. objective
10. Is this cake yours or mine? possessive

Exercise 2 Identifying Case
1. nominative, subject
2. objective, indirect object
3. possessive, to show ownership
4. objective, direct object
5. objective, object of a preposition
6. possessive, to show ownership
7. nominative, subject
8. possessive, to show ownership
9. possessive, to show ownership
10. possessive, to show ownership
11. possessive, to show ownership
12. nominative, subject
13. nominative, predicate nominative
14. objective, indirect object
15. possessive, to show ownership
16. possessive, to show ownership

17. nominative, predicate nominative
18. objective, object of a preposition
19. objective, indirect object
20. nominative, subject

24.1 The Cases of Pronouns (Nominative Case, Objective Case) (Page 133)
Practice 1
Exercise 1 Identifying Pronouns in the Nominative Case
1. I, S
2. he, PN
3. they, PN
4. She, S
5. he, S

Exercise 2 Identifying Pronouns in the Objective Case
1. her, DO
2. him, OP
3. us, DO
4. me, IO
5. us, IO

24.1 The Cases of Pronouns (Nominative Case, Objective Case) (Page 134)
Practice 2
Exercise 1 Using Pronouns in the Nominative Case
Sample pronouns are given.
1. They, subject
2. It, subject
3. you, subject
4. you, predicate nominative
5. We, subject
6. He, subject
7. she, subject
8. he, subject
9. She, subject
10. he, subject

Exercise 2 Using Pronouns in the Objective Case
Sample pronouns are given.
1. us, indirect object
2. us, object of a preposition
3. us, indirect object
4. us, indirect object
5. him, direct object
6. us, indirect object
7. us, indirect object
8. him, object of a preposition
9. her, indirect object
10. him, direct object

24.1 The Cases of Pronouns (Possessive Case) (Page 135)
Practice 1
Exercise 1 Using Pronouns in the Possessive Case
1. His
2. mine
3. our
4. yours
5. her
6. his
7. theirs
8. My
9. its
10. their

Exercise 2 Using All Three Cases
1. theirs
2. we

3. her
4. My
5. yours
6. him
7. me
8. us
9. its
10. their

24.1 The Cases of Pronouns (Possessive Case) (Page 136)
Practice 2
Exercise 1 Using Pronouns in the Possessive Case
1. his
2. yours
3. its
4. his
5. His
6. ours
7. his
8. Their
9. yours
10. it's
11. Our
12. mine
13. Your
14. hers
15. His
16. You're
17. our
18. my
19. It's
20. its

Exercise 2 Using All Three Cases
1. him
2. Their
3. she
4. We
5. her, him
6. its
7. them, they
8. we, our
9. them
10. he, she

24.2 Special Problems with Pronouns (Who and Whom, Elliptical Clauses) (Page 137)
Practice 1
Exercise 1 Using Who and Whom Correctly
1. Whom
2. who
3. who
4. Who
5. who

Exercise 2 Using Pronouns in Elliptical Clauses
1. me
2. they
3. he
4. me
5. I

24.2 Special Problems with Pronouns (Who and Whom, Elliptical Clauses) (Page 138)
Practice 2
Exercise 1 Using Who and Whom in Questions and Clauses
1. who
2. whom

3. whom
4. who
5. whom
6. whose
7. who
8. whom
9. whom
10. who
11. who
12. who
13. Who's
14. who
15. whom
16. whom
17. whom
18. whom
19. Who
20. who

Exercise 0   Identifying the Correct Pronoun in Elliptical Clauses
Sample clause completions are given.
1. I have
2. I do
3. she is
4. he does
5. she was
6. she is
7. I can
8. she gave him
9. he did
10. she did

25.1   Subject and Verb Agreement (Number, Singular and Plural Subjects) (Page 139)
Practice 1
Exercise 1   Determining the Number of Words
1. plur.
2. both
3. both
4. plur.
5. sing.
6. both
7. plur.
8. sing.
9. sing.
10. both

Exercise 2   Making Subject and Verbs Agree
1. has, S
2. are, P
3. were, P
4. is, S
5. leads, S

25.1   Subject and Verb Agreement (Number, Singular and Plural Subjects) (Page 140)
Practice 2
Exercise 1   Determining the Number of Nouns, Pronouns, and Verbs
1. singular
2. plural
3. plural
4. singular
5. singular
6. singular
7. plural
8. singular
9. plural
10. singular
11. singular
12. singular
13. singular
14. singular
15. both
16. singular
17. singular
18. singular
19. both
20. both

Exercise 2   Making Subjects Agree With Their Verbs
1. stands
2. were
3. grows
4. were
5. are
6. was
7. belong
8. was
9. sail
10. are

25.1   Subject and Verb Agreement (Compound Subjects) (Page 141)
Practice 1
Exercise 1   Compound Subjects Joined by *Or* or *Nor*
1. like
2. is
3. baby-sits
4. has
5. is
6. are
7. buys
8. warm
9. get
10. delivers

Exercise 2   Compound Subjects Joined by *And*
1. have
2. was
3. are
4. are
5. represents

25.1   Subject and Verb Agreement (Compound Subjects) (Page 142)
Practice 2
Exercise 1   Making Compound Subjects Agree With Their Verbs
1. are
2. has
3. are
4. have
5. belongs
6. buy
7. have
8. have
9. aren't
10. were
11. walk
12. haven't
13. is
14. annoy
15. was

Exercise 2   Making Compound Subjects Agree With Their Verbs in Sentences
Sample sentences are given.
1. Neither Jason nor Julie likes bananas.

2. Radio and television provide entertainment and information.
3. Computers and the Internet have changed the way the world does business.
4. Beets, carrots, or celery is a good addition to this recipe.
5. An apple or a banana was part of Brian's lunch every day.

25.1 Subject and Verb Agreement (Confusing Subjects) (Page 143)
Practice 1
Exercise 1   Deciding on the Number of Subjects
1. P
2. S
3. S
4. P
5. S
6. S
7. S
8. S
9. P
10. S

Exercise 2   Choosing Verbs to Agree With Difficult Subjects
1. is
2. disagree
3. are
4. have
5. follows

25.1 Subject and Verb Agreement (Confusing Subjects) (Page 144)
Practice 2
Exercise 1   Making Confusing Subjects Agree With Their Verbs
1. is
2. has
3. are
4. was
5. Do
6. has
7. have
8. was
9. Is
10. Here are
11. was
12. are
13. was
14. have
15. There are
16. is
17. is
18. is
19. is
20. have

Exercise 2   More Work With Confusing Subjects
1. was
2. have
3. seems
4. have
5. was
6. is
7. has
8. is
9. were
10. was

25.2 Pronoun and Antecedent Agreement (Between Personal Pronouns and Antecedents) (Page 145)
Practice 1
Exercise 1   Choosing Personal Pronouns to Agree With Antecedents
1. their
2. its
3. his
4. her
5. her
6. their
7. his
8. their
9. its
10. her

Exercise 2   Pronoun-Antecedents Agreement in Sentences
1. him
2. its
3. her
4. their
5. him

25.2 Pronoun and Antecedent Agreement (Between Personal Pronouns and Antecedents) (Page 146)
Practice 2
Exercise 1   Making Personal Pronouns Agree With Their Antecedents
1. her
2. her
3. its
4. his
5. their
6. she
7. her
8. it
9. they
10. our

Exercise 2   Making Personal Pronouns Agree With Their Antecedents
Joel and Henry ran along the path, each one wondering how much longer (1) he could last. It was a cool day, and (2) they both were in good shape. Still, (3) they had been running for about forty minutes, and for each of (4) them, this was a sufficient amount of exercise. Joel looked over at (5) his best friend and saw that (6) he did not even seem tired. Henry looked over at Joel and felt that (7) he was not even out of breath.

"Say, Joel," said Henry. "Are (8) you about ready to stop?"

"Not yet," said Joel. "Why? Is this too much for (9) you ?"

"Not at all," said Henry. "My mom just told (10) me this morning that she thought (11) I was getting stronger every day. Since you and (12) I started this program, I've been improving. I just thought that (13) you might be getting tired."

"No," said Joel. "(14) My stamina has increased during the past few weeks. Let's keep running."

As the two friends continued (15) their run, each one hoped that the other would stop soon.

25.2 Pronoun and Antecedent Agreement (With Indefinite Pronouns and With Reflexive Pronouns) (Page 147)

Practice 1

Exercise 1   Making Personal Pronouns Agree with Indefinite Pronouns

1. it
2. their
3. them
4. it
5. she
6. their
7. it
8. his
9. them
10. them

Exercise 2   Using Reflexive Pronouns Correctly

1. myself—me
2. ourselves—us
3. herself—she
4. myself—I
5. yourself—you

25.2 Pronoun and Antecedent Agreement (With Indefinite Pronouns and With Reflexive Pronouns) (Page 148)

Practice 2

Exercise 1   Making Personal Pronouns Agree With Indefinite Pronouns

1. their
2. his
3. her
4. his
5. her
6. his
7. their
8. their
9. her
10. his
11. her
12. their
13. their
14. his
15. their
16. her
17. his
18. his
19. her
20. its

Exercise 2   Using Reflexive Pronouns Correctly.

Each misused reflexive pronoun is followed by the correct pronoun

1. yourself, you
2. ourselves, we
3. myself, I
4. ourselves, us
5. myself, me

25.2 Pronoun and Antecedent Agreement (Four Special Problems) (Page 149)

Practice 1

Exercise 1   Solving Special Problems in Pronoun Agreement

1. contestants
2. Mike
3. the cartons
4. the fans
5. the children

6. guests
7. the judges
8. our cousins
9. students
10. flight attendants

Exercise 2   Correcting Special Problems in Pronoun Agreement

Samples of rewritten sentences are given.

1. Why do teachers always make tests so hard?
2. Without locking the car, Sandy left it in the garage.
3. That program requires a lot of independent work.
4. Paul told Steve that Paul's bicycle had a flat tire.
5. How do advertisers make that product look so attractive?

25.2 Pronoun and Antecedent Agreement (Four Special Problems) (Page 150)

Practice 2

Exercise 1   Correcting Special Problems in Pronoun Agreement

1. a young person
2. the station
3. William
4. the shelves
5. everyone
6. students
7. the meal
8. the players
9. Rita
10. the anonymous caller

Exercise 2   More Work With Special Problems in Pronoun Agreement

Each misused pronoun is followed by a sample correct answer.

1. she, my sister
2. you, a person
3. them, teachers
4. he, the captain
5. it, acting

26.1 Degrees of Comparison (Recognizing Degrees of Comparison, Regular Forms) (Page 151)

Practice 1

Exercise 1   Recognizing Degrees of Comparison

1. comp.
2. pos.
3. sup.
4. sup.
5. sup.
6. comp.
7. pos.
8. sup.
9. comp.
10. pos.

Exercise 2   Comparing Adjectives and Adverbs

1. more amazing, most amazing
2. fast, faster
3. rapidly, most rapidly
4. more modern, most modern
5. more oddly, most oddly

26.1 Degrees of Comparison (Recognizing Degrees of Comparison, Regular Forms) (Page 152)

Practice 2

Exercise 1   Recognizing Positive, Comparative, and Superlative Degrees

1. Sup.

2. Comp.
3. Comp.
4. Pos.
5. Sup.
6. Comp.
7. Sup.
8. Comp.
9. Comp.
10. Sup.
11. Sup.
12. Pos.
13. Comp.
14. Sup.
15. Comp.
16. Pos.
17. Comp.
18. Sup.
19. Sup.
20. Comp.

Exercise 2   Forming Regular Comparative and Superlative Degrees
1. tougher, toughest
2. heavier, heaviest
3. stronger, strongest
4. more comfortable, most comfortable
5. more interesting, most interesting
6. prettier, prettiest
7. more popular, most popular
8. more confusing, most confusing
9. more frightening, most frightening
10. more clearly, most clearly

26.1   Degrees of Comparison (Irregular Forms) (Page 153)
Practice 1
Exercise 1   Forming Irregular Comparative and Superlative Degrees
1. best
2. farther
3. worse
4. least
5. last
6. further
7. best
8. worse
9. worst
10. most

Exercise 2   Using Adjectives and Adverbs to Make Comparisons
Sample sentences are given.
1. The patient's condition is no worse today than yesterday.
2. I do worst in math.
3. Grandma makes the best apple pie in the family.
4. Many people eat less food in warm weather.
5. In the morning, Jim thought better of his idea.

26.1   Degrees of Comparison (Irregular Forms) (Page 154)
Practice 2
Exercise 1   Forming Irregular Comparative and Superlative Degrees
1. better
2. better
3. farthest
4. worst
5. worse
6. farther

7. better
8. better
9. later
10. more
11. more
12. best
13. later
14. better
15. better

Writing Application
Using Adjectives and Adverbs to Make Comparisons
Sample sentences are given.
1. Ted is hungrier than I am.
2. Her proudest moment was when she received an award.
3. Betty threw the ball farther than Ann threw it.
4. This time the construction work is moving along more quickly.
5. That's the fastest roller coaster of them all.
6. The most foolish clown threw a pie at the ring master.
7. The worst accident occurred on the expressway during the snowstorm.
8. I think this is going to be a good day.
9. The doctor said that the patient is well.
10. The antique model train locomotive ran well.

26.2   Clear Comparisons (Using Comparative and Superlative Degrees) (Page 155)
Practice 1
Exercise 1   Using the Comparative and Superlative Degrees Correctly
1. least
2. oldest
3. coolest
4. most
5. longest
6. more
7. more
8. fewer
9. fastest
10. most

Exercise 2   Recognizing Inappropriate Comparisons
1. more harder—harder
2. oldest—older
3. worser—worse
4. correct
5. more carefully—most carefully

26.2   Clear Comparisons (Using Comparative and Superlative Degrees) (Page 156)
Practice 2
Exercise 1   Using the Comparative and Superlative Degrees Correctly
1. better
2. most
3. hungrier
4. strongest
5. less
6. most
7. worse
8. cleaner
9. smaller
10. less

Exercise 2   Supplying the Comparative and Superlative Degrees
1. longest
2. worse

3. oldest
4. fastest
5. happiest
6. more capable
7. kindest
8. worse
9. more fluently
10. best
11. farther
12. better
13. youngest
14. most delicious
15. more versatile
16. more difficult
17. later
18. warmest
19. better
20. more comfortable

26.2 Clear Comparisons (Balanced Comparisons, *Other* and *Else* in Comparisons) (Page 157)
Practice 1
Exercise 1 Making Balanced Comparisons
1. than Angie's
2. than Aunt Polly's
3. than Len's
4. than Pete's
5. than Dad's

Exercise 2 Using *Other* and *Else* in Comparisons
1. than anyone else
2. than anyone else
3. than any other cook
4. than any other poet's
5. than any other road

26.2 Clear Comparisons (Balanced Comparisons, *Other* and *Else* in Comparisons) (Page 158)
Practice 2
Exercise 1 Making Balanced Comparisons
1. his chief rival's
2. than Mom's
3. than this hotel's
4. than Sandra's
5. her twin's
6. than Joan's
7. than my new bike's
8. than her brother's
9. than Keith's
10. than my sister's

Exercise 2 Using *Other* and *Else* in Comparisons
1. than any other I've ever tasted
2. than anyone else in the band
3. than any other senator's
4. than any other baseball player
5. than anyone else I know

27.1 Negative Sentences (Page 159)
Practice 1
Exercise 1 Avoiding Problems With Negatives
1. anything
2. could
3. can
4. was
5. any
6. anything
7. more than
8. ever
9. was

10. ever

Exercise 2 Using Negatives Correctly
Sample sentences are given.
1. Mom's keys are nowhere to be found.
2. The Chargers have lost but one game this year.
3. I shouldn't have told anyone the secret.
4. Hardly anyone was at the game.
5. I have never heard that old wives' tale before.

27.1 Negative Sentences (Page 160)
Practice 2
Exercise 1 Avoiding Double Negatives
1. anything
2. any
3. any
4. anywhere
5. none
6. any
7. any
8. anything
9. nothing
10. any

Exercise 2 Avoiding Problems With Negatives
1. anything
2. nothing
3. could
4. any
5. anything
6. were
7. can
8. anything
9. any
10. had

Exercise 3 Correcting Double Negatives
Sample sentence rewrites are given
1. I promise that I won't tell anybody.
2. Mary can hardly read the small print.
3. My father had never been to Athens.
4. I have but a few minutes left to work.
5. She had no lunch.

27.2 Fifty Common Usage Problems (Page 161)
Practice 1
Exercise 1 Avoiding Some Common Usage Problems
1. doesn't
2. lain
3. have
4. affects
5. among
6. take
7. from
8. healthful
9. fewer
10. teach

Exercise 2 Avoiding Other Common Usage Problems
1. raise
2. somewhat
3. into
4. sat
5. farther
6. Let
7. that
8. way
9. effects
10. as

27.2 Fifty Common Usage Problems (Page 162)
Practice 2
Exercise 1 Avoiding Usage Problems
1. anywhere
2. advise
3. except
4. isn't
5. all right
6. all together
7. all ready
8. effect
9. adapted
10. advice

Exercise 2 Avoiding Usage Problems
1. beside
2. Since
3. Bring
4. burst
5. from
6. wanting
7. I am
8. about
9. because
10. that

Exercise 3 Avoiding Usage Problems
1. doesn't
2. have done
3. fewer
4. have gone
5. less
6. Because of
7. Doesn't
8. have done
9. further
10. into

28 Capitalization (Sentences) (Page 163)
Practice 1
Exercise 1 Using Capitals to Begin Sentences
1. After
2. This, We
3. We
4. The, Exercise
5. How
6. The, We
7. How
8. My, Who
9. Mark
10. Have

Exercise 2 Using Capitalized Words
Sample capitalized words are given.
1. Meats
2. John
3. Robin
4. This
5. Bob
6. Mail
7. Who
8. Please
9. My
10. You

28 Capitalization (Sentences) (Page 164)
Practice 2
Exercise 1 Using Capitalization Correctly in Sentences
Words that should be capitalized are underlined.
1. show me what you are holding in your hand, young man.
2. getting my school schedule worked out for next year is causing problems.
3. "every hero becomes a bore at last," observed Emerson.
4. when will dinner be ready?
5. my grandmother taught me one important lesson: giving more than 100 percent is the surest way to get ahead.
6. we found a twenty-dollar bill on the sidewalk!
7. at one time Confucius warned, "the cautious seldom err."
8. the store down the street is holding a big sale today.
9. will you go on many weekend ski trips this winter?
10. sit still while the barber finishes cutting your hair.
11. "if you would wish another to keep your secret," advised Seneca, "first keep it yourself."
12. where did you take the camera to be repaired?
13. we saw quite a feat at the circus: a young man did a high-wire act without any safety nets below him.
14. the company gave us a substantial salary increase today!
15. many people put more salt on their food than is healthful.
16. they spent yesterday buying gifts: a stuffed panda, an electric razor, and a giant rubber plant.
17. "we can stay as long as we want," she said. "they have given us permission."
18. what in the world were you thinking of?
19. "why not try," she asked, "to climb a mountain?"
20. he was afraid: he had never climbed a mountain.

Exercise 2 Using Capitalization Correctly in Paragraphs
Words that should be capitalized are underlined.

karly said, "yesterday i was walking through the woods, and a porcupine crossed my path."

phil answered, "the porcupine is such a strange animal. did you know," he continued, "that people who live in the mountains often call the porcupine a quill-pig?"

"yes, i did know that," answered Karly. "the animal is certainly as clumsy and slow-moving as any pig, but it is not a pig at all. it is actually a rodent, with sharp teeth somewhat like those of a rabbit or a squirrel. even though it is a mere rodent, nearly every other wild creature in the forest is afraid to attack it. do you know why?"

"well, yes, i do," said Phil. "the reason is this: the porcupine's body is thickly sprinkled with stiff, needle-sharp quills. these quills are from half an inch to four inches long. a porcupine might have as many as 20,000 or 25,000 of these peculiar weapons. interestingly, when one is lost, a new one grows quickly to replace it. if you were a forest creature, you'd probably be afraid of porcupines, too!"

28 Capitalization (Proper Nouns, Proper Adjectives) (Page 165)

Practice 1

Exercise 1 Recognizing Proper Nouns and Proper Adjectives

1. Europe, France, Belgium
2. William Faulkner, Nobel Prize
3. Ted, American
4. Judy
5. Electrosonic
6. Chamber, Commerce
7. Cuban, American
8. God, Bible
9. Fortress, Louisbourg, Nova Scotia
10. French, Canadians

Exercise 2 Using Proper Nouns and Proper Adjectives

Sample proper nouns and proper adjectives are given.

1. Kannon
2. England, France
3. American
4. John Updike
5. Super Bowl
6. Tennessee
7. Alice, Ted
8. Mississippi
9. African
10. New Testament

28 Capitalization (Proper Nouns, Proper Adjectives) (Page 166)

Practice 2

Exercise 1 Capitalizing Proper Nouns

1. To see a play that has been running for twenty-five years, you should go to st. martin's theater in london.
2. One well-known suspension bridge is the golden gate, which spans san francisco bay.
3. Both the shoshone and the arapaho make up a part of the population of wyoming.
4. By checking a perpetual calendar, I found that benjamin franklin was born on sunday, january 17, 1706.
5. In the northeast winters are quite harsh and long.
6. Astronauts will probably visit jupiter some day.
7. The lowest point in all north america is in death valley.
8. thomas m ck ean, a lawyer from pennsylvania, signed the declaration of independence.
9. Some of the major airline companies that went bankrupt were eastern, national, and people's express.
10. In october 1976, congress repealed the homestead act of 1862 since there was no longer any land available for homesteading.
11. In ancient mythology the goddess athena dispensed wisdom.
12. The kentucky derby is held annually in the spring at churchill downs.
13. A well-known race horse, secretariat, won many races.
14. The torah, the talmud, and the midrash are the sacred writings of judaism.
15. You can find out about the great smoky mountains by writing to the chamber of commerce, 505 fesslers lane, nashville, tennessee 37210.
16. I think arabic is a difficult language to master.
17. The nebula award is presented for outstanding works of science fiction.
18. The nuclear regulatory commission regulates all civilian uses of atomic energy.
19. The white house uses the blue room as its official reception room.
20. About one half of our national leaders have been republicans and the other half have been democrats.

Exercise 2 Capitalizing Proper Adjectives

1. Open-air theaters are often used for the performance of elizabethan plays.
2. Many african american groups have held several conferences during the past few years to discuss their heritage.
3. Large crowds at an american political rally gave the police some crowd-control problems.
4. The anglo -saxon invasion of Britain took place in the fifth and sixth centuries.
5. Some early buddhist monasteries were caves that were elegantly carved and decorated.
6. Her old pictureperfect camera accompanied her on all her travels.
7. A sino -russian pact could have a significant effect on foreign policy.
8. Those who own pre-columbian sculptures have valuable art pieces in their possession.
9. A lovely indian woman in a sari came into the store asking for the manager.
10. The franklin d. roosevelt years were marred by World War II.

28 Capitalization (for Titles, in Letters) (Page 167)

Practice 1

Exercise 1 Using Capitals in Titles

1. Captain Perez
2. "The Most Dangerous Game"
3. Chief Justice
4. Doctor Gilbert
5. *Portrait, Lady*
6. *The Member, Wedding*
7. Bishop Wilson
8. Ms. Greer, Mr. Kelly
9. *Nature's Beauty Magazine*
10. *American Gothic*

Exercise 2 Using Capitals for Salutations and Closings

1. Dear Mr. Stevenson,
2. Respectfully yours,
3. My dear Uncle,
4. Very truly yours,
5. Dear Senator Brock:
6. Sincerely yours,
7. Affectionately,
8. Dear Colonel Cobb:
9. Dear Ms. Brody:
10. With deepest regret,

28 Capitalization (for Titles, in Letters) (Page 168)

Practice 2

Exercise 1 Capitalizing Titles of People

1. Could you direct me, sir, to this address?
2. We invited dr. and mrs. strutner to the play.
3. One of the greatest mystery writers of all time was dame agatha christie.

4. It is my great pleasure to present the president of the United States.
5. The ex-secretary of state is writing his memoirs.
6. Lieutenant governor taylor ran our state last week while governor hull was away on a business trip.
7. We expect colonel green to inspect the troops today.
8. We visited grandmother, who teaches in a small country school.
9. Please tell us, senator, how you expect to vote.
10. The reverend john hyder and father madison met to discuss some of the concerns facing their parishes.

Exercise 2   Capitalizing Titles of Things
1. *the financial journal* is a respected newspaper that presents news from the point of view of business people.
2. The only classes they are offering that I want to take are psychology, german, and art
3. The story "the lottery" by Shirley Jackson makes the reader contemplate some of humanity's baser instincts.
4. When registration opened, english 1A, biology 45, and all the calculus courses filled up immediately.
5. *the making of the past : the egyptian kingdoms* contains some excellent pictures of ancient tomb treasures.
6. Robert Graves based much of his novel *i, claudius* on the Roman historian Suetonius's *the lives of the caesars*.
7. Loren Eisley's *the man who saw through time* is a collection of essays about the Elizabethan scientist Francis Bacon.
8. Edgar Allan Poe once wrote a very fine poem entitled "a dream within a dream."
9. One of Phyllis McGinley's best books for children is *the horse who lived upstairs.*
10. *measure for measure* is one of Shakespeare's lesser-known plays.

29.1   End Marks (Page 169)
Practice 1
Exercise 1   Using End Marks Correctly
1. (?)
2. (.)
3. (.)
4. (!)
5. (.)
6. (.)
7. (?)
8. (!)
9. (?)
10. (.)

Exercise 2   Supplying End Marks
Sample sentences are given.
1. Who was that?
2. What a game they played!
3. This is our stop.
4. Are you ready?
5. You're here!

29.1   End Marks (Page 170)
Practice 2
Exercise 1   Using the Period Correctly
1. The American humorist S. J. Perelman was once a scriptwriter for the Marx Brothers.

2. My parents wondered what grade I received on the test.
3. Address the package to Mr. Arthur Grover, Jr.
4. I think Elizabeth Bishop is a fine modern American poet.
5. She prefers the title Mrs. to the title Ms.
6. I asked Mrs. Ramos to go with us.
7. Schedule a certain amount of time for studying every day.
8. Elizabeth P. Peabody started the first kindergarten in the United States in 1860.
9. The son of Efrem Zimbalist, Sr., a violinist, is an actor.
10. Dr. Elvira M. Thackery spoke at the seminar.

Exercise 2   Using the Question Mark Correctly
1. How much money did Lucille Ball make from her television series?
2. Many have wondered whether more people watched Lucille Ball or President Eisenhower's inauguration.
3. How did Dinah Shore customarily end her shows?
4. Who was known as Mr. Television?
5. What were two of the popular TV shows that children of the 1950's liked to watch?
6. Before 1951, what percentage of the American public was asleep by midnight?
7. Some wondered whether shows like the Steve Allen and Jack Paar talk shows were responsible for people staying up later.
8. In what TV show did Mary Martin fly through the air on wires?
9. In what show did audiences see Joe Friday?
10. During the 1953–1954 season, which show was rated first?

Exercise 3   Using the Exclamation Mark Correctly
1. Our dog had four puppies last night! exclamatory
2. There goes the thief! exclamatory
3. Quick! Hide Mother's birthday present! interjection, imperative
4. Help me! imperative
5. We have just three minutes before the plane takes off! exclamatory

29.2   Commas That Separate Basic Elements (Compound Sentences, Items in a Series, Adjectives) (Page 171)
Practice 1
Exercise 1   Using Commas Correctly
1. dark, wooded
2. Father, and
3. tomatoes, cucumbers, scallions, and
4. exhausted, discouraged
5. safely, or
6. correct
7. stopped, but
8. angry, determined
9. speech, but
10. salad, cooked a roast, and

Exercise 2   Understanding the Use of Commas
1. compound
2. series
3. adjectives
4. compound
5. series

29.2 Commas That Separate Basic Elements (Compound Sentences, Items in a Series, Adjectives) (Page 172)

Practice 2

Exercise 1 Using Commas With Compound Sentences

(1) Valentine's Day is celebrated by most Americans, yet few people know the story of how the holiday first began. (2) The holiday originated in ancient Rome, but the actual date of its origin is about A.D. 270. (3) According to legend Emperor Claudius II would not allow the troops of the Roman army to marry, for he felt that married men made poor soldiers. (4) A priest called Valentinus took pity on two young lovers, and he secretly married them against Emperor Claudius's orders. (5) Valentinus was arrested and thrown in jail, and Claudius had him beheaded several months later. (6) It was from this Roman jail that the first Valentine card was sent, for Valentinus supposedly cured the jailer's daughter of blindness and sent her a note signed "From Your Valentine." (7) You may want to believe this legend, or you may feel that this is just a romantic tale that was concocted to explain the origin of Valentine's Day. (8) The first Valentines in America were not covered with sweet verses, nor were they elaborate and lacy works of art. (9) Boys and girls of the late 1850's loved to send "Penny Dreadfuls" on Valentine's Day, and they looked forward to receiving them from their friends in turn. (10) A typical Penny Dreadful might contain a message such as this one: 'Tis all in vain your fluttering lids, your curly hair, your tinted cheeks, for finding you a Valentine will take at least a HUNDRED weeks!'

Exercise 2 Using Commas Between Items in a Series

1. The student driver nervously pressed down the accelerator, turned the key, and put the car in gear.
2. The flash flood raced through the narrow canyon, over the flatlands, and into the town's main street.
3. Mrs. Robertson offered the children peanut butter and jelly, bacon and avocado, or cheese and bologna sandwiches.
4. The children bowled, the parents kept score, and the grandparents watched.
5. He ate breakfast, she read the newspaper, and then they both left for work.
6. The sheepdog pushed and coaxed and prodded his stubborn charges into their pens. correct
7. Skiing, skating, and dancing burn up many calories.
8. The physician said he wanted to take some X-rays, check the results, and call us later in the day.
9. Did you pack a bathing suit, pajamas, a sweatshirt, and a toothbrush?
10. The ball flew over the pitcher's head, above the center fielder's glove, and into a spectator's waiting hands.

29.2 Commas That Set Off Added Elements (Introductory Material, Parenthetical Expressions) (Page 173)

Practice 1

Exercise 1 Recognizing Introductory Material

1. No,
2. To grow corn,
3. Determined,
4. If she sings,
5. Waiting patiently,
6. When I try,
7. Since you wrote,
8. Cary,
9. To improve our game,
10. Really,

Exercise 2 Using Commas Correctly

1. room, unfortunately,
2. Eriksen,
3. July, not
4. ballet, she
5. refusal, I am certain
6. happily, she
7. know, of course,
8. Yes, I
9. retreat, the
10. decision, consequently,

29.2 Commas That Set Off Added Elements (Introductory Material, Parenthetical Expressions) (Page 174)

Practice 2

Exercise 1 Using Commas After Introductory Material

1. After you hear about Sarah Winchester,
2. Following a short and romantic courtship,
3. Upon her husband's death,
4. Fearing the ghosts of people killed by Winchester guns,
5. With a great deal of determination,
6. To keep the ghosts confused,
7. Oh,
8. Testing their loyalty to her,
9. When she died,
10. Within her 160-room mansion,

Exercise 2 Using Commas With Parenthetical Expressions

1. The new plants, however, did not survive the frost.
2. I will vacuum, Hazel, if you will wash the windows.
3. He went to Harvard Law School, I believe.
4. The young rascal, furthermore, put salt in my sugar bowl.
5. Spread lime in the garden, not near the evergreens.
6. Typing your paper, you know, will make it easier to read.
7. The plane, therefore, did not arrive on time.
8. Tennis, not golf, is my favorite sport.
9. May I help you carry that package, Mr. Goodman?
10. If it rains, the picnic will be postponed until next week, I suppose.
11. Did you know, Cynthia, that tomorrow is Dan's birthday?
12. Aunt Marie, similarly, enjoys wearing large hats.
13. The twins, in any case, will be here by noon.
14. Dr. Sanchez, not Dr. Monroe, is my dentist.
15. Did you have an appointment, Ms. Martinez?
16. The backyard, on the other hand, is well tended.
17. The newspapers and paperbacks, however, should be recycled.
18. She is friendly enough, in my opinion, to be a good social coordinator.
19. Dina likes apple, not pecan, pie.

20. The leaves, of course, should be raked.

29.2 Commas That Set Off Added Elements (Nonessential Expressions) (Page 175)
Practice 1
Exercise 1 Using Commas With Nonessential Expressions
1. Robinson, a fine hitter,
2. correct
3. Mendelssohn, who was born in 1809,
4. Alex, who works after school,
5. correct
6. Ottawa, the capital of Canada,
7. correct
8. correct
9. Hill, the home of Theodore Roosevelt
10. Nashville, which is near the center of Tennessee,

Exercise 2 Writing Essential and Nonessential Expressions
Sample expressions are given.
1. sitting at that desk
2. , two cities I had always wanted to see
3. , which is not my favorite month,
4. , our nearest neighbor
5. that we were watching
6. , a new blue one,
7. , who is retired,
8. provided by the theater
9. , Boston and Denver,
10. that was chained

29.2 Commas That Set Off Added Elements (Nonessential Expressions) (Page 176)
Practice 2
Exercise 1 Using Commas With Nonessential Expressions
1. My orthodontist, who just came back from a trip to Hawaii, tightened my braces.
2. The woman who was hired as a company consultant made some fine suggestions to the management.
3. The President's wife is the one boarding the plane right now.
4. Calligraphy, the art of beautiful writing, takes practice and skill in order for one to become proficient at it.
5. The suit worn by the model on the left probably costs a fortune.
6. The museum held the saddle of John Wayne, one of the most famous Hollywood cowboys.
7. Have you ever visited the Alamo, a fascinating building in Texas?
8. Yosemite Falls, which drops 2,425 feet to the river below, almost dries after a hot summer.
9. Joanne Lewis, who happens to be my cousin, writes news articles for local television.
10. Pélé, a famous soccer player from Brazil, played in the United States many years ago.
11. This strange locust, which spends seventeen years developing in the earth, lives only six weeks as an adult.
12. Dinosaurs, the animals that dominated the earth for over 140 million years, became extinct 65 million years ago.
13. The newborn guppy, called a fry, must swim to the surface and take a gulp of air before it can swim well.
14. Mark Twain, the author of The Adventures of Huckleberry Finn, used a riverboat term as his pen name.
15. Patricia's last vacation, a bicycle trip across China, did not cost as much as she had anticipated.

Exercise 2 Writing Sentences With Nonessential Expressions
Sample sentences are given.
1. Paul, Alex's best friend, is tall for his age.
2. Felicity, my neighbor's cat, is very shy.
3. Perry, the first one to taste the soup, said it was too salty.
4. The six o'clock news, Tim's favorite program, was not very interesting today.
5. My grandmother, who means a great deal to me, knitted this sweater.

29.2 Commas That Set Off Added Elements (Places, Dates, Titles, Other Uses) (Page 177)
Practice 1
Exercise 1 Adding Commas to Sentences
1. Trucks, Avenue, Norwalk,
2. science,
3. 42,375
4. remarked,
5. Briggs, Jr.,
6. storm,
7. June 20, 1793,
8. 1,558,691; 6,818
9. time," Sue,
10. spring,

Exercise 2 Punctuating a Letter
Los Angeles, October 12, Pam, March 1, 1932, Hopewell, $50,000 September 15, $14,000 April 3, friend,

29.2 Commas That Set Off Added Elements (Places, Dates, Titles, Other Uses) (Page 178)
Practice 2
Exercise 1 Using Commas With Places, Dates, and Titles
1. Microtec, Inc., opened
2. Little Rock, Arkansas.
3. "Allison Evans, R.N."
4. On July 4, 1884, the Statue of Liberty
5. St. Louis, Missouri, to San Francisco, California, by
6. Professor John H. Coleman, Ph.D., accepted
7. Tuesday, August 8, to Sunday, August 19.
8. Randall Knudtsen, Sr., and Randall Knudtsen, Jr., working
9. Stuttgart, Germany.
10. Bridgetown, Barbados, on

Exercise 2 Using Commas in Other Situations
1. 1318 View Ridge Drive, Missoula, Montana.
2. 2,189 miles
3. the children, to school.
4. September 15, 1972, in Honolulu, Hawaii.
5. Outside, the house
6. said, "A grandparent
7. P.O. Box 900, Cupertino, California
8. When reading, the boy
9. correct," Benjamin Disraeli
10. the second, a quarter horse; the third, a thoroughbred

29.3 The Semicolon (Page 179)
Practice 1
Exercise 1 Using Semicolons Correctly
1. money;
2. nectarines;
3. barked;
4. Joey;
5. $100;
6. swim;
7. lawn;
8. now;
9. cities;
10. before;

Exercise 2 Writing Compound Sentences With Semicolons
Sample sentences are given.
1. The show started on time; however, it was longer than expected.
2. Some birds cannot fly; for instance, penguins can only waddle and swim.
3. You must fasten your seat belt; otherwise, a buzzer will sound.
4. Joe baked a cake; his sister made an apple pie.
5. I'd love to go to the movies; on the other hand, I wouldn't mind getting to bed early tonight.

29.3 The Semicolon (Page 180)
Practice 2
Exercise 1   Using Semicolons to Join Independent Clauses
1. trees; they
2. intelligent; they
3. food; when
4. fish; others
5. sounds; one
6. babies; they
7. pets; usually
8. farmers; they
9. neighborhoods; they
10. days; raccoon

Exercise 2   Using Semicolons and Commas to Join Clauses

(1) Stockholders hoped to get rich when their stocks rose in price; therefore, many borrowed money to buy stocks. (2) On Black Thursday in October 1929, stocks tumbled to forty percent of their original value; as a result, many people lost almost everything they owned. (3) Pandemonium broke out on the stock exchange floor; fist fights, for instance, were common. (4) Frantic orders to sell came into the exchange; many orders to sell, however, could not be completed because there were no buyers. (5) Some stockholders were forced to sell their homes, businesses, and other possessions to pay back money they had borrowed; others could not pay their debts at all. (6) There were several short rallies in stock prices; nevertheless, prices generally spiraled down. (7) Some tragedies were caused by the stock market crash; in fact, the president of Union Cigar jumped to his death when his stock dropped over $100 in one day. (8) The President assured the public that business was good; many business leaders continued to buy stocks. (9) Some of the richest people did manage to survive the stock market crash; most people, however, had barely enough left to survive. (10) The collapse of the stock market almost destroyed the business world; it is a tragic lesson to people today.

29.3 The Colon (Page 181)
Practice 1
Exercise 1   Using the Colon as an Introductory Device
1. ingredients:
2. mirror:
3. citizen:
4. transportation:
5. experience:
6. weather:
7. announced:
8. actress:
9. sports:
10. month:

Exercise 2   Using Colons in Special Writing Situations
1. 23:1
2. 6:05; 6:37
3. *Cooking:*
4. X: 132
5. Note:

29.3 The Colon (Page 182)
Practice 2
Exercise 1   Using Colons as Introductory Devices
1. city: Athens
2. order: A
3. purpose: It
4. prediction: "I
5. name: bannerets
6. times: This
7. correct
8. seen: barnyard
9. symbols: flags
10. buildings: barns

Exercise 2   Using Colons in Special Writing Situations
1. One of my favorite stories in the Bible is Mark 4:3.
2. Dear Mr. Harrison:
3. The schedule indicated that the train from Chicago should arrive at 5:38 P.M.
4. Note: The following information has not yet been verified by the main office.
5. Our coach suggested that we read *Playing Team Soccer: A Study in Offense and Defense Skills.*
6. My teacher suggested I check in *Business News* 61:12 for further information for my report.
7. Dear Mrs. Phillips:
8. I took out a reference book called *Rules for Writing: A Guide to Better Compositions.*
9. The minister asked the congregation to turn to Exodus 6:2.
10. Are we supposed to leave at 6:15 A.M. or 6:45 A.M.?

29.4 Quotation Marks With Direct Quotations (Introductory, Concluding, Interrupting Expressions) (Page 183)
Practice 1
Exercise 1   Punctuating Direct Quotations
1. "This ... process," ... said.
2. "In ... heart."
3. "This report," ... said, "does ... footnotes."
4. asked me, "Don't ... telephone?"
5. "What ... news!" ... exclaimed.
6. "Which bus," ... visitor, "should I take?"
7. "What ... mean?" ... Alice.
8. said, "We ... finals"
9. "I ... basketball," ... said, "much ... baseball."

10. "the great … class."

Exercise 2   Writing Direct Quotations
Sample sentence completions are given.
1. Are we leaving now
2. We have to wait for Mr. Jones
3. If you'll sit down … we can begin
4. What a jump
5. I know … this was a difficult job

29.4 Quotation Marks With Direct Quotations (Introductory, Concluding, Interrupting Expressions) (Page 184)
Practice 2
Exercise 1   Recognizing Direct Quotations
1. Christine said that <u>she would like to play badminton tomorrow afternoon.</u> indirect
2. Each fact that a person learns is, in the words of E.L. Youman, "<u>a key to other facts.</u>" direct
3. Eleanor Roosevelt once said, "<u>No one can make you feel inferior without your consent.</u>" direct
4. Carlyle once defined endurance in two precise words: "<u>patience concentrated.</u>" direct
5. After listening to a weather forecast, our coach announced that <u>there would be no practice today.</u> indirect
6. You must know which song contains the words "<u>in the dawn's early light.</u>" direct
7. During the first lap, Andrea decided, "<u>I must win today since my parents are watching.</u>" direct
8. Later in the race, she decided that <u>they would have to be satisfied with second place this time.</u> indirect
9. "<u>A book with an unhappy ending</u>" were the words he used to describe his checkbook. direct
10. Emerson once wrote, "<u>The creation of a thousand forests is in one acorn.</u>" direct

Exercise 2   Writing Direct Quotations With Introductory, Concluding and Interrupting Expressions
1. Persuasively, the sales clerk added, "This particular radio won't be on sale much longer."
2. "The park will be closed," the ranger said, "so that we can repair the picnic area."
3. "That jacket looks nice on you," my father said as he walked in the door.
4. With growing irritation, the taxi driver asked, "Have you decided where we are going yet?"
5. Henry Ward Beecher once made this important distinction between work and worry: "It is not work that kills me; it is worry."
6. "He who has imagination without learning," warns Joubert, "has wings but no feet."
7. "When you get to the rodeo," my cousin warned, "watch out for wild horses and bulls."
8. "Don't forget June 15," his wife reminded him. "That's our anniversary."
9. "You've got to keep your eye on the ball every second," instructed my coach.
10. "When the dance is over," my date informed me, "we are going to go out for some pizza."

29.4 Quotation Marks With Direct Quotations (With Other Punctuation Marks, Special Situations) (Page 185)
Practice 1
Exercise 1   Punctuating Direct Quotations
1. station,"
2. explanation," … thought,
3. stormed,

4. 'See you soon,'
5. agree," … said,
6. now,"
7. said, … atlas."
8. 'Good luck,'
9. OK"!
10. efforts," … captain,

Exercise 2   Paragraphing Dialogue
I, How, I, Mother, All

29.4 Quotation Marks With Direct Quotations (With Other Punctuation Marks, Special Situations) (Page 186)
Practice 2
Exercise 1   Using Punctuation With Direct Quotations
1. The boys shouted, "We won the championship!"
2. "When the film comes back," Jim announced, "we will set up a slide show."
3. The teacher said, "You will need to study hard for this test"; he also said we should get plenty of rest the night before the test.
4. The salesperson in the shoe department asked, "Do those boots pinch your toes?"
5. Carlos shouted frantically, "The man in the gray parka stole my wallet!"
6. The clerk asked, "Are you certain you want just a one-way ticket?"
7. My mother felt my forehead and said, "You get into bed right this minute!"
8. She constantly reminded us of "the keys to success": hard work, a goal, and a little luck.
9. Did the coach say, "Be at the field at eight in the morning" or "at eight in the evening"?
10. The garage attendant said, "Your exhaust pipe has a hole in it"; however, he didn't offer to fix it.

Exercise 2   More Work With Punctuation
1. I got the lead in this year's one-act play: "Roses and Wine."
2. My friend asked, "Why don't you go jogging with me in the morning before school?"
3. "The plane will take off," the flight attendant stated, "as soon as the fog clears a bit more."
4. The new father proudly announced, "We have a beautiful baby girl!"
5. Are you certain the doctor specifically said, "Take two pills fifteen minutes before eating"?
6. She gave us her list of "absolute travel necessities": makeup, hair dryer, and bathing suit.
7. Did Emerson say, "If a man owns land, the land owns him"?
8. Angela confessed, "I should read the newspaper more."
9. "We must try harder," he said, "if we truly want to win this debate."
10. I heard him ask, "Can you tell me where a drinking fountain is?"

29.4 Underlining and Other Uses of Quotation Marks (Page 187)
Practice 1
Exercise 1   Punctuating Different Types of Works
1. <u>The Saturday Evening Post</u>
2. correct
3. <u>If Morning Ever Comes</u>
4. <u>The Grapes of Wrath</u>
5. "The Magic Barrel"
6. <u>Keep It Real</u>
7. <u>The Bridge Over the River Kwai</u>

8. Awareness
9. "The Rock Pile"
10. correct

Exercise 2   Choosing the Correct Form
1. The Christian Review
2. "The Last Leaf"
3. "Why I Write"
4. Romeo and Juliet
5. the Old Testament

29.4   Underlining and Other Uses of Quotation Marks (Page 188)
Practice 2
Exercise 1   Underlining Titles, Names, and Words
1. David Copperfield
2. The Concert
3. Gemini 5
4. occasion
5. correct
6. Childe Harold
7. déjà vu
8. The New York Mirror, Direct Line
9. The Mikado
10. correct

Exercise 2   Using Quotation Marks With Titles
1. We were studying the chapter called "The Character Sketch."
2. "Trifles" by Susan Glaspell can be found in a collection called Plays.
3. We listened to the "Surprise Symphony" from The Complete Symphonies of Haydn.
4. Almost everybody in California knows the song "California Here I Come."
5. I read an article in Science World entitled "Frog Talk: Chirp, Chuckle, and Thump."
6. Edgar Allan Poe wrote a good horror story when he wrote "The Masque of the Red Death."
7. Emily Dickinson wrote an interesting poem on death called "I Heard a Fly Buzz—When I Died."
8. Public Broadcasting Television showed The Prince and the Pauper on Once Upon a Classic.
9. "Once More to the Lake" by E. B. White is an essay that looks back to the childhood of the writer.
10. Eleanor Clark's short story "Hurry, Hurry" begins and ends with the activities of a poodle named de Maupassant.

29.5   Dashes (Page 189)
Practice 1
Exercise 1   Using the Dash
1. tennis—all
2. library—it, day—and
3. novels—The, Wrath —portray
4. built—you, amazing—in
5. class—oh

Exercise 2   More Work With Dashes
1. belts—all
2. parents—unfortunately, included—are
3. presidents—I'm, Kennedy—have
4. now—I
5. in—of, places—the

29.5   Dashes (Page 190)
Practice 2
Exercise 1   Using the Dash
1. Food, housing, and clothing—all of these are getting more expensive.

2. Tobogganing sounds like something—oh, here comes Mario.
3. We will play tennis—or at least attempt to play tennis—at school today.
4. The man underwent an emergency appendectomy—the surgical removal of an appendix—and is now recovering.
5. Our guest speaker—who had a flat tire as he was coming here—was a little late.
6. I'd like to introduce you to—what did you say your name was?
7. That the plane burned huge amounts of fuel—this was the concern voiced by the conservationists.
8. The Crusades—there were four major ones, weren't there?—were not an overwhelming success.
9. Some of the instruments—the drums, guitars, and piano—still need to be loaded onto the truck.
10. The parents say that their talented—they use this term loosely—daughter will perform in a piano recital.
11. Pencils, paper, book covers, and pens—these will all be required in this course.
12. That old table—which is on its last legs, to say the least—was the first item sold at the flea market.
13. Feeding, exercising, and providing the necessary medical care—all of these constitute important aspects of pet ownership.
14. I got Danielle a bracelet for her—why, Dani, what a surprise to see you!
15. Our club raised fifty dollars—more or less—for the U.S. Olympic team.
16. Some horror writers—for instance, Stephen King—have wonderful imaginations.
17. It bothers me when you continually—oh, never mind.
18. Eating, watching fireworks, and being with friends—there is no better way to celebrate the Fourth of July.
19. They sent me four identical forms—why, I'll never understand—for the insurance claim I'm submitting.
20. Some bad habits—biting your nails, grinding your teeth, and drumming your fingers—seem almost impossible to break.

Exercise 2   Using the Dash in Paragraphs
Fishing—Don's favorite sport—is something that he can do any time of the year. His favorite time—if he had to choose one—is in the winter. During this time—I'm sure you already know this—many lakes in the eastern and midwestern United States are frozen solid. Don likes to chop a hole in the ice and fish through it—a fishing method that was developed long ago by the Native Americans. Ice fishermen like Don build small sheds and put them on sled runners—can you just imagine doing this? The shed is pulled out onto the lake and a hole is chopped in the ice with an axe or a heavy iron rod—this rod is called a spud. The ice is then chipped away—what a tedious task!—to make an opening about twelve inches square. The shed is then pulled over the hole and the fisherman sits in a comfortable chair—if you can believe this—to do the fishing. Because it is dark inside the shed, the fisherman can see the fish swimming in the water below—it hardly seems fair to the poor little fish. Just give Don a fishing

shed, a frozen lake, and fishing gear—that's all he needs to be happy.

29.5 Parentheses (Page 191)
Practice 1
Exercise 1 Using Parentheses
1. (1825–27)
2. (In … one.)
3. (the one … road)
4. (Can … old?)
5. (a) (b) (c) (d)

Exercise 2 More Work With Parentheses
1. The most important point (we hope you agree) is to do this as cheaply as possible.
2. If I understand you correctly (I think I do), the work was satisfying.
3. Paul did a report on Mozart (1756–1791), who began composing at the age of five.
4. The highpoint of the concert (What a concert it was!) came just before intermission.
5. Jane Lawson called you (Do you know her?); however, your line was busy.

29.5 Parentheses (Page 192)
Practice 2
Exercise 1 Using Parentheses
1. (held only twice a year at Bueners)
2. (Italy)
3. (Chapter 6 in the text)
4. (1900–1980)
5. (16-ounce size)
6. (1), (2), (3)
7. (more often than not, broken)
8. (a fisher who uses a hook and line)
9. ("The Night They Drove Old Dixie Down")
10. (a favorite event on Picnic Day)
11. ($64.10)
12. (having been up thirty-six hours straight)
13. (a), (b), (c)
14. (though getting up so early is a strain)
15. (seventeen, to be exact)

Exercise 2 Capitalizing and Punctuating With Parentheses
1. I have an appointment today (right after the game).
2. Will you meet me at 716 Elm Street (the building right across from the library)?
3. The dress (It was the most beautiful shade of blue!) fit perfectly.
4. When we go to Seacliff Beach (a resort just south of Santa Cruz), we will have a picnic on the beach or possibly a clambake.
5. Something in the refrigerator smelled (Some meat had gone bad!), so I cleaned it out.
6. I watched the ants. (There was an ant hole within three feet of me.) They were busy gathering crumbs from the sandwich I was trying to eat for lunch.
7. She has honey-blonde hair (Do you think it is natural?) and blue eyes.
8. Using the flowers (dahlias, I think), I created a lovely centerpiece.
9. The road appears to be lined with oaks. (Do you think that is the right type of tree?)
10. I slowly savored the pistachio ice cream (My favorite flavor!) until it was gone.

29.5 Hyphens (Page 193)
Practice 1
Exercise 1 Using Hyphens
1. three-fourths
2. sister-in-law, father-in-law
3. able-bodied
4. anti-French
5. governor-elect
6. man-of-war
7. bright-eyed
8. well-educated
9. old-fashioned
10. twenty-two, thirty-five

Exercise 2 Hyphenating Words
1. ath-lete
2. (drudge)
3. cus-tom
4. (study)
5. par-tridge
6. moun-tain
7. com-pound
8. ten-nis
9. in-cite
10. re-mark

29.5 Hyphens (Page 194)
Practice 2
Exercise 1 Using Hyphens With Compound Numbers, Word Parts, and Words
1. able-bodied, well-loved
2. Central-American
3. far-fetched
4. quick-witted
5. ninety-nine
6. Western-European
7. sought-after
8. post-Renaissance
9. mass-produced
10. correct

Exercise 2 Dividing Words
1. self-explanatory
2. cat-tle
3. correct
4. heady
5. down
6. Superintendent
7. gal-loped
8. Ellinsworth
9. correct
10. Zealand

29.6 The Apostrophe (With Possessive Nouns, Joint and Individual Ownership) (Page 195)
Practice 1
Exercise 1 Writing Possessive Forms
1. women's books
2. week's vacation
3. City College's campus
4. actress's career
5. Ken and Pam's children
6. two dollars' worth
7. Jim's and Susan's coats

8. pupils' absences
9. sister's textbook
10. father-in-law's pizza

Exercise 2   Using Possessives
Sample possessive nouns are given.
1. Dave's
2. Jenny's
3. parents'
4. students'
5. horse's

29.6   The Apostrophe (With Possessive Nouns, Joint and Individual Ownership) (Page 196)
Practice 2
Exercise 1   Using Apostrophes to Make Singular Nouns Possessive
1. student's
2. Phyllis's
3. dog's
4. Andrew's
5. representative's
6. college's
7. Jim's
8. cat's
9. Robert Graves'
10. month's

Exercise 2   Using Apostrophes to Make Plural Nouns Possessive
1. ladies'
2. children's
3. twins'
4. governors'
5. critics'
6. people's
7. relatives'
8. women's
9. visitors'
10. cities'

Exercise 3   Using Apostrophes with Compound Nouns
1. Secretary of State's
2. Colbert and Nelson's
3. father in-law's
4. police chief's
5. Camp Fire Girls'

29.6   The Apostrophe (With Pronouns) (Page 197)
Practice 1
Exercise 1   Using Apostrophes Correctly With Pronouns
1. theirs
2. everyone's
3. somebody else's
4. their
5. one's
6. Someone else's
7. her
8. its
9. ours
10. one another's

Exercise 2   Writing Sentences With Pronouns
Sample sentences are given.
1. June is everybody's favorite month.
2. The cat washed its kittens.
3. Can we borrow anyone's CD player for the party?
4. Josh mumbled his answer.

5. We'll have to use someone else's house for the meeting.
6. Are these jackets theirs?
7. One's success depends on hard work.
8. The instructor honored our request.
9. We like to try on one another's jewelry.
10. The skates with the yellow laces are hers.

29.6   The Apostrophe (With Pronouns) (Page 198)
Practice 2
Exercise 1   Using Apostrophes With Pronouns
1. his
2. correct
3. correct
4. Hers
5. correct
6. Everybody's
7. theirs
8. nobody's
9. correct
10. else's

Exercise 2   Using Possessive Forms of Pronouns
Sample pronouns are given.
1. everyone's
2. your
3. Someone's
4. his
5. each other's

29.6   The Apostrophe (With Contractions, Special Uses) (Page 199)
Practice 1
Exercise 1   Using Contractions Correctly
1. It's
2. they're
3. George's
4. *and*'s
5. she'll
6. Who'll
7. don't
8. *m*'s, *w*'s
9. Aren't
10. Sue'll

Exercise 2   Supplying Contractions
Sample contractions are given.
1. you'll
2. I'll
3. Weren't
4. She'd
5. he's

29.6   The Apostrophe (With Contractions, Special Uses) (Page 200)
Practice 2
Exercise 1   Using Apostrophes With Contractions
1. man is
2. do not
3. didn't
4. couldn't
5. they would
6. It's
7. are not
8. they are
9. we have
10. we would
11. he's
12. 1930's, 1940's, 1950's

13. you will
14. shouldn't
15. they are
16. that'll
17. should not
18. thing is
19. We will
20. work has

Exercise 2   Recognizing Special Uses of the Apostrophe
1. *8*'s
2. *s*'s, *c*'s
3. *?*'s
4. *f*'s
5. *4*'s

Diagraming Basic Sentence Parts (Subjects, Verbs, and Modifiers: Adding Conjunctions) (Page 201)

Practice 2

Exercise 1   Diagraming Subjects, Verbs, and Modifiers
1.

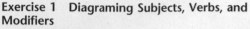

2.

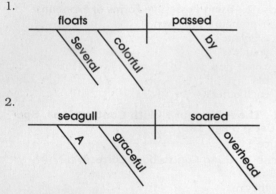

Exercise 2   Diagraming Sentences with Conjunctions
1.

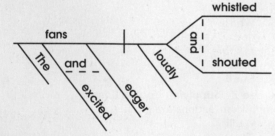

Diagraming Basic Sentence Parts (Subjects, Verbs, and Modifiers: Adding Conjunctions) (Page 202)

Practice 2

Exercise 1   Diagraming Subjects, Verbs, and Modifiers
1.

2.

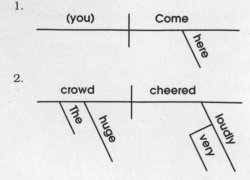

3.

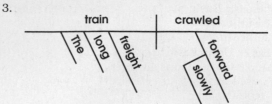

Exercise 2   Diagraming Sentences with Conjunctions
1.

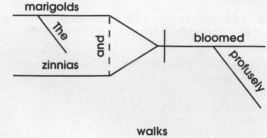

2.

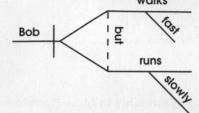

3.

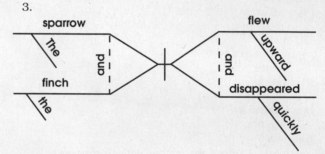

Diagraming Basic Sentence Parts (Complements) (Page 203)

Practice 1

Exercise 1   Diagraming Complements
1.

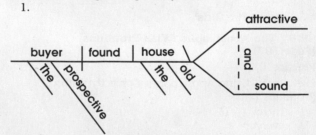

Exercise 2   More Work with Complements
1.

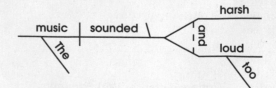

Diagraming Basic Sentence Parts (Complements) (Page 204)

Practice 2

Exercise 1 Diagraming Complements

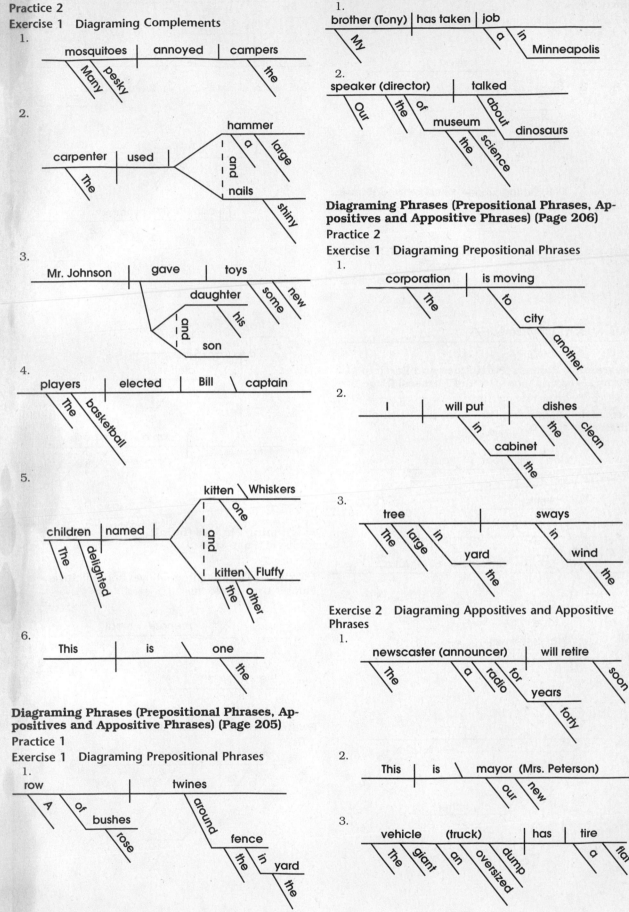

1.

mosquitoes | annoyed | campers
Many pesky   the

2.

The carpenter | used | hammer and nails
a large / shiny

3.

Mr. Johnson | gave | toys
daughter and son | his | some new

4.

The basketball players | elected | Bill \ captain

5.

The children | named | kitten \ Whiskers one and kitten \ Fluffy the other
delighted

6.

This | is \ one
the

Diagraming Phrases (Prepositional Phrases, Appositives and Appositive Phrases) (Page 205)

Practice 1

Exercise 1 Diagraming Prepositional Phrases

1.

A row | of bushes | rose | twines
around fence the in yard the

Exercise 2 Diagraming Appositives and Appositive Phrases

1.

My brother (Tony) | has taken | job
a in Minneapolis

2.

Our speaker (director) | talked
the of museum the science | about dinosaurs

Diagraming Phrases (Prepositional Phrases, Appositives and Appositive Phrases) (Page 206)

Practice 2

Exercise 1 Diagraming Prepositional Phrases

1.

The corporation | is moving
to city another

2.

I | will put | dishes
in cabinet the | the clean

3.

The large tree | in yard the | sways | in wind the

Exercise 2 Diagraming Appositives and Appositive Phrases

1.

The newscaster (announcer) | will retire
a radio for years forty | soon

2.

This | is \ mayor (Mrs. Peterson)
our new

3.

The giant vehicle (an oversized dump truck) | has | tire
a flat

Diagraming Phrases (Participles and Participial Phrases, Gerunds and Gerund Phrases) (Page 207)

Practice 1

Exercise 1   Diagraming Participles and Participial Phrases

1.

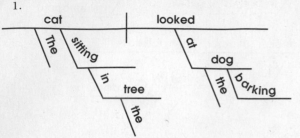

Exercise 2   Diagraming Gerunds and Gerund Phrases

1.

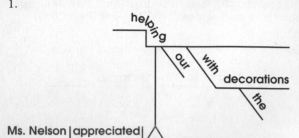

Diagraming Phrases (Participles and Participial Phrases, Gerunds and Gerund Phrases) (Page 208)

Practice 2

Exercise 1   Diagraming Participles and Participial Phrases

1.

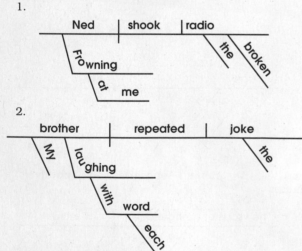

2.

3.

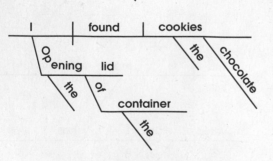

Exercise 2   Diagraming Gerunds and Gerund Phrases

1.

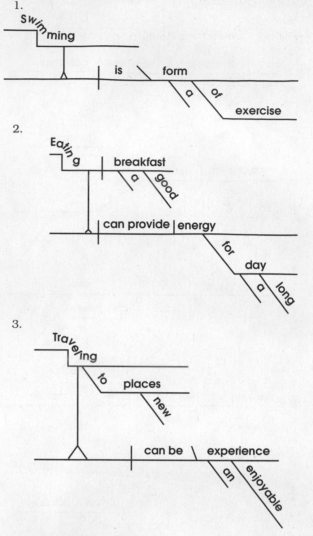

2.

3.

Diagraming Phrases (Infinitives and Infinitive Phrases) (Page 209)

Practice 2

Exercise 1   Diagraming Infinitives and Infinitive Phrases Used as Nouns

1.

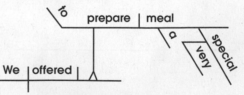

Exercise 2   Diagraming Infinitives and Infinitive Phrases Used as Adjectives and Adverbs

1.

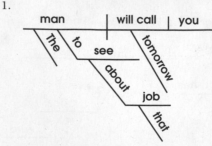

Diagraming Phrases (Infinitives and Infinitive Phrases) (Page 210)

Practice 2

Exercise 1 Diagraming Infinitives and Infinitive Phrases

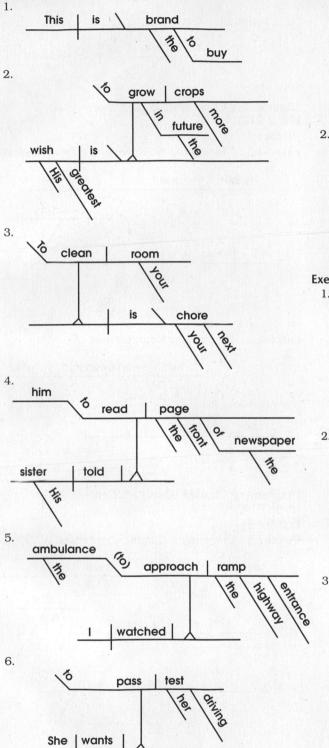

1.

2.

3.

4.

5.

6.

Diagraming Clauses (Compound Sentences) (Page 211)

Practice 1

Exercise 1 Diagraming Compound Sentences

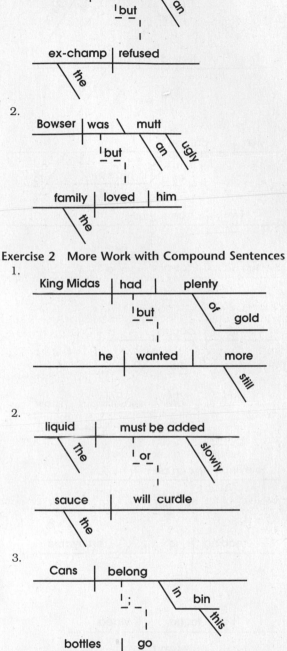

1.

2.

Exercise 2 More Work with Compound Sentences

1.

2.

3.

...iagraming Compound Sentences

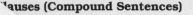

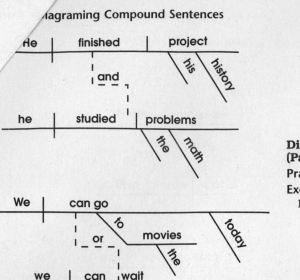

2.

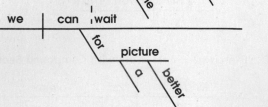

3.

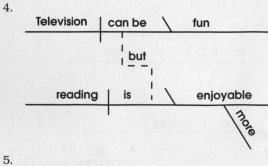

4.

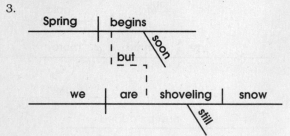

5.

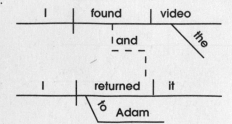

6.

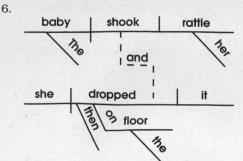

Diagraming Clauses (Complex Sentences)
(Page 213)
Practice 1

Exercise 1 Diagraming Adjective and Adverb Clauses

1.

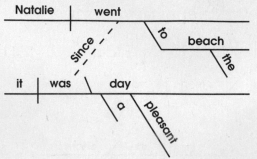

Exercise 2 Diagraming Noun Clauses

1.

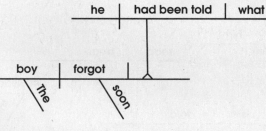

Diagraming Clauses (Complex Sentences)
(Page 214)
Practice 2

Exercise 1 Diagraming Complex Sentences

1.

2.

3.

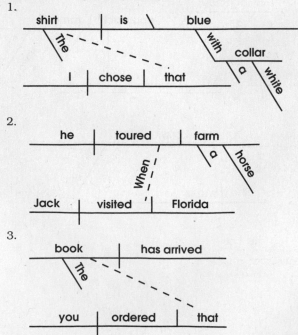

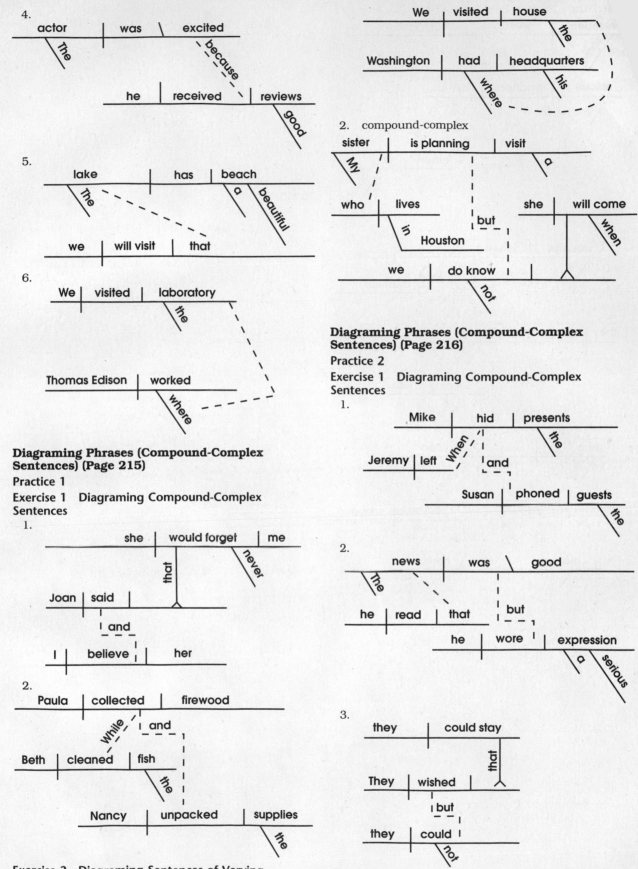

4.

5.

6.

Diagraming Phrases (Compound-Complex Sentences) (Page 215)
Practice 1
Exercise 1 Diagraming Compound-Complex Sentences
1.

2.

Exercise 2 Diagraming Sentences of Varying Structures
1. complex

2. compound-complex

Diagraming Phrases (Compound-Complex Sentences) (Page 216)
Practice 2
Exercise 1 Diagraming Compound-Complex Sentences
1.

2.

3.

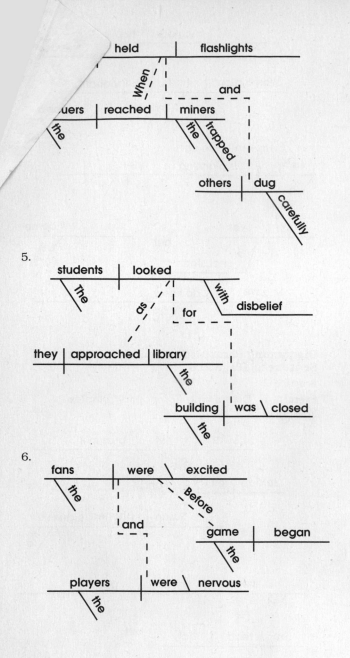

5.

6.